PSYCHIATRY AND RELIGIOUS EXPERIENCE

PSYCHIATRY

AND

RELIGIOUS

EXPERIENCE

By

Louis Linn, M.D., *and Leo W. Schwarz*

 RANDOM HOUSE · NEW YORK

First Printing

To Miriam and Ruth

PREFACE

Today the cooperation of psychiatry and religion as a moral force has become more than ever decisive for the control of power and the improvement of human relations. Scientists, physicians, and religious leaders have spoken much and eloquently on the necessity for such control and improvement, but a workable plan has yet to be proposed. It is the aim of this book to show how the insights of psychiatry and religion may be used for the relief of human suffering and the release of creative human energies.

Psychiatry and the social sciences have undergone an enormous development in our time, and increasing efforts are being made to incorporate this development into religious belief and practice. Yet we are only on the verge of understanding the character of either domain, to say nothing of their inter-relations and differences. The literature in both fields is as inconclusive as it is vast. Many areas are still unexplored and many principles and techniques remain unprecisely formulated.

In our own study of the ways in which religion and the social sciences, especially psychiatry, may join forces, the method we adopt is clinical as well as analytical. All our material is based upon situations with which psychiatrists, psychologists, social workers, and religious leaders have actually been confronted. Religious leaders have a traditional method of dealing with the problems they face in everyday life. The authors believe, and hope to show here, that psychiatry has much to teach the religious leader in the management of these problems. Both the medical techniques of psychotherapy and the healing methods of religious counseling are described. The clinical examples in the book have been altered to protect identity. Besides the material generously made available to us by religious leaders of all faiths and denominations and their congregants and parishioners, we have availed ourselves of the case histories of psychiatrists; psychoanalysts; social workers; teachers; psychologists; chaplains in the armed forces, hospitals, colleges, universities, and correctional and penal institutions; and the diversified agencies serving them.

The plan of the book is both developmental and topical. The first four chapters deal with the religious growth of the individual and the basic principles of religious counseling. The remaining six chapters comprise applications of these principles to the major cycles and problems of adult life. In all, the emphasis is not on ritual or theology, but on ethical and moral values; not on personal judgments, but on objective appraisal. It is the province of the religious leader to deal with dogma and ritual; it is the purpose of the psychiatrist to evaluate, from a scientific point of view, the influence of the moral aspect of religion upon human behavior. While the techniques of analytic psychology are stressed, the approach is generally psychiatric. We have avoided the use of technical terms, but when such terms occur, they are defined. Readers interested in further study may refer to the notes and bibliography, where our debt to the work of others is fully acknowledged.

We have had the benefit of critical readings of all or parts of the book by the following friends and colleagues, to whom we express our sincere appreciation: Miss Anna Freud, London, England; Professor Seward Hiltner, Federated Theological Faculty of the University of Chicago; Professor Florence Hollis, New York School of Social Work, Columbia University; Dr. Lawrence Kubie, Clinical Professor of Psychiatry, School of Medicine, Yale University; Dr. Earl A. Loomis, Professor of Psychology and Religion, Union Theological Seminary, New York City; Dr. Margaret S. Mahler and Dr. Mary O'Neil Hawkins, Faculty, New York Psychoanalytic Institute; Dr. Bernard L. Pacella, Associate Attending Psychiatrist, Presbyterian Hospital, New York; Miss Ollie A. Randall and Dr. Jeanette Regensburg, Community Service Society, New York City; Dr. Israel S. Wechsler, President, American Neurological Association.

Of the numerous associates and colleagues who have generously made material available and taken the time to discuss difficult problems, we are particularly indebted to Dr. Benjamin Balser, College of Physicians and Surgeons, Columbia University, New York City; Major Dorothy Berry, Prison Welfare Bureaus, Salvation Army, New York City; Rev. Ernest Bruder, Chaplain Services Branch, Saint Elizabeth's Hospital, Washington, D. C.; Professor Waldo W. Burchard, Hollins College, Virginia; Dr. Louis Finkelstein, President, Jewish Theological Seminary, New York City; Rabbi I. Fred Hollander, Director, Institute of Pastoral Psychiatry, New York Board of Rabbis; Mrs. Eva J. Meyer, Librarian, New York Psychoanalytic Institute; Mr. Philip W. Russ, Personal Service Consultant, Armed Services Division, National Jewish Welfare Board, New York City; Father Joseph J. Quinlan, President, Association of Mental Hospital Chaplains; and Dr. Jack Sheps, Assistant Attending Psychiatrist, New York Psychiatric Institute. For grants to facilitate special clinical research, especially in the religious factors in family life, we are grateful to the Sol Wechsler Associates of New York City, and to the Gralnick Foundation, High Point Hospital, Port Chester, New York.

We are heavily indebted for counsel and help to Albert Erskine, of Random House, and Dr. Leo Roberts, Cambridge, Mass.

L. L.
L. W. S.

CONTENTS

Contents

4.

The Basic Principles of Religious Counseling   80

5.

Religion in Sex and Marriage   117

6.

Understanding Illness   146

PSYCHIATRY AND RELIGIOUS EXPERIENCE

A chapter in the history of Earth closed with the appearance of man. In man, the Weltstoff *had been made to think and feel, to love beauty and truth—the cosmos had generated soul. A new chapter then began, a chapter in which we all are characters. Matter had flowered in soul. Soul has now to mould matter.*

That moulding of matter by spirit is, under one aspect, Science; under another, Art; under still another, religion. Let us be careful not to allow the moulding forces to counteract each other when they might be made to cooperate.

JULIAN HUXLEY

THE DOMAINS OF PSYCHIATRY
AND RELIGION

1.

THE PSYCHOLOGICAL REVOLUTION OF THE LAST DECADES of the nineteenth century began in hospitals and laboratories, and today has penetrated the home, the school, courts, business, entertainment, government, and welfare and religious institutions. Psychiatry, the spearhead of that revolution, has had an immense impact upon almost every facet of contemporary life and society. The daily newspapers give striking evidence of how deeply the psychiatrist is involved in private and public life.

Perhaps the most dramatic aspect of psychiatry, besides its practice in hospital and clinic, is the way in which it was first rejected and then embraced by religious leaders and institutions. The initial rejection fits in with the attitude that religion has displayed towards science in general for centuries. With each scientific advance, religion seemed obliged to surrender part of its domain, and psychiatry, especially that branch of it called psychoanalysis, appeared to be its deadly enemy. Freud's *The Future of an Illusion* was, in effect, a declaration of war upon religion. Religious belief, he argued, is an illusion that man clings to because of his emotional immaturity. Once he has achieved emotional maturity, religion is fated to disappear. It is not surprising that this thesis aroused militant opposition among religious leaders.

In recent years, however, there has been a rapprochement between religion and psychiatry. Several factors brought this about. The great advances in the social sciences fired the imagination of everyone, religious leaders included. In the light of new findings, many religious leaders came to feel that their traditional techniques were inadequate. In some instances, at least, this conclusion was the result of a crisis or failure in the faith of the religious leader, so that he was moved to substitute psychiatry and social work for religion and religious counseling. He explained his adoption of new attitudes in various ways, but the upshot was usually a point of view that was neither religiously valid nor psychiatrically sound. Other religious leaders, although their convictions remained unshaken, were so impressed with the psychological revolution that they became interested in its implications, not only as they might affect their own work, but as they bore upon the contribution by religious leaders to the welfare services of the community.

The most vital factor of all in the rapprochement is the moral crisis of our time. Freud's faith, or rather that of his more intemperate followers, in science as a panacea appears naïve in the light of nuclear warfare and the apparent readiness of unprincipled politicians to risk the extermination of the entire human race. The man of science has finally come to ask himself whether his ideal is to be pure research or service to his fellow man. The example of Nazi Germany, especially, has emphasized the fact that moral purpose and social responsibility must direct the search for scientific knowledge and the acquisition of power.

Preoccupied at first only with the psychologically pernicious effects of an excessively punitive moral code, psychiatry is now prepared to recognize that normal psychological development cannot occur except on a firm moral base. In fact there has been a tendency among some psychiatrists to go to the opposite extreme and to gloss over the differences between their own role and that of the religious leader. There are psychiatrists and religious leaders who claim that, since both professions are engaged in reducing human suffering and increasing happiness, their methods are identical. "Between my own techniques and those of a psychiatrist," writes one minister, "I recognize no particular difference." [1] Most religious leaders would reject this view when it is stated so baldly, yet in their discussions of the topic, while they stress differences in theory, they often propose practices that imply common techniques. Some psychiatrists also assert that a division between religion and psychiatry is no longer possible. In fact, many psychoanalysts veer towards this view. For example, Erich Fromm writes: "The analyst . . . as a physician of the soul . . . is concerned with the very same problems as philosophy and theology: the soul of man and its cure." [2]

The motive behind this effort to bring religious leaders and psychiatrists into a cooperative relationship is commendable, but to speak of identical aims or techniques is a mistake that can have unfortunate consequences. The marriage between religion and psychiatry can only be one of temporary convenience; and lest the partners again turn on each other, it is imperative that their situation and prospects be carefully examined.

The paths of the religious leader and the psychiatrist often meet, sometimes converge, but they are never identical. The two professions are never enemies, and they do indeed share a similar task in facing human conflict and suffering. But there are vital differences, and it is essential that they be made explicit, so that members of each profession may function properly in helping those who turn to them. To this end, we shall begin by explaining what we mean by religion, what by psychiatry.

The Domain of Religion

RELIGION is a word with a long history and many meanings. No one has yet formulated a definition that does justice to the whole complex of emotion, beliefs, and patterns of religious behavior that are found in the cultures and societies of recorded human history. Listed in an appendix to James H. Leuba's *A Psychological Study of Religion* are forty-eight different definitions of religion from various writers. We are not eager to add another definition to this list, but in our view religion is first and foremost the repository of a moral code. Central to this code, in the three great Western religions, is the belief that it is primarily in group life (family, community, national, and international) that human beings achieve those things which are of lasting value. Secondly, religion enshrines the belief that if one obeys the code certain important satisfactions ensue, the chief of which is immortality. Religion stands also for the belief that the universe has a purpose and that it is a purpose favorable to man. This belief in turn presupposes the existence of an organizing principle of some kind, which is commonly called God. Finally, religion is associated with a kind of emotional experience which is taken as revelatory of the true nature of the universe, as proof, in a word, of the existence of God. Such experience may be actively sought, as in meditation and prayer, or it may occur in a seemingly unpredictable way, though often within the setting of an emotional upheaval.

The detailed contents of the moral code vary widely from one religious system to another. Accounts of the nature of the satisfactions which follow obedience to this code (or the dissatisfactions which follow its disobedience), of the concept of immortality, and of the nature of the organizing principle which is God, vary widely under different circumstances, even within a given religious system. They vary as between the child and the adult, or one cultural setting and another, or one historical epoch and another.

The present study is limited to contemporary religious experience in Western democratic society, and confines itself further to the activities of Catholic, Jewish, and Protestant religious leaders. Thus delimited, our study deals with principles, psychiatric and religious, that figure in the work and thought of the entire clergy. Indeed, it is these principles that are implied in our use of the term religious leader. At the same time it is of the first importance to bear in mind the divisions that exist within both Christianity and Judaism. American Catholicism differs in certain practices from European Catholicism, and both differ from Greek Orthodoxy. Further, within each Catholicism there are differences owing to cultural variations, as, say, between Italian, Irish, and Polish communicants. Similarly, the beliefs and practices of Protestant denominations and sects produce an extraordinary variety of social relationships and patterns of behavior. And the same thing is to a large extent true of Judaism. The religious experiences of individuals and institutions are also influenced considerably by their local cultural milieu, depending upon whether it is urban, rural, or regional. Many of the problems that children have, such as social identification, arise from the fact that they belong to a religious minority in a particular community or neighborhood, even though the institution with which they are affiliated may actually constitute a religious majority in the country at large or in other neighborhoods.

Our procedure, therefore, is based upon the assumption, supported by clinical evidence, that religion is not merely an individual concern, but part of the cultural pattern of our society, and that it expresses itself in many forms. In our view, religious experience is socially and culturally differentiated, so that the problems it raises can be understood only within specific contexts.

The Domain of Psychiatry

W H I L E the religious leader is primarily concerned with normal human experience and only secondarily with the pathological, psychiatrists practicing their branch of medicine are concerned above all with the abnormal. But this is not to imply that the boundary line between health and disease can be sharply drawn; disease, like health, is life and function, impaired as the latter may be. So we may say that disease is a condition in which a living organism functions under a handicap. Medicine is constantly in search of improved methods of etiologic diagnosis—that is, diagnosis based on a knowledge of the cause of disease—for such diagnosis opens the way to specific treatment. It is the ideal of the physician first to identify the handicap and its causes, then to remove them, and so restore the organism to health. The techniques which the physician employs for this purpose are referred to collectively as therapy.

In general, mental illness is characterized by a discrepancy between the thoughts, feelings, and actions of an individual, on the one hand, and the requirements of external reality, on the other. Weeping over the loss of a loved one is normal behavior, but uncontrollable and excessive weeping, without adequate cause, is grounds for suspecting an abnormal state of depression or melancholia. Thus the religious leader, in attempting to evaluate the mental state of a person presenting himself for help, will ask himself: To what extent is this person's mental state recognizably and understandably related to the circumstances of his life? He will therefore want to acquaint himself as thoroughly as possible with the individual's behavior and his relation to those around him. How does the person adapt socially, physically, and psychologically to the demands of day-to-day living? How does he relate to other people in and outside the family group? How realistic are his judgments of the world about him and how well is he able to accept frustration? Does his home situation worsen his problem, or can it be mobilized to help him solve it? In order to answer these questions appropriately, the religious leader must have an understanding of the general principles and areas of psychiatry.

Most serious among the diagnostic categories of mental illness are the psychoses. In the psychoses the manifest deviation from reality is greatest and is commonly associated with an inability to realize that one is sick. The aberrant mental state may express itself in delusions of grandeur or persecution, hallucinations, and bizarre behavior. A psychotic person may, for example, accuse his marital partner of infidelity, though the charge is groundless. Hence it is important for the religious counselor to bear in mind that such accusations may be delusional.

The psychoneuroses, not as serious as the psychoses, and commoner, are usually less fantastic and less extreme in the impression they make on others. Inappropriate fears and obsessive thoughts may make the afflicted person afraid to be alone, or to travel, or to be in crowds. He may consult doctors frequently out of fear of physical illness, though the symptoms he presents are without any basis in physical disease. There is often a considerable disparity between his actual achievements in life and his true capabilities. At times, in spite of outward evidence of success, he is hounded by a sense of failure.

Similar to the psychoneurotics in the fact that they are not psychotic, are those whose behavior prevents satisfactory social adjustment. They suffer from what are usually referred to as character disorders. Unlike psychotic people, they are usually aware that their thoughts, feelings, and actions are inappropriate, but they remain powerless to control them.

Among the most difficult cases in psychiatry are the people in a fourth category, those in whom mental illness expresses itself in antisocial behavior. We have to do here with the psychopath. He breaks laws and usually ends up in court and prison. He belongs to a class which is probably the least understood in our time, subject as he is to the same punitive attitudes that psychotics were centuries ago, when they were among those persecuted as witches. For example, many so-called hardened criminals have a pathological fear of society. To them breaking the law is frequently a device for getting out of the jungle of free society into the relative security of the prison. In their panic-stricken flight from human relationships they unconsciously follow a path that leads to self-defeat. They may be likened to the hero of Lamb's essay on roast pig who burns his house down in order to get a ham sandwich. To view the antisocial act in this light is of course not to condone violation of the law, but to explain why punishment so often fails to alter the behavior of criminals. It also provides a theoretical basis for a new and possibly more effective approach to treatment. The psychiatrist here is not concerned with creating a new moral code, but with a more effective way of enforcing the old one for a specific group of mentally ill people.

It should be clear by now that if the psychiatrist or religious leader, or for that matter any other professional who serves people, is to be effective he must aim at understanding the whole person and his environment. It is here, in the psychosocial area, that the psychiatrist and the religious leader share a common domain. Only by recognizing the physical, social, and psychological forces involved in human behavior is it possible for the religious leader to determine where and how religion may be employed to meet an individual's needs, or whether psychiatry may be more appropriate, or religion and psychiatry together.

Areas of Overlap and Confusion

THE fact that in certain areas psychiatry and religion border upon each other has made it easy to confuse their respective roles. And fostering this confusion is the change that has taken place in the concepts of medicine and religion. Throughout the history of medicine, doctors have been confronted with diseases which they could not diagnose or which they could diagnose but were unable to cure. In these circumstances the physician's first injunction was *Primum non nocere*, If you can't help, at least do no harm! He was called upon to comfort the sufferer, to ease his pain, both physical and mental, and to aid him in accepting the inevitable if his illness was progressively disabling or ultimately fatal. These interventions constituted much of what has been euphemistically called the "art," in contrast to the "science," of medicine. In the beginning the best physicians were those most noted for their "art," but as medicine progressed, the art became less important than the science. Although the good physician must be able to call up maximal art as well as maximal science, the fact is that much effective therapy proceeds today with a minimum of art. A doctor vaccinating hundreds of people in a day may prevent a major epidemic without displaying one whit of the art of medicine. Or he may have no more contact with a patient than a drop of blood on a slide, but the advice he gives the family doctor based on what he sees may save the patient's life.

Much of what was once counted as the art of medicine has now been taken over by auxiliary groups—occupational therapists, recreational therapists, bibliotherapists, etc. Among the auxiliary groups which bring comfort to the sick, religious leaders must surely rank high. Perhaps it is because of the earlier fusion of the art and the science of medicine that some who are called upon to practice the art are liable to the confusion of thinking that they are practicing the science. This is especially true with the relatively new field of psychiatry, so that people who are presumably well trained in disciplines designed to improve human welfare still punish or exhort such mentally ill cases as the incorrigible criminal, the alcoholic, the narcotic addict. But even nonpsychiatric fields of medicine still witness the intrusion of primitive pseudo-religious ideas. For example, a few years ago police in Texas jailed the father and two brothers of a young woman because the men, members of Jehovah's Witnesses, refused to let doctors give her a needed blood transfusion on the ground that "eating blood" violated their religion.

Examples of this sort could be multiplied indefinitely. The lesson they bring home is simply that in matters of disease the religious leader must avail himself of the best medical knowledge, including that of psychiatry. For psychiatry studies and treats human behavior under conditions of stress. In such conditions, behavior patterns tend to emerge which are categorized under the various diagnostic classifications of psychiatric illness. Various treatments are employed in an attempt to replace these behavior patterns with patterns that more satisfactorily fulfill the needs of the individual and the demands of society.

It should be realized that religion is no more identical with psychiatry than with any other branch of medicine. There is an unfortunate tendency to speak of "psychiatric values," but there are no "psychiatric values" any more than there are "values" in other branches of medicine, except perhaps as physicians favor health against disease, or life against death. Developments in psychiatry are no more related to religion than parallel developments in other branches of medicine. For example, when it was discovered that "general paralysis of the insane," once a widespread mental disease, was due to syphilis, effective methods of treatment were devised and the disease was practically eliminated as a public health problem. The insanity due to pellagra was eliminated for all practical purposes when it was learned that a specific vitamin deficiency was its cause and that it could be remedied by proper diet. Electroshock therapy remains an important means of treating certain forms of melancholia, and the new tranquilizer drugs have transformed many aspects of psychiatric practice. None of this had to do with religion.

Another psychiatric technique consists of maintaining an objective attitude to the patient, but it must not be supposed that because he imposes no set of moral values upon the patient, the psychiatrist is indifferent to such values. His technique is merely a means to an end, which is to get the patient to develop his personal values and to share in the positive values of society. And these values are neither invented by the psychiatrist nor derived from psychiatry. They are the moral and spiritual values that have developed from the experiences of group life in the past. They are a heritage transmitted by religious and social institutions.

Since the goal of the psychiatrist is to improve his patient's contact with reality, psychiatry adopts an attitude of neutrality in order to help the patient see the extent to which his understanding of the world is distorted. In the process of correcting these distortions the patient develops an ever increasing capacity for accurate perception of reality and for taking that reality into account in conducting his life. The moral code of the Western world is, of course, part of that reality, and as the patient improves, his capacity to accept what is socially useful in the code increases. In this respect the goals of psychiatry and those of religion seem to coincide.

The objective attitude of the psychiatrist has proved to be an eminently useful device in his hands. By means of it he is able to foster emotional growth and insight in the patient. It has been employed not only by the psychiatrist but by others in the helping professions, in particular the psychiatrically oriented social worker and the nondirective psychotherapist. But failure to understand the limitations of this approach is extremely dangerous for all concerned. The approach is a technique, not a substitute for a moral code, and to confuse the two is to invite catastrophe. And it is a technique utterly alien to the work of the religious leader.

In his earliest formulations, Freud pointed out that the inhibition of certain desires sets up a conflict out of which mental illness is generated. It was fallaciously concluded from this that the way to eliminate mental illness was to eliminate all frustration. But clinical experience showed nothing of the sort. They showed rather that a child has to learn to inhibit certain desires or he will develop abnormalities that are no less severe than those resulting from an excess of inhibitions and controls. Yet there are all too many people even now who take the objective attitude of the psychiatrist—an attitude that he maintains only during the analytic hour—as a prescription for a way of life, who believe that to do away with frustration is to do away with mental illness. To these people anxiety, guilt, sadness, anger, all are pathological. The normal state would thus be indistinguishable from Nirvana, and tranquillity nothing less than the ultimate good. Such a point of view sometimes passes for a religious one, yet it would be hard to imagine anything less seemly in a religious leader than counseling or maintaining tranquillity at any price. For his task is to keep alive a capacity for sadness over matters that truly warrant it, to stir the conscience, to speak with prophetic indignation against injustice and persecution.

In mapping out the respective domains of psychiatry and religion, we encounter another source of confusion in the fact that symptoms of mental illness may assume a religious guise, the guise especially of hyperreligiosity. When the manifestations are grotesque and extreme, as in schizophrenia, they present no diagnostic problem to the religious leader. The schizophrenic patient has been known to burn, castrate, or blind himself, gouge his feet and hands with sharp instruments in imitation of the crucifixion, and carry out other horrifying acts of self-mutilation. In typical fashion the schizophrenic will explain that he intends all this as a sacrifice to God in order to convince Him of his sincerity and to atone for sexual thoughts and actions.

But the emotional disorder may take subtler forms of religious expression. A chaotic history of repeated religious conversions is usually proof of a mental disorder, and excessive religious zeal in the confessional, sometimes referred to as "scrupulosity," is not an uncommon symptom of psychoneurosis. Since emotional imbalance may be expressed in various ways within the idiom of religion, it follows that not all religious expressions are necessarily wholesome. Thus alerted, the religious leader will be on the lookout for devotions and observances that signify a neurosis rather than an aspiration to give life greater meaning. Religious feeling may range from infantile escapism at one extreme to a healthy acceptance of one's limitations as a human being at the other. It can be an expression of security in a mature person who is unabashed by a cynical world; but it can also be an expression of extreme insecurity. It can lead to self-righteous separation from the world; but it can also lead to wholehearted solidarity with one's fellow men. It can express itself in the symptoms of schizophrenia, or in the language, ritual, and ceremony appropriate to the highest human aspirations. The sense of duty can range from compulsive legalism to a moral outlook which fosters the creative cooperation of impulse and conscience. Religious study can stress the memorization of verbal formulas or the need for moral and spiritual growth. It can try to justify personal retreat from obligations to the community and humanity, or it can inspire social action of significance.

It was stated earlier that psychiatrists have not been immune to confusion in mapping out their proper domain. Freud, for example, was impressed by the fact that certain psychoneurotic patients have personal rituals which, in their repetitiveness and attention to detail, can be compared to religious rituals. He was able to trace these abnormal rituals to the persistence into adult life of infantile attitudes of helplessness and dependency. Yet Freud himself recognized that there is a normal need for protection even in the grownup, so that it is surely a mistake to confound the devices for handling abnormal infantile yearnings for protection with those used by the emotionally mature adult in response to needs appropriate to his age and station in life.

The discussion of religion by Freud's colleagues and disciples in the last half-century or so reveals three major tendencies. First, there is the one represented by C. G. Jung and Otto Rank, who rejected some of the major Freudian principles and established schools of their own. Instead of explaining religion away, they have made religious ideas and symbols the core of their psychology and world view. By and large, they have surrendered observation to speculation and have concerned themselves with belief rather than behavior. The result has been a pseudo-scientific psychology and a pseudo-scientific vocabulary. In Jung's *Modern Man in Search of a Soul,* God is a symbol standing for energy in the human psyche, energy emerging from the unconscious as a pattern of the "archetype" of life. Rank's view, as stated in his book *Beyond Psychology,* is that man lives and dies beyond psychology and ideology—through conversion, revelation, and rebirth. Actually the Rankian concepts of "world spirit" and "world consciousness" are obscure and their expression is shrouded in mystery. Typically, an official magazine of the Rankian analysts is called *Journal of Psycho-*

therapy as a Religious Process; and the title is significant of Jung's point of view as well as Rank's. Both abandon psychoanalytic concepts for the religious concepts of soul, grace, and healing.[3]

Besides that of Jung and Rank, there is the point of view adopted by Erich Fromm, whose statement that the psychoanalyst is concerned with the same problems as theology and philosophy has already been quoted. In his *Psychoanalysis and Religion,* we find Fromm using traditional religious and philosophic language, like "physician of the soul" and "the All," which only serves to cloak an essentially secular viewpoint. It is Fromm's belief that organized religion has violated the spirit and practice of its humane ideals by an overconcentration on dogma, and that in setting up an omnipotent God, it is responsible for the creation of a passive, dependent, submissive type of individual. He equates such religion with what he calls secular authoritarian religion, of which Nazism is an example. In contrast to these meretricious types of religion, Fromm suggests that there is a meritorious humanistic religion. "Religious experience in this kind of religion," he asserts, "is the experience of oneness with the All, based on one's relatedness to the world as it is grasped with thought and with love." Such, he thinks, was the religion of Isaiah, Jesus, Socrates, and Spinoza.

To Fromm, humanistic religion represents the reality which psychoanalysis—neither as ally nor as enemy—is engaged in studying. He concludes that whether we are religious or not, we can perhaps more easily find a common faith in a negation of modern idolatry, that is, the deification of brute power, the state, and the machine, "than in any affirmative statements about God." The thesis is best understood in the context of Fromm's other writings, where it becomes clear that in his view the destructive drives in man stem from an iniquitous society. Man can become healthy, and his culture "sane," through the reconstruction of society into a kind of syndicalist order of communities that assure the individual freedom and independence.

Fromm's thesis is questionable at more than one point. Is it possible to separate, as he does, the religious beliefs of men from the practice of the human virtues? And is the religious belief in authority necessarily authoritarian? It is a fact that social reforms and democratic movements have been inspired and aided by organized religion, and that modern religious movements can boast of many forceful, independent, humanitarian leaders and followers. Actually Fromm is talking, not as a psychoanalyst, but as a cultural sociologist and political scientist. In abandoning biological instinctual drives as a source of human conflict and substituting social factors for them, and in assuming further that man is innately rational and good, Fromm parts company with the empirical findings of medical psychology. He denies Freud's biological naturalism; he rejects Jung's and Rank's theology; he embraces a liberal-humanistic utopianism.

The Freudian Hypothesis

N O T all psychoanalysts agree with Freud's thesis, stated in *The Future of an Illusion,* that both religion and religious morality are negative elements in our culture and that religion should be replaced by a psychoanalytically oriented psychiatry.[4]

The presuppositions and conclusions of the militantly antireligious psychoanalysts have been challenged by many of their colleagues. Karl A. Menninger may be taken as representative of this group. At the same time that he questions the speculative opinions of Freud on religion, he adheres rigorously to his scientific method. While not overlooking the pathology that expresses itself in the form of seemingly religious behavior, he recognizes the positive elements in normal religious experience. His position is that religious faith may not only help to control human aggression, but may foster life by inspiring compassion and love.

It is interesting to note that one of the first and most famous of Freud's case histories involves a religious experience. We refer to the remarkable case known throughout psychoanalytic literature as the "Wolfman." The patient presented himself for treatment in 1910, when he was twenty-three years old and had been incapacitated for six years by a severe emotional illness. In connection with this case Freud was able to demonstrate a point which is basic to psychoanalytic theory: that a precursor to emotional disturbance in adult life is severe emotional illness in childhood. Most of Freud's case report is a reconstruction of his patient's childhood illness, based upon memories that emerged during the psychoanalysis.

Without going into all the life circumstances which precipitated the childhood illness, we may note that when the patient was three years old he developed a behavior disturbance, which was characterized at first by irritability and "naughtiness," and then by anxiety that grew gradually more severe and expressed itself primarily as a fear of wolves and a fear of falling asleep. As his symptoms grew gradually worse, the patient's mother decided on her own to try the therapeutic effect of religious instruction. In Freud's words, "His mother determined to make him acquainted with the Bible story in the hope of distracting and elevating him. Moreover, she succeeded; his initiation into religion brought the previous phase to an end . . ." The animal phobia and the fear of falling asleep disappeared. The religious instruction his mother administered took the form of Bible stories to him, and his nursemaid, taking a hand, discussed religious problems with him. Freud states that "the battles which now began to convulse his mind ended in a victory for faith."

These battles were induced primarily by the boy's fear of his father. He first tried to cope with the problem by expressing this fear as a fear of wolves, and then, after the period of religious instruction, as a fear of God. His fearful attitude at bedtime was overcome by a series of bedtime rituals which consisted of kissing holy pictures, reciting prayers, and making the sign of the cross. These acts, of which the apparent object was to placate a presumably angry God, were really calculated to placate his father. His attitude to God was one of great respect and love on the one hand and great irreverence and even blasphemy on the other. In short, his attitude to God paralleled his attitude to his father.

As the result of his mother's religious teaching, "the wolf phobia," writes Freud, "quickly vanished, and, instead of sexuality being repudiated with anxiety, a higher method of suppressing it made its appearance. Piety became the dominant force in the child's life. These victories, however, were not won without struggles, of which his blasphemous thoughts were an indication, and of which the establishment of an obsessive exaggeration of religious ceremonial was the result." Yet Freud, who has been characterized in some quarters as the greatest "anti-Christ" of all time, goes on to say: "Apart from these pathological phenomena it may be said that in the present case religion achieved all the aims for the sake of which it is included in the education of the individual. It put a restraint on his sexual impulses by affording them a sublimation and a safe mooring; it lowered the importance of his family relationships, and thus protected him from the threat of isolation by giving him access to the great community of mankind. The untamed and fear-ridden child became social, well-behaved and amenable to education." [5]

Such passages in Freud point up the fact that when he is speaking on the basis of the clinical data, he exhibits an attitude towards religion which differs from that exhibited in his more purely philosophical excursions into the subject.

At the ages of eight and ten Freud's patient had brief periods during which the obsessional exaggeration of his religious observance became particularly prominent. When he was ten he came under the influence of an atheistic German tutor, in response to whom his strict piety gradually dwindled away. He remained in comparatively good mental health from then until he was seventeen, when neurotic symptoms returned following a venereal infection. This was the beginning of the emotional breakdown, which grew gradually worse.

Freud states that under the influence of the German tutor, all of the boy's "strict piety dwindled away, never to be revived." Although there is no way of answering the question, it is still reasonable to ask what the course of this emotionally unstable young man's life might have been if he had been introduced to wholesome, positive religious experiences at the time of puberty or before; whether he might not have gone on from the ambivalent religious attitude of his childhood to a more mature form of religious expression. Nor is it an unreasonable hypothesis that even his childish and neurotic religious attitude might have rescued him from his adult emotional illness, just as it did from that of his childhood. It is perhaps a commentary on the psychoanalyst's feeling about religion that none of the few follow-up reports on the "Wolfman" contains material, either by inference or as a result of direct inquiry, concerning the patient's subsequent religious attitudes. In view of the prominence which Freud himself gave to the patient's childhood religious experience in his original case report, it is not unfair to suggest that this omission represents an unfortunate scientific flaw in the follow-up studies.

Another case which illustrates even more graphically that religion and psychiatry are not implacable foes but that they actually supplement each other is one described by Helene Deutsch. It concerns a seventeen-year-old girl from a devout Catholic home. The picture she presented when first examined by the psychiatrist was one of profound mental illness. She lay on her bed mute and immobile, displaying muscular rigidity in a variety of bizarre postures. The onset of this acute disturbance followed a series of personal tragedies, including the death of her father when she was sixteen, her brother's suicide after a venereal infection, and her mother's death from tuberculosis. In childhood the patient was described as being "naughtier than the naughtiest boy," slovenly in her personal habits, cruel to her younger brothers and sisters, as well as to animals, and unable to get along with her playmates. At the age of twelve she underwent a dramatic alteration of character. She became extraordinarily clean, conscientious, pedantically exact in all she did, hypersensitive towards her family, extremely truth-loving, ready to renounce all worldly pleasures out of sympathy and love for others, correct and reliable, with a trace of asceticism. In Deutsch's words, "The little devil had become an angel incarnate."

We need not go into the details of this patient's emotional conflicts, how she tried to cope with them, which of her life experiences lay behind them. In any case, they were kept under control for five years, only to erupt in the form of a severe mental illness when she was seventeen. She first attempted to cope with her problems by flight into a convent as a novice. Her superiors soon recognized that she was mentally ill and referred her to a psychiatrist for treatment. Three years of psychoanalysis resulted in a great improvement, and she resumed her plans to become a nun. In the new world of the convent she was able to remain, for all practical purposes, healthy. The patient herself was completely satisfied with the result of the analysis.[6]

From the analyst's point of view, two points may be made

about this case. First, the convent provided a modus vivendi which was socially useful and personally fulfilling, and which, in addition, served to protect the young woman from life stresses in the outer world that were beyond her capacity to handle. The framework of Catholicism provided her with devices and techniques without which this degree of restoration to mental health might not have been possible. Second, psychoanalysis, by effecting a cure, if only a partial one, enabled the patient to resume her chosen way of life. Far from destroying beliefs, as it is often accused of doing, psychoanalysis in this case enhanced the patient's capacity for participation in the religious community.

To Freud religion is an illusion that will wither away as mankind achieves emotional maturity. It is easy to dismiss this claim with the observation that mankind, even with Freud's help, shows no signs of maturing. It is even questionable whether mankind will survive long enough to make it possible to determine how emotional growth will affect its religious attitudes. In any case, there are already sufficient data at hand to cast serious doubts on Freud's contention. In the clinical material presented in the following chapters, it will be found that there is considerable evidence for a thesis that would surely have been a paradox to the author of *The Future of an Illusion*. The thesis is that emotional growth by way of psychoanalysis can result in an upsurge of religious feeling, where none was consciously present before; that it can result further in the replacement of the distorted religious expressions that accompany mental disease with forms of religious experience that are at once deeply satisfying and consistent with emotional maturity. In short, Freud's own technique, applied with apparent clinical success, has resulted, in case after case, not in a dissolution of religious feeling but rather in its augmentation and stabilization.

The Next Step

IT IS generally agreed that the role of the religious leader in modern society stands in need of clarification. It may be said at once that in the fulfillment of this role, he will avail himself of whatever light psychiatry and the allied disciplines can shed upon the religious attitudes and problems of children and adolescents, upon religious needs in such situations as sickness, catastrophe, and death. But since psychiatry and religion are not simply two names for the same thing, and are not the same in either techniques or purposes, how is religious counseling—as quite separate from psychiatry—to be characterized, and what are its professional standards? How are individuals affected or changed by religious counseling? Do religious affirmations and practices contribute to emotional adjustment and maturity, or do they, as some have contended, foster unwholesome dependency attitudes? Can there be cross-fertilization of the professions that make up the modern psychological treatment team, and if so, to what extent? Granted that all the helping professions have a common basis in the need to understand human behavior, we still have much to learn about the methods whereby the religious leader can make his unique contribution. It seems reasonable that the best way to learn is to study systematically and critically a large body of clinical material.

At any rate, such is the complex task which has been set for this book. Whatever may be the case with the theoretical constructions suggested here, and obviously they await further cooperative effort, the authors believe that most of the clinical findings are conclusive. They indicate unmistakably that the religious leader is an indispensable member of the treatment team. The psychiatrist, the psychologist, the social caseworker, and members of allied disciplines need his help, just as he needs theirs to round out his own contribution to the community. Further, it has become apparent that the religious leader participates in the total treatment program in a specific way. As wielding a unique instrument, he helps where other members of the team cannot help. Their training forbids them from trespassing on the religious domain, and the community consults them with other than religious expectations. Similarly, the role of the religious leader on the team is such that he cannot assume the roles of the other members without diluting and impairing his own. He needs to understand the goals and techniques of other members, but he has methods and goals of his own, goals that are capable of definition and clinical illustration. It is also clinically clear that psychiatric treatment need have no adverse affect upon religious feelings and practices, but on the contrary can and does enhance a person's capacity for religious faith and fellowship. Above all, the various findings explored in this book encourage the belief that continuing research and cooperation among all the helping and healing professions will make for the enhancement of life.

RELIGIOUS DEVELOPMENT IN

CHILDHOOD

2.

THE EXPERIENCES OF CHILDHOOD HOLD THE KEY TO ALL later behavior, religious or other. Parental love and a happy family environment usually assure the child's development into an emotionally mature adult, while the absence of these things generally has damaging effects on character and personality. There are exceptions, of course, but the evidence of psychiatry overwhelmingly bears out the close correspondence between childhood experience and adult behavior. And this being so, we may say that religious feelings and ideas in an adult are not merely the result of reasoning or inspiration. Even when they occur later on in life, taking adult forms and influenced apparently by none of the person's childhood associates, in actual fact they go back to childhood relationships and the unfolding of self and conscience. It is for this reason that we open with the relatively little understood psychological development of religious attitudes from infancy to adolescence.

Religion of the Preschool Child

UNTIL the child has learned speech, he cannot communicate his religious experiences. The Bible stories he hears, the prayers he is taught, the observances in which he participates in the life of the family, are the nucleus of his first religious ideas. They are the ideas he usually employs in working out the life problems which concern him most at this time. This period is characterized initially by a conception of God which differs little from the child's conception of his own parents. At this phase of development, the child commonly pictures God as possessing the attributes of his father, or occasionally his mother. He may say that God is like his father, only larger. Gordon W. Allport cites the case of a six-year-old boy who refused to recite the "Our Father" prayer because his earthly father was a drunkard.[1] The opposite reaction is exemplified by a girl of five who was excessively attentive to her father both in public and in private. He filled all her thoughts and made her happy and wholly overshadowed even her religious life. When at prayer, she felt far more religious fervor if she was looking at her father as she prayed. Later, she used to go to church, where the minister was a friend of her father's; during the prayers she would keep her eyes fixed on the pastor in order to strengthen her devotion. Because of the equation of God with the parents at this early period, an understanding of normal parent-child relations helps the religious leader interpret God to the child of the preschool age, in terms of his emotional needs and intellectual capacity.

After the child learns to talk, a more complex phase of development begins. His interests begin to broaden. He plays with other children and adults and often imitates their behavior. Typical of this is the religious experience of Michele and Carol, three-year-old twins, which at first was confined to saying prayers at bedtime. In the beginning they enjoyed this, but afterwards repeated the prayers routinely. Yet if for any reason their parents tried to leave out this ritual, they objected and insisted upon saying the prayer. One day some friends of the twins' parents came to dinner with their three-year-old daughter, who said grace at the table. The twins watched with interest, folded their hands and bowed their heads like their parents and the visitors. The little girl was complimented for saying grace so well. The next day the twins insisted on saying grace and continued for several months. Here one can clearly see the role of imitation and social experience in the development of religious practices.

During periods of stress—when a new baby is born, or some other upsetting event occurs—there may occur a reawakening of a previously submerged pattern of behavior that is characteristic of an earlier phase of development—a "regression."

As the child observes the satisfaction of the baby during feed-ing, he too may wish to be fed and to reexperience that pleasure. He longs for the contentment and even ecstasy that he felt in his own infancy as his imperious demands of hunger were gratified at his mother's breast—a gratification which helps to lay the groundwork for faith and optimism in later life.[2] More-over, the child may again soil himself for a brief period in order to gain the mother's attention. If in connection with bowel con-trol the mother is too critical or severe, a serious struggle may ensue, which may exert a distorting influence upon later be-havior. Bowel movements performed at the right time and place are a positive way of placating authority, but when such ex-periences dealing with cleanliness are invested with too much emotion, they may be a basis for a subsequent excessive con-cern with ritual and religious observances—prayers said in the proper manner and at the right time, for instance, become a way of placating authority in the person of God. Freud's "Wolfman" case, which was discussed in Chapter One, is an instance of this. Another instance is a psychoanalyst's case of a man whose father died when he was four years old, and whose mother, a fanatically religious person, was also unloving and hypercritical. She filled her son's mind with terrifying su-perstitions, above all that of a bogeyman who supposedly in-habited the cellar of their home. The result was that the little boy developed a fear of going out into the street alone. One day when he was six, his mother forced him out into the street to run an errand, and suddenly, in a state of panic and despera-tion, he prayed to God for help. All he remembers is that he soon found himself back home, in front of the door, the errand accomplished and his fear gone. Thereafter he found that he could master the fear of the bogeyman in the cellar by the expedient of saying a prayer. So began a lifelong attitude of piety, or perhaps one should say of hyperreligiosity. For he would spend hours each day in detailed and exhausting re-ligious rituals, designed to placate the bogeyman who at times was confused in his mind with the idea of an angry God who had to be placated. He developed such perfectionistic tendencies that they later interfered with his happiness as a husband and his efficiency as a businessman. In a word, the boy grew up an emotionally stunted person. Analysis revealed that in God he regained the father he had lost as a child, a God who was an idealized figure powerful enough to protect him against his emotionally abnormal mother, and was at the same time an angry person who might abandon him as his father had done.[3]

Another case of a child's difficulties, which seemed to result from a mother's overconcern with bowel training and preoccupation with cleanliness, and which had unfortunate religious consequences, is that of a five-year-old Jewish girl who suddenly took a dislike to her grandmother. One day she asked her mother. "Why did Granny kill Jesus Christ?" "After a bit of conversation," the mother relates, "I learned that one afternoon while she was playing in the yard with the six-year-old son of my neighbor, a Catholic with whom we have very friendly relations, the boy said to her, 'I don't like you. You killed my God, Jesus Christ.' After insisting that she didn't, she finally replied, 'I did not kill Christ. Maybe Granny did, but I didn't.' " Neither mother nor rabbi could do anything to restore the child's once friendly attitude to her grandmother. The little girl, it seems, was also suffering from nightmares in which she was pursued by a witch. Finally she was taken to a psychiatrist, who confirmed the mother's impression that the youngster was an essentially wholesome child. After she had won the friendship of the child, the psychiatrist inquired, "Do you think your granny is the sort of person who would kill anybody—Jesus Christ or anyone else?" The response to this inquiry was a flood of tears and the outcry that her granny was a cruel person and she feared her. Discussion with the mother revealed that the grandmother was really a "Craig's wife," widowed and grown old. She had an obsessional hatred of dirt and disorder. Most horrifying to the child was the grandmother's relentless pursuit of the field mice that constantly invaded their suburban home. She set traps for them and disposed of their mangled bodies with manifest pleasure. Further inquiry by the psychiatrist brought out the fact that the child felt she was bad and dirty, that her grandmother had told her so when she was caught playing with her genitals. The child was reassured about her exploratory play, and told that she was a clean little girl and that her granny had no intention of punishing her. As the parents came to understand the nature of the problem, they were better able to handle the child's hostile attitude towards her grandmother. After months of treatment, the sleep disturbance improved and the hostility subsided to a great extent. It wasn't always possible to get the grandmother's cooperation and as a result the child's symptoms would flare up from time to time. However, she improved enough so that she became amenable to the teachings of the rabbi, and as a result of a priest's intervention with the boy, the two children of different faiths began to play together again.

One of the problems with which the preschool child has to contend, however carefully the parents may have prepared him, is the birth of a new baby. The younger the child, the greater the hurt, especially if he is the first-born. Sympathetic as the mother may be, she must attend to the needs of the newcomer, so that the older child receives less attention than before and feels anger against the baby who has displaced him. If he gives direct expression to this anger he may be scolded and punished, and his feeling of alienation from the mother will become even greater.

The child may succeed in curbing his outward expressions of anger towards the newborn baby and towards his mother, but inwardly he may cherish a wish that the hated rival would die. To a young child an angry wish is comparable to an angry deed, for in his limited understanding of the world he overestimates his own powers and believes that such a wish can actually, magically, cause death. As a consequence he suffers much guilt, with feelings of unworthiness and expectations of punishment. In such cases of "sibling rivalry," religion can be used wisely to relieve guilt or unwisely to aggravate fears, and a knowledge of the particular home situation will help the religious leader to understand the problem when a child has a negative reaction to religious teaching.

An interesting example of how religion offered effective help in the resolution of a sibling conflict occurs in an eighteenth-century tract by the Reverend Jonathan Edwards.[4] Shortly after the birth of a baby sister, four-year-old Phoebe became conspicuously involved in curious bits of religious behavior. She would acknowledge loudly that she loved God more than she loved her new baby sister. When her older sisters returned from school she would greet them with tears and expressions of alarm for their salvation. She expressed the fear that her sisters would end up in hell in spite of her entreaties in their behalf. Her precocious religious fervor excited great interest in the community and she had opportunities to talk at length with various clergymen, especially Reverend Edwards. It would appear that these religious activities provided her with a socially acceptable outlet for expressions of hostility to her newborn sister, her older sisters, and probably her mother as well, besides bringing her to the attention of a number of important father figures. If the particular religious form in which Phoebe solved her emotional problems can hardly be cited as exemplary, the case does indicate the possibilities of the religious approach to such problems.*

The following case also throws light upon both the good and bad effects of religion in connection with the problems of sibling rivalry. A five-year-old boy, Jim, developed a fear of death coincident with the birth of a brother. Above all he was afraid he would die in his sleep. As a result, bedtime was a dreadful occasion for all concerned. Shortly before the birth of his brother he had ridden past a cemetery with his parents, and in response to his questions had been told that it was a place where dead people were buried; that their bodies slept there forever while their souls went to heaven. At about this time, too, he had learned to say the well-known prayer, "Now I lay me down to sleep . . . if I should die before I wake, I pray the Lord my soul to take . . ." After the birth of his brother he stopped saying this prayer and in its place began expressing a fear that he would die before he waked. Reassurances by his parents and by the family doctor were to no avail. In desperation sleeping medications were administered, but they too proved unsatisfactory. Nor could the minister help at first, but learning the details of the home situation, such as the birth of a

---

* In an unpublished study on "The Family Romance of the Artist," Phyllis Greenacre, M.D., of New York, suggests that gifted children who are destined for greatness are prone to religious awakenings in early childhood. Such awakenings occur around the age of five and are associated with ecstatic experiences and a sense of union with God. Greenacre suggests that the highly gifted child suffers a sense of alienation from his peers and from his family, that his heightened perceptivity sets him apart from others and makes him a lonely individual. Greenacre regards the turning to God as part of the struggle against loneliness. Thus the availability of religious devices to the gifted child facilitates the solution of the problems of his emotional growth, which are more complex than those of the ordinary child.

brother and the child's handling by the mother, he recommended a psychiatrist.

Using play therapy, one of the special treatment techniques of child psychiatry, the psychiatrist brought out the boy's intense but repressed hostility and death wishes towards his newborn brother. The youngster was given ample opportunity in play therapy to vent his rage against the intruder whose birth had toppled him from the position of the favorite and only son. These controlled and harmless expressions of rage were interpreted to him by the psychiatrist, who told him that feelings of resentment against his new little brother were understandable, but that he would be able to control these feelings. In time he might even find in him a playmate with whom he could have lots of fun. Meantime his mother had several talks with a caseworker, who helped her to see that she had managed Jim in a highly inconsistent manner, by turns excessively affectionate and punitive. Through this double attack on the problem, a striking improvement in the boy's sleep soon took place. It is interesting to note that, with his improvement, he resumed his bedtime prayers spontaneously. No sooner had he mastered his angry feelings against his younger brother than he ceased to feel threatened by the words of the prayer. Now that he no longer felt like a bad boy who deserved punishment for his evil thoughts, he derived comfort from the warm, fatherly minister's assurances that God protected him while he slept. And such assurances made it easier for him to share his mother's love with the new baby.

This case history is typical of a common emotional disorder of childhood, in which primarily unconscious death wishes towards a newborn brother or sister are combined with intense attachment to the mother. Until this problem was brought out into the open, none of the ordinary methods of common sense and reassurance were of any help to Jim, but when the special techniques of the psychiatrist revealed the nature of the problem, even the ordinary methods could be addressed to the proper target and began to take effect, and rapid improvement followed. Not only was religious consolation of no avail at the height of the boy's fears, but he reacted against it. Yet with his knowledge of the behavior of the child and of the home situation, the religious leader was able to understand this fearful reaction to religious teaching, and referred the child to a psychiatrist. As the child's neurosis subsided, his capacity to relate to a father figure in the form of the minister and to participate in religious observance returned. Once restored to a more or less normal state, he was able to avail himself of the minister's teaching in coping with his problem.

The Oedipus Complex and Religion

AS THE ability to communicate develops, children learn the difference between the sexes. The boy often interprets the absence of a penis in the girl as a mutilation inflicted as a punishment, and as a result, physical injury and death come to be feared as a punishment for misbehavior. With awareness of the difference in the sexes, the child begins to identify with the parent of his own sex; the boy normally takes the father's behavior and aspirations as his model, and the girl takes the mother's. A by-product of this "identification" is an infantile ambition to displace the parent of the same sex from his or her major role in the family. The ideas and behavior patterns associated with this ambition are referred to as the Oedipus complex. During this period, masturbation occurs, and it is associated with fantasies involving the parents. Because of the prominence of the Oedipus complex, this is called the "oedipal phase" of development, which occurs roughly at the age of four to six years, when the child has developed speech and some social experience. Typically the complex is associated with a wish for the death of the parent of the same sex, who is now regarded as a rival. But the child loves this parent, too, so that he suffers guilt for harboring unfilial thoughts. Moreover, he fears that the parent will learn of these death wishes and punish him. Since, in the child's logic, to wish for someone's death is tantamount to killing him, his anticipation of parental punishment can be terrifying. During this period the religious leader may exert a powerful influence, not only upon the child's later religious beliefs and character formation, but by steering his normal aggressions in the direction of forgiving authority figures through the medium of Bible stories, play symbols, and rituals. The religious leader will take advantage of the fact that the child, at this stage of his development, is especially receptive to the environment and eager to develop new relationships and experiences.

That the Oedipus complex may express itself in religious terms is illustrated by the following case history, which also shows understanding by the religious leader involved and the use of a Biblical story to meet the emotional and intellectual needs of a child going through the oedipal phase of his psycho-sexual development. A five-year-old boy who had previously been active and gay became fretful and sleepless. He refused to go to sleep at night, and was afraid of the dark. He would not close his eyes even when the lights in his room were blazing. The parents reasoned with the child and tried to reassure him, but their efforts were of no avail. The pediatrician had to resort to sleeping pills. In discussions with the doctor and with his parents the boy indicated that his fear had something to do with a bookcase in his room. With some encouragement he finally revealed that it was a particular volume in the book-case which was the cause of his terror. The book turned out to be an illustrated collection of Bible stories for children, among which was the story of Abraham's preparations for the sacrifice of his son Isaac. The incident was luridly portrayed in a full-page picture. With this discovery, the problem rapidly became clear, for it happened that the boy's father was named Abraham. Deeply attached to his mother, the boy had been fearful of the consequences of what he imagined was his father's resent-ment. Now the boy was enabled to tell his father of his worry, while the father, in turn, was able to reassure him that he did not resent his expressions of affection for his mother. The father explained that a mother loves her son in one way and her husband in another, and that when he grew up he would have a wife of his own, and a child of his own, and that he would love his child dearly, even as he, the father, loved him. Further, as the result of consultation with his minister, the father reminded the boy that even in the original story the father did not injure the son, that God, who is Father to all, is all-loving. The minister also suggested other religious ma-terials, and in consequence of all this the sleep disturbance disappeared almost at once.

Here, then, an experience associated with religion precipi-tated a neurotic reaction. Although, as the minister showed,

the offending Bible story could be turned into a source of reassurance, it is still true that every care must be exercised in
selecting religious teaching materials for the young. Children
are extremely impressionable, and such stories as that of Isaac
might reasonably be kept from a youngster of five, certainly in
the illustrated version that appeared in our case history. Stories
emphasizing forgiveness and the role of God as a protector
and provider—in a word, stories related to the emotional needs
of the child in the oedipal period—are likely to have the best
effect of all in fostering emotional growth.

The home of the preschool child is his world. His ideas about
men are based almost exclusively on what he sees in his father;
about women, on what he sees in his mother; about the relations
between men and women, on his parents' relations. His ideas
about the way figures in authority treat relatively helpless individuals like himself are based on the way he has worked out his
feelings within the family.

The Quest for Personal Identity

IT IS not always possible for the child to model itself
after the parent of the same sex. The parent may be
dead or divorced, or the child may be unable to accept him as
a model. Or the other parent may exercise an unduly powerful
influence in the home and interfere with the normal growth and
development of everyone else in it. In all these cases the process
of establishing personal identity may be hampered. When the
child is old enough to go to school, he encounters many other
parent figures upon whom he may model himself: teachers,
religious leaders, parents of friends, and public heroes. But a
damaging experience in the preschool period may subsequently
hamper the child's freedom in this respect. He may fail to achieve
a positive sense of personal identity, or, coming into contact
with children who have achieved this sense in a religious setting,
he may fall into confusion.

The parents of a young boy reported the following experience. They themselves were brought up in homes in which
there was a moderate observance of Jewish religious traditions.
Their own home, on the contrary, was devoid of any evidences
of religious interest, except for that indicated by some visiting

friends, both Jewish and non-Jewish. With the birth of their son, they adopted the custom of decorating their home and exchanging presents at Christmastime. When he was five, the boy's best friend was a youngster, from an Episcopalian home, who attended church and Sunday school and derived considerable pleasure from doing so. The boy became envious of these activities and told his parents he would like to accompany his friend to church. The parents were troubled but gave their permission. A few weeks later they received a telephone call from their son's public school teacher, who told them that there had been a discussion of religious affiliations during which one boy after another stood up and identified himself readily as a Christian or a Jew, but that their boy arose hesitantly and stated that his parents were Jews but he was not sure what he was, except possibly "just an American." Adding to the boy's confusion and unhappiness was his exposure to anti-Jewish remarks made by other children, and in one instance by an adult.

The rabbi whom the parents now consulted told them that Judaism could be taught only as a religion. On his advice the boy was enrolled in a religious study group, and the parents themselves became members of a synagogue. Although of a skeptical turn of mind, the boy attended his religious classes regularly, learned his lessons well, and at confirmation carried off his role in the ceremonials with distinction. He became an active member of the synagogue's "teen-age group," where he made many sound friendships.

In thus taking a positive stand with regard to their religious identity, the parents aided their confused son to arrive at a clearer picture of himself. And it was the religious leader who made this possible. In general it may be said that, given the opportunity for identification with a religious group, the child who is developing normally will achieve an unequivocal notion about his religious affiliation by the age of six.

Nothing could be more mistaken than the common parental attitude that formal religious affiliation should be deferred until the child is "old enough" to make his own decision. This attitude is encountered especially often in interfaith marriages. To defer affiliation until the school years or adolescence is to by-pass an important developmental phase in the life of the child; it has unfortunate effects, not only on the problem of personal identification, but on other psychological problems as well. Our clinical data indicate that parents should make the decision for the child, and make it before he has reached the age of five.

Parents belonging to minority groups will sometimes deny their children the opportunity for religious affiliation, thinking to protect them against unnecessary conflict, or to spare them the problem of "double allegiances." Of the latter, Kurt Lewin rightly remarks: "Parents should not be afraid of so-called 'double allegiances'; belonging to more than one overlapping group is natural and necessary for everyone. The real danger lies in standing 'nowhere'—in being a 'marginal man,' an eternal adolescent." [5]

Play Aspects of Religion

APART from the fun which play affords them, children learn and grow through play, and resolve important personal conflicts as well. Religious notions may figure in their play, as the following story related by the mother of two little girls illustrates. "Before the Christmas festival, Eva was 'the Christ-child.' She flew through the room with outstretched arms bringing gifts to all children . . . The little one also claimed an office, and was promoted to the position of 'Angel Choir,' to sing and mingle with the angels. After Christmas Eve the holy persons were represented by building blocks . . . In Heaven —a stage-like structure, with stairs leading up to it—stood the Saviour, the Lord Jesus, the Guest, and the Christ-child. The relation between the Christ-child, the Saviour, Jesus, and the Guest was remarkable. The children knew quite well that the Christ-child was called Jesus, and that He grew up to be the Saviour, yet they maintained that their Christ-child was always small. They knew, too, that at our meals we 'pray that Jesus may be our Guest'; but this did not hinder them at all from attributing a separate personality in their play to each of these names." [6] This last observation is of special interest in bringing out a peculiarity of childish thought, which is by no means confined to the religious sphere. It is the capacity of the child's mind to tolerate contradictions without the discomfort usually

experienced by the more logical-minded adult. Freud refers
to this illogic of the child as the primary process. Under normal
circumstances it is encountered mainly in early childhood and
in the dreams of adults.

Children often take the same playful attitude towards prayer
as these girls did towards a religious holiday, and make their
nightly prayers an occasion for bedtime romping. To the child
learning to talk, the appeal of rhymed prayer is especially great.
But the natural playfulness of children erupts spontaneously
in any medium at its disposal, and this suggests that the religious leader might well provide young children with every
opportunity to play at religious games, choosing materials suitable to their age, experience, and imagination. Play can be an
effective stepping stone to a more formal program of religious
instruction.

Religion in the School Years

U P   T O about the fifth year the child's wishes are very
often in conflict with those of the parent. In spite of
his best efforts to obey he is not always able to. Fearing physical
punishment and loss of love on the one hand and unable to
control himself on the other, the child finds himself in a dilemma. Until the conflicts are resolved the child may suffer
from night terrors, transient fears, behavior disturbances, and
other symptoms.

Initially a child obeys out of a direct fear of punishment from
a parent who is physically present. This has been characterized as the period of external morality. In time the child develops internalized controls, and the concept of God plays
an important role in facilitating this process. The fear of ret-
ribution is projected heavenwards, that is, towards God in the
image of the parent. God becomes a super-parent, all-seeing and
all-knowing, from whom it is not possible to hide one's wrong-
doings. Parent and God are more or less literally equated.
There follows the formation of conscience. The kind of relationship the child has with his parents, and the values instilled by them, determine the child's concept of God and the
quality of his conscience. If the relationship is a positive one,
the child gradually accepts the parents' conceptions of right

and wrong as part of himself. He comes to refrain from wrong-doing out of a sense of guilt rather than from fear of detection and actual physical punishment. The external parent is replaced by a group of ideas whose regulatory influence is no less severe. The process of separating the conception of God from the image of the parent begins at this time and introduces the next phase of religious development. God is still primarily a God of anger who is feared and who can be loved only ambivalently. This combination of love mixed with fear of the power of the parent constitutes awe and respect, and characterizes the child's emerging concept of God. As Jean Piaget points out, respect and awe cannot have their origin in a relationship between equals, but between "the small and the great."

The main problem for the growing child at this time is the development of adequate control over his impulses. Here is a case history that illustrates the way religion contributes to this development after the child has acquired a conscience. An eight-year-old boy attended a parochial school where the discipline was strict, but fair and not punitive. He apparently accepted the limits of this environment without noticeable psychological effect until he contracted measles. The period of acute illness was without incident, but with recovery some four weeks later, a recovery that coincided with the beginning of Easter vacation, the boy underwent a curious and striking change in behavior. Previously well behaved, he now became mischievous, overtalkative and overactive. At mealtimes he would drop his silverware and spill his food in ways that were interpreted at the time as misbehavior. At night he slept restlessly, often crying out in his sleep. On the third day of this altered behavior he became tearful and frightened, reiterating that he didn't want to be on vacation, that he was unable to study and improve himself with his teachers away. A pediatrician whom the family consulted found that the boy was showing peculiar movements which were unmistakably caused by chorea (St. Vitus dance). Proper treatment was instituted at once and the child made a satisfactory recovery. In retrospect it was clear that his spilling of food at table was due to the clumsiness associated with the onset of chorea.

The most striking thing here is the fact that the child reacted to his increasing disability with a wish to return to school and to his religious teachers, as if their continued disciplinary influence would bolster his crumbling self-control. What this case particularly illumines is the need, less evident in normal circumstances, for external discipline in the problems that accompany emotional growth. In this area, religion plays a role of preeminent importance.

Religious discipline may be applied to help free the child from his infantile attachments and open up for him a capacity for relationships with other adults and a broadened social horizon, both indispensable to his emotional development. But religious discipline, while it is of the first importance in fostering normal growth, may also be applied to hinder such growth. It is not rare for children to develop a fear of going to school, which may express itself in a variety of ways, particularly in the form of headaches, colds, and "stomach upset" in the morning; some children will vomit their breakfast or wet the bed regularly. Of course these symptoms are often the result of other anxieties that are now focusing on the school itself, but some pediatricians believe that such symptoms occur more frequently in children who go to parochial schools, where the discipline is stricter than in most secular schools. Whether this is true or not, the following case illustrates the effect of excessive religious discipline. A bright, sensitive boy of six, whose parents were devoutly religious, was enrolled in a parochial school. He was a bedwetter and tended to blink his eyes nervously, but otherwise he showed no abnormalities of behavior. The youngster returned from school one day in a highly agitated state. Between sobs he related how he had been scolded by the teacher in front of the class for unruly behavior. His father stormed at him for his misbehavior, and locked him in his room without food for the rest of the day. The next day the boy went off to school in a greatly subdued state, but was brought back in the middle of the school day, crying uncontrollably and saying, "God has made me blind!" To the horror of his parents, whose initial reaction was again punitive, the youngster did seem to be blind. When the minister arrived on the scene he found the family helpless and telephoned an eye specialist to come to the house at once. Physical examination revealed no disease, which convinced the doctor that what was involved here was a severe state of anxiety. With this in mind he reassured the boy, as well as the parents and the minister, that he was not in serious danger and that his sight would return quickly. Talking to the minister, the boy said that he had tried hard to be good, and related in detail the unhappy circumstances of the preceding day. The minister pointed out that boys his age were not expected to be perfectly behaved all the time, that self-control came gradually as one grew up, and that it was ridiculous to suppose that God, who helps people, would strike a six-year-old boy blind for acting like a six-year-old boy. During the afternoon the boy's vision returned completely. Aware of the emotional basis of the disturbance, the minister proceeded effectively to deal with it by appropriate reassurances of a religious character. Further, he made it plain to the parents that unless they showed more understanding in conducting the religious education of their son, the result could only be, not acceptance but fear of religion, with predictable consequences in misbehavior.

Not only is the child faced with the task of developing control over his impulses, but if he is to grow intellectually, he must liberate his mind from infantile misconceptions. Here, too, religion plays a constructive role, especially in the development of the concept of causality, which represents a momentous step in a child's intellectual growth. Piaget writes: "The explanation of movement is the central point to which all the child's ideas about the world converge . . . It shows, above all, that the distinction between a body's own movement and that which is determined from the outside is only reached after much groping and many difficulties . . ." [7] Up to the age of five or six, the child has a feeling of magical omnipotence. "The moon moves," he declares, "because I make it move. It follows me because it wants to follow me." To the child, the moon is subject to a kind of perpetual moral restraint whereby it is obliged to follow him. At this stage of his development, the child conceives of causality in moral terms. He visualizes himself as a parent who dictates the movement of the moon in the sky in much the same way as parents dictate his own movements.

By the time he reaches the age of ten, the child has arrived at an explanation of the movements of the moon that is more in accord with reality. How does he achieve this? How does he pass from infantile ideas of magical omnipotence to a realistic grasp of the world around him? Failure to make this vital step in the process of normal maturation, or going back upon it later in life, accounts for certain thought disorders characteristic of mental illness. The step itself is commonly brought about by the idea of God. "The moon moves," the child now says, "because God makes it move." And this represents a long and important step in the direction of reality.

Thus infantile ideas of magical omnipotence give way to the God-concept of causality. In this concept, moral considerations mingle directly with physical, indeed are hardly separated. It is the earliest notion of causality and the one that survives longest. As mental development proceeds, increasingly the separation between moral and physical considerations occurs, and teleology is more and more excluded from the explanation of natural phenomena. In times of great crisis the earlier notion of causality tends to be revived.

In the light of the change that takes place in the mental life of the child around the age of six, it is not surprising that the interest in religion reaches a peak at this age, as Gesell has noted in his statistical studies of childhood. The fact has not gone unsensed in traditional religion. It is celebrated with impressive ceremonies designed to set the stage for the next period of growth. So we have first communion in some Christian groups, and in Judaism the beginning of the child's religious studies at this age is celebrated with a party in his honor.

As inner controls develop, the child forgets—"represses"— many of the wishes which were the source of his troubles. Not only does he achieve these more dependable controls, but there is an enlargement of his social horizons in school and in play. The acquisition of new skills, physical and intellectual, opens new channels for self-expression, and unacceptable impulses begin to be directed into socially acceptable channels, that is, sublimated. Early conflicts are gradually resolved, and in the normal course of events a relatively peaceful period sets in, which is called the latency period. This is a period of learning during which the child masters many new physical skills and vastly expands his knowledge of the world about him. He goes to school, where he meets many parent substitutes. Group life becomes much more important to him and the infantile emotional bonds to his family undergo a considerable loosening.

The conception of God undergoes further development, coming to embrace love and forgiveness. Good behavior becomes the rule, not out of fear or guilt but out of love. The parents' standards become the youngster's standards, not because the parents are feared but because they are respected and loved, and at the same time God becomes a being separate from them. Whatever the limitations of the real parents, the divine Parent becomes a psychological reality that can be loved, and whose moral prescriptions can be followed because of that love. As the earlier conception of God makes room for love, the attitude of awe towards Him gives way to reverence. At this period, too, altruistic feelings and concern for fellow human beings make their appearance. An ideal Father Figure gradually takes shape in the mind of the child, a figure who has an infinite capacity for love and forgiveness, and who in turn can be loved without question. This figure is rarely built up solely on the basis of experiences with the parents. Schoolteachers, parents of friends, heroes in the public eye and in books and in religious literature—all these contribute to the formation of the ideal. The upshot is that the period of storms inaugurated by the attempt to obey a figure who is hated and loved at the same time is replaced by a period of calm, marked by a capacity for loving obedience.

The degree to which idealized religious figures may take the place of parents during the latency period is well illustrated by the following case. A girl of nine accompanied her divorced mother to a large midwestern city. The mother was obliged to work long hours, so that the girl was left to her own devices for the larger part of the day. In her loneliness she playfully responded to the attentions of a man who was known to have made sexual overtures to young girls in the neighborhood. His attentions soon became aggressively sexual, and the terrified girl fought him off and fled in tears. As a result of this painful incident the girl developed a paralyzing fear of going out alone. The fear continued for several months, until she made the acquaintance at a nearby Catholic convent of Sister Frances, with whom she entered into a loving and understanding relationship. For the first time the girl could unburden herself freely. Sister Frances urged her to fight her fears with faith, just as she herself had done as a little girl, and with Sister Frances as her model, the child quickly mastered her fears. Now instead of coming from school to an empty house she would go directly to the convent, where she made herself useful in a variety of ways. Although many knew her and showered her with affection, Sister Frances remained her special confidante and ideal.

Another case that illustrates the importance of extrafamilial figures in the latency period is that of a nine-year-old boy who was conceived out of wedlock. While still pregnant the mother met another man, who married her in spite of her indiscretion, of which he was aware. So far as anyone in the community knew, the boy was her legitimate offspring. But the mother reacted to her son with great hostility, convinced that a sinful beginning could have only a sinful end. She was merciless in her discipline and always insisted that he was a "good-for-nothing," and the boy inevitably came to accept his mother's opinion of him. He became unruly in school and committed minor acts of delinquency. The mother would greet each new crisis with a triumphant, "I told you so!" Although the family lived in a housing project which maintained an excellent recreational program, the mother refused to allow him to participate in the games, of which he was very fond. Instead, she compelled him to attend religious classes, insisting that he had a much greater need for moral instruction than for play. Here he met with as little sympathy as he received from his mother; indeed, owing to her influence on the teacher he was subjected to particularly strict discipline. The boy went from bad to worse.

Finally, as the result of a more serious legal offense, the boy and his parents were referred to a family social agency by the court. To the trained eye of the social worker the nature of the boy's plight soon became evident. Fortunately, the father was able to see the problem and assume a much more protective role within the family. Equally important were the social worker's conferences with the teacher, who readily saw that the church was simply repeating the deficits of the boy's family life; that it was doing less than nothing to provide him with a substitute group experience. Accordingly the teacher assumed a more accepting and understanding role towards the boy. She sanctioned a considerable curtailment of his formal class work, so that he was able to participate in the neighborhood recreation program. Informed of the family situation, the minister too became warm and encouraging. He guided the father in his relationship with the boy and did what he could to make the mother less punitive. Together the social agency and the neighborhood church worked out a program which resulted in improvement in the boy's relationship with his family and even more improvement in his relationship with the church group.

Another characteristic of the latency period, the strong urge to associate in play with other children, has an important bearing upon religious upbringing. Given the child's need to conform to the group pattern of his contemporaries, a religious observance which brings him into opposition with the general mores is likely to result in conflict. Yet where appreciation of the problem exists it is usually possible to work out a solution compatible with the emotional needs of the growing youngster on the one hand and the religious convictions of his family on the other. For example, a boy was in the habit of sneaking into the neighborhood movie without paying. Repeated warnings had no effect and he was turned over to the authorities. The solution of the problem proved to be simple when the facts of the boy's life and background came to light. He came from an orthodox Jewish home, where handling money on the Sabbath was strictly forbidden. Thus he had been punished severely several times when his father caught him carrying money for his ticket to the Saturday afternoon movie which was the high spot of the week for him and his "gang." In his dilemma, the boy had resorted to sneaking into the movies. Aware of the true situation now, the mother adopted the device of taking the boy to the theater on Friday, paying for the ticket in advance, and instructing the cashier to let him in on Saturday. Never was a case of "juvenile delinquency" dealt with more easily.

The case which follows further illustrates how strong is the child's wish in the latency period to conform to the mores of his peers. A Protestant mother was quite distressed when her seven-year-old daughter, Joan, came home and asked, "Can I be a Catholic like Mary?" The mother's first thought was that the child was being subjected to proselytizing influences in the home of her little Catholic friend. It turned out, however, that

Joan's question had been inspired by the beautiful communion dress which she had watched Mary trying on. In dealing with the situation the mother spoke in a respectful, open-minded fashion of the Catholic traditions observed in Mary's home. At the same time she threw out gentle reminders of the happy occasions when Protestant observances were celebrated at their home and in church. In this way, while fostering a wholesome attitude in the girl towards her Catholic playmate, she tried to augment her sense of belonging to her own religious group. And it is the best way of dealing with such inquiries from children.

In view of the great importance of group play in the latency period, the destructive psychological effect of a chronic illness that cuts a child off from his playmates can easily be imagined. The following case history illuminates this, and it demonstrates the vital psychological function that religion may play in the emotional development of a physically handicapped child. It also shows that if the psychological needs of a child are such that religion can fulfill them, he will find his way to religious help, even when the environment does not proffer such help. Our case concerns an attractive girl endowed with superior intelligence, an only child, whose parents were militant atheists. Not only was there no religious observance in the home, but the parents were bitterly opposed to religion. The child's governesses were instructed not to take her to church or fill her head with "religious claptrap."

At the age of seven, the girl developed a disorder of the brain, with fainting spells that occurred several times a day, and even oftener under circumstances of excitement or fatigue. In consequence she was not allowed to play much with other children. Naturally unhappy about this, she felt that her illness was somehow related to her not being a good girl. But especially noteworthy is the fact that the girl, raised in an environment presumably sealed against religious influences, still developed a strong religious belief. She became firmly convinced that if she would only declare her love for God with sufficient fervor she would be cured of her illness. Accordingly, her prayers were long and elaborate, and she attempted to improve upon them each night. The neurotic nature of these long-drawn-out religious rituals is obvious, but it would be a mistake to deny them genuine religious content. In any case, the child's belief in her ultimate cure never wavered, although her illness continued for several years. When in her fourteenth year the condition disappeared, the girl was grateful but not surprised. Although unaffiliated with any church, she remained throughout her life a deeply religious person, sustained in her later as in her earlier trials by prayer.

Attitudes of Children Towards Death

BETWEEN the ages of three and five the child tends to deny the existence of death as an irrevocable event. To the child, wedded as he is to the concrete, death is an abstraction. Life and consciousness are alone real to him, so that he regards the dead person as merely asleep. For example, he will want to know how such a person is able to move in his coffin. So the concept of life after death is very much part of the thinking of the preschool child.

The idea that we "protect" children by hiding from them the realities of death is mistaken. Such efforts only hinder their emotional development. It is interesting to observe that the child's reactions to death in some ways resemble those of the adult. Thus a boy of six had a pet dog which was killed by an automobile. His initial reaction was one of stunned dismay, which was followed by an outburst of rage against his parents, whom he blamed for not taking proper care of the dog. In other words, the boy behaved like the adult who rages against God for neglecting his charges. At first the boy objected to a burial ground away from home, but he accepted the idea when he ran across two of the dog's favorite rubber toys and one of his own, which he turned over to his parents with instructions that they be buried with the dog. It would appear from this gesture that the boy harbored a belief in life after death. So far as the parents could tell, he had not been exposed to the idea either within the home or outside it. He had arrived at it spontaneously in an effort to console himself for his loss. Moreover, it seemed to his parents that, in spite of his initial reaction of rage against them, the boy had feelings of guilt about the death of his dog, for he had on occasion expressed the wish to be rid of "that pest." Thus the toys served as a kind of peace offering to the "soul" of a possibly offended pet. Free of anxiety now, the boy agreed with his parents upon the place of burial, and, soon after the burial, went about his usual affairs without further evidence of concern.

Such adjustment to the death of a pet provides some insight into the mourning behavior not only of children but of adults as well. The modes of assuagement are often very similar. They fulfill a deep-seated human need which, as it occurs in the child, has a special poignancy. Some years ago a noteworthy French film called *Forbidden Games* showed a child who had lost her parents in an air raid comforting herself by playing a game of "funeral," in which she would provide any dead creature she could find with an elaborate funeral service, including the use of ornate metal crosses and floral decorations stolen from the village cemetery. "Playing" at burying dead things helped the girl to relive, digest, and ultimately master the shock of the death of her parents. The fact is that for the child as for the adult, "doing something" in the form of a ritualistic observance brings comfort and helps tide over a difficult period of mourning. We will return to the problem of bereavement in childhood in a later chapter.

Teaching Religion to Children

SO FAR we have discussed some of the psychological needs of childhood which generate what it seems no exaggeration to call a craving for religious experience. The child is in a constant state of psychological readiness to take up religious ideas. And this readiness exists even when the parents exert every effort to insulate him against religious influences. Usually, however, the child is subjected to a steady flow of religious influences outside the home, and these may not coincide with the teachings, even religious ones, within the home. For example, a five-year-old boy attending a new Sunday School was shocked to hear that he would have to be washed in the blood of the Lamb. "I just won't do that!" he said. It took some little effort on the mother's part to convince him that the teacher did not mean a real lamb or real blood, that it was a way of saying his heart should be pure. Such teaching obviously was beyond the boy's comprehension, and if his misconception had gone uncorrected, it could very well have had serious psychological consequences.

Given the wide variety of religious influences pouring in upon the child, the problem that confronts the parent is whether to control these influences in terms of some set of religious convictions of his own, or to leave the whole matter to chance. The dangers of the latter course are plain. It is to leave the child's religion in the hands of baby sitters, domestic servants, friendly neighbors, other children, and so on. All these can, and often do, make a lasting impression upon a child, sometimes healthful, but more frequently harmful.

For example, how profound the influence of a nursemaid may be is pointedly demonstrated by the experience of Sigmund Freud. When he was two years old, Freud had a nursemaid, an old Czech woman, to whom he was much attached. She took the little boy to church with her, told him about heaven and hell, and other religious matters as well, no doubt. When they got home from church, the boy would play at preaching sermons. Unfortunately, the old woman was soon dismissed for theft. It is fair to surmise that Freud's hostility to religion and religious ceremonies goes back to his disappointment with the very person who first introduced him to religion.[8] There was no one in a position to counteract this unhappy experience, for the rest of the Freud household, it appears, were indifferent to religion.

In the religious education of children, as indeed in their education generally, it should be borne in mind that up to the age of six, children think in highly concrete and literal terms. They have little capacity for abstraction and not much grasp of symbolic meanings. Such meanings are commonly taken by the child at their face value, so that, as in our story of the "blood of the Lamb," they may have adverse effects. So may luridly illustrated stories from the Bible. The boy who reacted with terror to the picture of Abraham's intended sacrifice of Isaac is a case in point. It is clear, therefore, that the selection of religious materials in the instruction of the young calls for great care. According to one religious educator, "Children would be far more richly rewarded if parents and teachers made less effort to give them the word 'God,' and more effort to share with them experiences contributing to curiosity and wonder. We do not believe that children should have to discard early, immature concepts of God; rather through spiritually nourishing experiences, they should develop an ever-deepening concept." [9] Yet over against this is the opinion of a five-year-old girl who asked her mother, "What is God?" The mother hesitated and finally fumbled out the words, "It's just when you do good and feel good inside." The child left in thoughtful silence and returned to her mother a little later with the comment, "You're wrong, Mother. God is way up high. I'm connected to him with invisible strings and he says if I'm a good girl or bad girl."

Religious formulations of the most literal sort may be, as we have seen, a source of comfort to the child in periods of stress associated with illness and death. The following example is at the same time a sad commentary on the world we live in. A five-year-old boy listened with wide-eyed horror to an adult conversation about hydrogen bombs. Contamination of the air by radioactive substances came in for discussion, as did the holocaust that would follow upon the detonation of a hydrogen bomb. Unable to contain himself any longer, the child exclaimed, "Daddy, will the whole world really be destroyed by hydrogen bombs?" The father answered at once, "Of course not! That is utter nonsense!" "How do you know?" queried the child. His father said, "Do you remember the story of Noah that I read to you from the Bible? Do you remember how God put a rainbow in the sky after the flood? And do you remember what God told Noah about that rainbow? He said He put it there as a proof that never again would He let the world be destroyed." The child recalled the story and was reassured, which is perhaps as well, since no other reassurance is available.

The readiness of the child to accept the opinions of his elders, parents especially, places a heavy responsibility upon them. Up to approximately the age of six the child not only accepts these opinions, but turns them into absolutes. Thus Piaget speaks of this early phase of psychological development as a phase of "moral absolutism," by which he means the tendency of the young to accept rules as self-evident or as "axiomatic givens" rather than as human contrivances to facilitate personal relationships. This reaction to moral standards as though they were sacred no doubt stems from the child's conception of his parents as infallible and omniscient beings. But this phase of "moral absolutism" begins to break down after the age of six, as the child comes to realize that there are other authorities besides his parents, just as there are other moral codes than theirs. What often saves the child from moral bewilderment at this time is the emergence of the notion of God, the highest authority of all. Hence the immense importance of early religious training, the object of which should be not the reestablishment of the absolutism of the earlier period but the inculcation of a humane and flexible scheme of moral and social values. At the thirteenth annual Institute for Teachers of the Archdiocese of New York, Chaplain John J. O'Connor, director of the Navy's Character Education Program, criticized his audience of nuns, priests, brothers, and lay teachers for placing too much stress on the esoteric and mystical aspects of religion and too little on moral values. Fortunately it is those moral values, religion in the concrete, that the growing child grasps most easily and which are the most momentous for the development of character.

As we will see in the next chapter, puberty appears to set in with great suddenness, but the fact is that many psychological rumblings signal its approach. As the child's mastery of his infantile drives becomes more complete, his interest in religion tends to subside. The religious fervor which commonly marks the period between five and seven gives way to indifference. And at the approach of puberty this attitude in turn changes to one of increasing skepticism. Thus the Santa Claus myth, accepted uncritically by the four-year-old child, is dismissed with total disbelief by the time he is nine. By this age, too, he understands what death is, and its inevitability. Sexual interests begin to evince themselves now, as well as feelings of revolt against society. Behavior disorders and other evidences of emotional disturbance are likely to appear. But it is only as the physical changes of puberty set in that the chief problems of this period occur and that steps are taken toward their mature solution.

RELIGIOUS CONFLICT AND

VALUES IN ADOLESCENCE

3.

WHEN ADOLESCENCE BEGINS—AT AROUND THE AGE OF thirteen—no aspect of the child's life remains unaffected. This is especially true of his religious interests. Overtly expressed disbelief in God is more frequently encountered at the start of adolescence than at any other age, yet it is typical of the paradox of adolescence that it is also characterized as the most religious period of all. The fact is that these extremes may be encountered at different times in the same youngster. Adolescence is a period of decision as well as indecision. It is an age when religious experiences may be enormously helpful in paving the way to maturity. Hence it is that religious confirmation ceremonies represent wise psychosocial planning.

But religion may also be mishandled, with permanently damaging effect on the life of the adolescent. In one case, a young Jewish woman under the care of a psychiatrist was full of misgivings about the forthcoming bar mitzvah of her son, and it turned out that she had grown up in a state of bitter rivalry with a young brother. She recalled the pomp and ceremony of his confirmation with great envy, and the parental indifference to herself. The analyst drew a parallel between her feelings about her brother's confirmation and those which assailed her now, and pointed out that she was identifying her son with her younger brother and reliving the pain of her unsuccessful sibling rivalry. But this insight did nothing to lessen her mounting anxiety. Finally she suggested rather timidly, "Do you think that some of my nervousness might be the result of the way the cantor is treating my son?" The patient proceeded to relate that in her congregation the training for confirmation was exclusively in the hands of the cantor, in this case a severe taskmaster who was constantly holding over the heads of his charges the threat that he would cancel the entire proceedings if they did not show themselves more apt and diligent. Nothing mattered to him except that they should chant the prescribed scriptural readings to perfection. To a boy whose parents had sent out hundreds of invitations to relatives and friends, the cantor's threat, if carried out, would be the acme of humiliation. In describing this situation the patient expressed herself rather bitterly towards her rabbi. She felt that he had abdicated to the cantor and so failed her son. The hysterical fears of this mother, added to the over-strictness of the cantor, resulted in prolonged adverse effects on the boy's attitude towards religion. Such a case history shows that the values inherent in such ceremonies as confirmation may be nullified entirely if there is no understanding of the psychological issues involved. The rebelliousness and ambivalence that characterize adolescence are intensified if the boy or girl is caught in a power struggle between adults.

Adolescence is marked by periods of emotional regression and readoption of religious attitudes that were originally symptoms of infantile conflicts. This is one way of achieving emotional growth and corresponding growth in religious concepts. The fact that religious attitudes undergo a range of development and redevelopment during adolescence was brought out in a questionnaire study [1] of three groups of boys and girls—twelve-year-olds, fifteen-year-olds, and eighteen-year-olds. In the youngest group, beliefs were concrete, exhibiting the personalized qualities associated with the preschool phase of religious development. For example, a majority of the twelve-year-olds believed that God keeps a watch over the behavior of each person and punishes for bad behavior. Most of them had no doubt that heaven exists and that only good people go there, just as there was hardly any doubt about hell as a place where the wicked are punished for their sins on earth. No less common was the literal acceptance of every word in Scripture, to doubt which was regarded as a sin.

The most striking changes occurred when this group had reached the age of eighteen. God came to be conceived in more abstract terms, as an indefinable force working for the general good rather than for the welfare of separate individuals. Not so much a punisher of wrongdoers, God was thought of rather as a source of help in times of trouble. So the number of boys and girls in this age group who believed in the efficacy of prayer was greater than in the twelve-year-old group, for whom prayer was mainly a way of assuaging guilt.

On the basis of the evidence provided by this study, we may say that while the belief in God hardly varies from one age group to the other, the conception of God changes from the concrete to the abstract. At the same time this momentous alteration in the notion of God has no marked effect, it seems, on the concrete observance of prayer and ritual.

The changes with age in the character and intensity of religious belief were noted by Edwin D. Starbuck as long ago as 1899. In his *Psychology of Religion* he says, "It is a singular fact . . . that . . . conversions do not distribute themselves equally among the years; in the rough, we may say that they begin to occur at seven or eight years and increase gradually to ten or eleven and then rapidly to sixteen; rapidly decline to twenty, and gradually fall away after that, and become rare after thirty. . . . The event comes earlier in general among the females than among males, most frequently at thirteen and sixteen. Among males it occurs most often at seventeen and immediately before and after that year." [2] Gesell and his group found peaks of religious fervor at six and thirteen. Figures apart, the important thing here is that religious belief is a dynamic process, whose specific motivations can be brought to light only by the psychosocial study of children.

Religion and the Needs of Adolescents

A STUDY of over a thousand autobiographical essays written by students in their later adolescent years shows the variety of their worries: feelings of inferiority, inability to control daydreaming, sexual problems, social situations, breaking away from their parents. In all this turmoil religion appears to be a major concern. God, heaven, hell, immortality, and the reason for human existence are fervently debated. Conspicuous, too, is the desire to do something to improve the world. Gesell found that before the age of thirteen, children were predominantly concerned with material possessions, health, and personal appearance, whereas at about thirteen a substantial number of them began to express a concern for world peace, a concern that became even more prevalent a year later, and though declining when they were about fifteen, it became more pronounced again thereafter.

In a climate of political conformity the teenager is less likely to find expression for his idealism in the socialist schemes which used to excite the interest and energy of earlier generations. But guided by the religious leader, the adolescent can find opportunities for social action within the framework of a religious group. He might draw inspiration from the messianic ideals of the Bible and take as his model the religious man who fights for social justice. In any case, the psychological origins of the adolescent's social idealism lie in his yearning for peace within himself, and this in turn arises as a reaction to the inner struggle that erupts at puberty. The adolescent tends to project his feelings of helplessness and turmoil onto the outer world, so that his yearning for inner peace may take the form of a wish for world peace. The parallel in this regard between the adolescent and the schizophrenic patient is illuminating. Suffering from a chronic state of inner war, these patients in their responses to psychological tests will echo the adolescent's yearning for world peace. And like the adolescent they react to conflicts in their environment by becoming more irrational and violent. With the resolution of these conflicts the patients tend to improve.

Adolescents often seem so self-confident, so full of swagger and bluster, that we are apt to miss the fact that they, like the schizophrenic patients, need the steadying influence of rational behavior, moral strength, and unity in the world around them. Periods of turmoil in the outer world intensify their inner conflicts. Today the turmoil is greater than ever, and its effect is to still further intensify the instability that goes with adolescence. Hence the importance of an environment which can meet the emotional needs of the conflict-ridden youngster. Hence the importance of religious observances which introduce a stable rhythm into family life, as do recurrent holidays, with their festive ceremonies and ancient symbols.

Infantile attitudes die hard, and the teenager goes through

many a battle before he sloughs them off. The main psychological fact about the adolescent is his continued helplessness and dependence. In his efforts to achieve emotional independence he will often put on a great show of rebelliousness, whose violence only betrays his inner feelings of helplessness. In every adolescent there dwells a child in need as much as ever of supervision and instruction. To overlook this is to court disaster in dealing with the adolescent. In the interests of encouraging independence and maturity, parents may permit actions which they know to be wrong, at times even sacrificing their deepest convictions in an ill-conceived attempt to be "modern."

When parents yield to the adolescent's claims to independence, it is usually out of the mistaken notion that they are thereby helping the child towards self-sufficiency. Actually the psychological effect may be paradoxical. The adolescent may feel that he has been abandoned and as a result his anxiety may increase. He becomes more rebellious than ever. In connection with this ambivalent desire for independence, the results of a conference of sixty high school students called by the Methodist ministers of Minneapolis are instructive. Questioned about their attitude to the church, these students, in characteristic adolescent fashion, complained that they were given no opportunity to work out their problems free of adult supervision and in the same breath complained also that the church failed to provide adequate adult leadership. They made recommendations for a more effective program. In other words, though they expressed a desire for independence, they had insight enough to realize that they were not yet ready for full independence and needed competent leaders.

Such leaders, as some congregations and parishes have realized, should have experience in dealing with groups and in program planning. Above all they should be able to turn the experiences of the group to ethical ends. Failure of the group leader to understand the moral needs of the adolescent leads to the kind of situation illustrated in the following story. A young man on his first job as a recreation leader in a community center was extremely anxious to be accepted by his charges and so decided to "meet them at their level." He began spending a good deal of time at their local hangouts. After several months he thought he had been accepted as "almost" a member of the gang, and in this spirit he joined a crap game one night and rolled the dice like a veteran. He noticed a stiffening in the group around him and an uneasiness later as they all walked home. Finally one boy said, "You know, Doc, you get more like us instead of us getting more like you!"

The task of the youth leader is to grasp the twofold nature of the adolescent problem: the quest for independence on the one hand and the need for continued adult supervision on the other. The leader should encourage boys and girls to air their views, especially their religious views if he is working with a church or a synagogue. He must have the respect not only of his charges, but of their parents and elders. And the latter should be encouraged to express their views on the issues aired by the children, and to help plan religious programs. All concerned will thus have a similar orientation. Discussion will touch upon all important points, such as health, safety, property, law, social responsibility, and ethical attitudes and actions. It will recognize that there is an acceptable time and place for dating, that the church or synagogue can offer its facilities in an atmosphere that is attractive rather than repressive. It will also recognize that such decisions as when to seek or accept the first kiss are personal ones. Coeducational activities conducted under stimulating ethical leadership will contribute to the sublimation and social control of the adolescent's intense sexual urges.

Actually a moral code fulfills a great need for adolescents. It provides limits which they themselves want. If such limits are not set for them, they react with anxiety, in the course of which they may commit foolish and dangerous antisocial acts. A code that has been laid down in a cooperative manner establishes barriers without destroying the adolescent's sense of independence, for he himself has participated in establishing those barriers.

Religious Interaction and Authority

DISAPPOINTMENT and chagrin follow upon the adolescent's discovery that his parents have human limitations. Having overvalued them before, he now takes up an attitude of depreciation, the one extreme being as unrealistic as the other. The pedestals once reserved for his parents have now to be provided with other heroes. Once more, as in early childhood, he tends to equate God with his father, but this time with antireligious results. Thus we have the case of the sixteen-year-old boy who developed such nervous symptoms as a pounding heart and breathlessness at the morning church services. It was all he could do to control an impulse to rush out of the church. In discussing the matter with the minister the boy spoke of his unhappy relationship with his domineering and punitive father. The boy had expressed the wish to run away from home, and it suddenly occurred to him that his urge to run out of the church came at a point in the prayers in which God is described as a Father of love and forgiveness. It was at this point that he became particularly conscious of feelings towards his father. His emotional turmoil in church would seem, therefore, to have been due to his inability to separate his idea of his father from his idea of God. The minister assured the boy that the Father of all did not have the failings of earthly fathers. He was able to enter into a friendly, paternal relationship with his young parishioner, which tided the boy over a difficult period in his home life.

Rebellion against paternal authority took a very different form with an eighteen-year-old boy who indulged in hyper-religiosity as a device for harassing his parents. He delighted in proclaiming the superior qualities of his religious counselor in the presence of his father, comparing the two to the latter's disadvantage. The father could only approve of the boy's display of piety, but at the same time it imposed upon him a variety of inconveniences—for example, going to church more frequently than if he had been free to follow his own inclination. In such subtle ways the boy expressed aggression against his father. When he became aware of this through psychiatry, his relationship with his father became more realistic and mature. And with this change his abnormally intense religious preoccupation subsided.

Sometimes conflict with parental authority takes the paradoxical form of an inability to tolerate success and its rewards. Fame and fortune may lead to such an intensification of guilt as to cause a mental breakdown and even self-destructive behavior. People afflicted in this way may try to ward off the calamity by setting obstacles in their own path so as to postpone success. In the process they become agents of their own undoing. For example, a very religious young man succeeded his father as the head of the family business. In the course of treatment for symptoms of anxiety and depression, he mentioned that he always experienced feelings of self-effacement and humility in his business operations. Time and again he failed to seize the initiative in situations that required his active intervention. He was satisfied that it was the "will of God." To his psychiatrist he confessed that he was troubled by the fact that the death of his father had caused him no sadness. It began to be clear that his attitude to his father was deeply competitive and that he was plagued by neurotic fears of paternal retaliation. When all this came to light, his superstitious dread of success melted away, and in consequence the business grew beyond the limits established by his father. The young man's previous failure to take advantage of his opportunities, which he ascribed to the will of God, had been a way of warding off depression. Now that he was restored to a healthier frame of mind, his religious observances, if less frequent, were more wholesome, more positively oriented toward life, and more genuinely religious.

The growing youngster is faced not only with the restraints placed upon him by his elders, but by those that, developed so painstakingly during his latency years, exist within himself. While parents and others in authority may be, at times, too strict in their supervision of the teenager, it is as often as not the case that the teenager attributes qualities of strictness to them which as a matter of fact exist within himself. He is in militant opposition to his own self as well as to the outside world. This is one reason why the rebelliousness of adolescents is so confusing to their elders, and why conflict with authority inevitably has an important place in the psychology of adolescence.

We have already noted that the inability to resolve the conflict results in a reawakening of attitudes which prevailed at an earlier stage of development, such as a reversion to the earliest notions of God, for example, God being more or less literally equated with the father. For normal emotional growth the youngster has to recapture the psychological ground which he has surrendered in this process of regression. The majority of adolescents accomplish this on their own, though not without suffering—for the most part, time is on their side, bestrewn with difficulties as its passage may be—but occasionally an adolescent will need the help of a social caseworker or psychiatrist. However it comes to pass, forward movement in his emotional development is commonly accompanied by a corresponding change in his religious attitudes. Hyperreligiosity, obsessional blasphemous thoughts, and other distorted manifestations of religion are replaced by religious expressions which are spiritually more satisfying.

The Quest for a Concept of Self

O N E of the psychological problems which confronts the child during latency is the acquisition of a concept of self. As we have seen, religion plays a role in this connection. Now, with the advent of adolescence, a new concept of the self must replace the old one. The process culminates in the emergence of adulthood, with its more clearly defined goals and aims. In primitive societies, where the role of the adult is relatively simple, the transition is made in a short time. A few weeks or possibly months of training culminate in the rites of puberty, and in one leap the status of the individual is changed from that of a child to that of a man. In our society this change usually takes place gradually, over a period of years. Assuming adult responsibilities in civilized society involves more drastic changes than those which take place among primitives, and new skills which are more complex and more numerous must be learned. It is only in late adolescence that the process approaches completion. In early adolescence it is the child self that still predominates; only in late adolescence does the adult self come to the fore. Since the change from one self to the other involves a change from one set of values to the other, it is not surprising to find the process attended by conflict and anxiety.

The following case histories are intended to illustrate this conflict and anxiety in adolescents of varying ages, and to show the ways in which religion may come to the assistance of the adolescent in his quest for self-identification. A thirteen-year-old girl, the only child of a Catholic father and a Protestant mother, was referred for psychiatric treatment. Her schoolwork had deteriorated and she suffered from sleeplessness and feelings of depression. The parents' marriage had ended in divorce after a series of sexual escapades by the mother, and the father had custody of the child. She had been witness to the religious dissensions between her parents, so that when the psychiatrist inquired about her religion, she answered, "I'm a Catholic; no I'm not; I don't know what I am. I'm not what my mother is, that's for sure." This ambivalence indicated a desire to identify with her mother on the one hand, and a rejection of her for her misconduct on the other. The girl feared her own sexual impulses, thinking they might cause her father to abandon her just as he had already abandoned her mother. The confusion about her religious identity went along with the confusion in her personal life, and the one contributed to the other. It may be said that when positive identification with the religion of the parents is lacking, as it was in this case, the path to selfhood, thorny as it is, becomes all the thornier; just as, contrariwise, the presence of such identification may facilitate the achievement of selfhood.

Part of the equipment of the adolescent is his ability to exercise inner control over his impulses, but in the absence of such control and until it is developed, religion can provide certain outer controls. The case we turn to now is that of a girl who was referred to a family agency for help because she was depressed, anxious, and confused. Her mother had died when she was nine, and her father had been hospitalized for severe mental illness shortly thereafter. She was cared for in an orphanage until she was sixteen, when quarters were found for her in a girl's residence. There she witnessed cases of Lesbianism, which caused her no little disquiet. Although scrupulously honest at other times, in periods of anxiety she would indulge in compulsive petty stealing from department stores. She found relief in confessing to the caseworker, and expressed a desire to affiliate with a church, which she did with the assistance of a religious counselor to whom the caseworker directed her. Until she came to understand the real cause of her compulsive behavior, she was able, as the result of her participation in the church program, to control her impulse to steal. This homeless girl, without relatives or close friends, was thus helped by religion to do what she could not have done unaided. And it provided her with an interim period, free of anxiety and guilt, in which she could come to grips with her problem psychologically and so pave the way to the establishment of inner controls. Nor is this all the present case illustrates. It shows the good effects of collaboration, in this instance, of caseworker and religious counselor.

Our next case is concerned once more with family conflict about religion and its effects upon the adolescent. Charles, a boy of seventeen, was arrested for delinquent sexual behavior. He had first been referred to a family agency when he was thirteen years old. His Jewish mother had been hospitalized the year before because of a severe mental illness. His father was Catholic. During his early childhood he had received Jewish religious instruction from his mother, but as she became incapacitated, Charles at the age of eight came under the increasing influence of his paternal grandmother, a devout Catholic, who moved into the household. She had him baptized, though it appears that the father, an unskilled laborer, had planned to let Charles choose his own religion, hoping that he would decide to be a Christian. The boy told the caseworker that he was Jewish, but she noted that his room was decorated with Christian pictures and insignia. When Charles was fourteen his father died. Thereafter he actively resisted his grandmother's pressure to attend mass, contending that Catholicism was contrary to scientific fact. At the age of seventeen he was returned to the family agency, having been arrested on a sexual delinquency charge involving a Jewish girl his age. Psychiatric evidence showed that this sexual situation was part of an unresolved childhood attachment to his mother. In court, when urged by the judge to return to Catholicism, he declared that he was not a Catholic but a theosophist. He was unhappy with the probation officer to whom he had been assigned, a Catholic who brought pressure on him to return to his father's faith. The youngster was floundering. On the one hand his interest in religion was obvious, on the other hand he actively fought all efforts to channel this interest into Catholicism. With Charles's permission, the caseworker discussed his history with an extremely understanding priest, who talked to the boy and pointed out that no one could be forced to accept a religion; though the priest gave literature to Charles, he assured him at the same time that he was under no pressure to change his views. And he offered to talk to the probation officer to get him to stop bringing pressure on Charles. Just as Charles's divided religious background contributed to his confused sense of self, so it was reasonable to hope that a consistent and wholesome relationship with a religious leader might help him to find himself. Towards this goal the caseworker and the priest continued to work in close cooperation.

The concept of self is usually compounded of elements that derive from both parents. In early childhood, when the child's whole world is the family, the absence of one parent may constitute a serious handicap. At such times religion may be a means of holding on to the departed parent until further emotional development makes it possible to accept the separation. There is the case of a girl of eight who suffered from such various symptoms as fear of darkness and hyperactivity. The father, an extremely religious man, ruled the family with an iron hand, and there was considerable marital disharmony. Much of the child's abnormal behavior was traceable to a guilt-ridden conflict with her mother arising out of an overintense attachment to the father. Both the daughter and the mother were given psychiatric help, and as the mother became more independent and self-sufficient, she separated from her husband, taking the girl with her. During the subsequent stormy period of readjustment the youngster became, like her father, extremely pious. In her religious observances she was able to pretend that the beloved father was still with her, participating in her prayers and rituals. Her concern with religion at this time was manifestly excessive and it was the impression of the psychiatrist that it was part of an obsessional state. By the time the girl had reached the age of eighteen, and was becoming more successful in coping with her life problems, her need for obsessional religious observances ceased. Her religious interests took a more normal form. It is reasonable to conclude that the hyperreligiosity that erupted when the girl's parents separated was a device that helped to preserve the emotional satisfactions of her relationship with her father, though she was separated from him. Meanwhile she was able to work out a reasonably satisfactory concept of self.

It is this concept of self upon which catastrophes may have a shattering effect. So the loss of an identifying passport in a sinking ship may seem as great a misfortune to an immigrant as the loss of life itself. On the other hand, the simple act of recording one's name on a survivor list may result in the restoration of one's esteem. In times of shattering adversity, religious affiliations may provide the very help needed. Thus a brother and a sister, aged twelve and fourteen respectively, came to this country with their family as refugees from behind the Iron Curtain. As Catholics, they had fled their homeland, unable to practice their faith there. In the parochial school in America the teachers instilled in them a deep sense of personal pride as Catholics and an optimistic certainty that their Communist persecutors would inevitably go down to destruction. So bolstered, the children were tided over the emotional stresses incident to their refugee status.

The way in which religion came to the rescue in a case of psychosis is illustrated by the story of a thirteen-year-old girl, an only child, who developed a severe emotional disorder in a setting of chronic discord between her parents. The child withdrew from all childhood activities and relationships into a dream world where she fancied she was the wife of Robin Hood. In the hospital to which she had been removed she was often heard to say, "In order to live, one must first die." It may be remarked here that this is a common fantasy in the religious ecstasies of schizophrenics. The idea of death, often expressed in the form of a wish for martyrdom, is inextricably interwoven with the idea of rebirth. Death is conceived of not as an end to being but rather as a flight from an intolerable reality. Reborn, the sufferer finds his previous tortured state replaced by one that is ecstatic and free of conflict.

Not only was there this fantasy of rebirth, but the girl conceived of herself also as a missionary who must go South and end all discrimination against Negroes. Here again, lofty social aspirations of this sort are not uncommon among schizophrenic patients. Themselves in the grip of an irresolvable inner conflict, they respond to conflict wherever they encounter it. As we saw earlier, it is quite common to hear the adolescent and the schizophrenic alike express a yearning for inner peace under cover of a wish for world peace and social justice.

In the first stages of treatment our patient expressed the fear that the doctor would take her dream world away from her. With the establishment of a trusting relationship between her and the doctor, she decided on her own to give up her Robin Hood fantasy. In its place there appeared a strong hyperreligious trend. No longer did she put her trust in Robin Hood to right the wrongs of the world, but in God. The turn to religion at this point marked a step away from her dream world and into reality. In place of her previous isolation she now socialized more normally with her fellow patients. The girl gradually improved, and it became possible for her to resume relations with the real world as she encountered it in the hospital. She continued to daydream, but these dreams were now based on reality and involved her friends. In this process of self-healing, as we may characterize it, the patient was helped by her faith in God.[3]

Physical illness as well as external mishaps may disrupt a previously successful emotional adaptation. In such cases the availability of support in the form of religion may exercise a critical influence on the way a patient weathers the crisis. A poignant account of how religion fortified the shaken psychological defenses of a youth suffering from a fatal physical disease is contained in John Gunther's *Death Be Not Proud*. Although religious instruction was not included in his upbringing, the boy showed an unmistakable religious trend during his illness, one which contributed to the inspiring courage he displayed throughout his suffering. At his insistence his mother spent many hours reading to him from the Bible, particularly the Book of Job, to which he returned repeatedly. Perhaps the most interesting thing in the story is that the boy made a great outward display of agnosticism. One of his poems was entitled "An Unbeliever's Prayer." Yet his religious needs were plain and fortunately his mother was able to meet them, in spite of her own nonreligious inclination.

Adolescent Sexuality and Religious Expression

FROM a biological point of view, the most significant fact about the adolescent is that he has become capable of procreation. The sex drive is now imperious and almost irresistible, but equally imperious is the social prohibition against it, with the result that nowhere do the conflicts of adolescence achieve such acerbity as in the realm of sex. Indeed, it is not too much to say that all the chief problems are rooted in sexuality, and that no serious exploration of adolescence can afford to overlook the fact. At this point perhaps more than at any other, the religious leader and the psychiatrist come together in their mutual concern for the welfare of the adolescent. At the same time it needs to be stressed that their respective roles in the resolution of the sexual conflict of the adolescent are quite different.

Although their attitudes to sex differ in certain respects, each of the religions discussed in this book—Catholicism, Protestantism, Judaism—has a definite sexual code. And it is the task of the religious leader to teach his particular code and to encourage acceptance of it. Not only will he strive to understand the normal sexual needs and patterns of behavior of adolescence, but he will recognize the sexual behavior that is symptomatic of an abnormal psychological condition. So we may cite the case of an eighteen-year-old girl who was bringing shame on herself and her family by a series of sexual escapades in the community. She refused to see a psychiatrist, but agreed to see the minister. The latter, in his discussion with her, dwelt only on the fact that he had reason to believe that she was a desperately unhappy young woman, suggesting at the same time that a doctor might be of more help to her than himself. In the minister's mind, what was involved here was not simply a question of right or wrong, but also of emotional illness. In further conversations with the minister the girl expressed hatred of herself as a woman, relating that her parents seemed to favor her two brothers, whose attitude to girls was one of contempt. She admitted the possibility that her sexual behavior was part of her rebellion against them. Finally she agreed to see a psychiatrist. As a result of treatment, she became more reconciled to herself as a woman, and with this her sexual promiscuity subsided. Ultimately she married, had a child, and appeared to be reasonably content. At no time did the minister in this case give the appearance of condoning the girl's behavior, even though he chose to speak of it as the symptom of an illness requiring psychiatric help.

What happens when the religious leader is uncertain about his role in questions involving sex is well illustrated by a case brought up at a round-table discussion. The case involved a seventeen-year-old girl who had been having sexual intercourse with several boys in the community. In fear that she might have become pregnant, she prayed to God and promised that if her menstrual period arrived at the proper time she would abstain from all sexual activity for three months. She had her period and was grateful, but it was not long before she was again experiencing strong sexual desire and being importuned by her boy friends. When she told one of them about her promise to God, he laughed and told her that such a prudish attitude towards sex was not at all in keeping with the Jewish religion. Not knowing herself what to do, she addressed herself to the rabbi. Was she really bound to keep this promise to God? The rabbi was shocked by her apparent amorality, so devoid did she seem to be of shame or guilt. He felt that such a person could have no real religious feelings and was skeptical that anything he could say to her would have any effect. But he was most emphatic in saying that he could not possibly sanction breaking a promise to God. Without much confidence that any words of his would influence the girl, he advised her to look out for some man whom she could love and marry.

In a round-table discussion of this case, it was contended by one theological student that injunctions to sexual continence were outmoded, and might even be harmful to the emotional development of the young woman in question. Another said that there was nothing wrong with her sexual activities, provided that she cleansed herself beforehand in a ritual bath. In any event, he said, the young men were more culpable than she. An animated discussion followed as to whether or not the young woman's sexual behavior could be condoned by the Jewish moral code. At the end of forty-five minutes of heated debate the consensus was that it could not—a fact so obvious that only theological students could overlook it. But even after this agreement one student was left wondering whether the girl's behavior was contrary to the teachings of modern psychiatry. Hence the group had to be reminded that moral values originate, not in psychiatry, but in religion. It is not the business of the psychiatrist to condemn or criticize sexual behavior that deviates from the normal, but to understand it as far as it may be a symptom of emotional disorder. And the goal of his treatment is the replacement of the deviant sexual pattern by one that is more consistent with the prevailing social mores. Not that this goal is always practicable, for there are cases in which the deviant sexual pattern is the only possible one. The psychiatrist accepts this fact in the same way that a cardiologist accepts the invalidism of a patient with an incurable heart ailment. He accepts and does not judge, without however losing sight of the fact that invalidism is a handicapped way of living. So far as the moral values worked out within the framework of religion go, the psychiatrist does not reject them; rather he presupposes them. The religious leader's job is to uphold them, not inflexibly, but with the concrete needs of his congregants and parishioners always in mind.

Next coming up for discussion at this round table was the girl's presumed lack of a religious and moral sense. To the rabbi who so judged her it was pointed out that she had after all prayed to God and made a promise of her own free will, which she was unwilling to break at her boy friend's instigation. Only the rabbi, she thought, was in a position to annul the promise. It was pointed out that some religious leaders tend to underestimate the capacity for religious feeling of those who seek their help, and that such was the case in the present instance. Nor could it be maintained, in view of her voluntary consultation with the rabbi, that the girl was amoral and devoid of guilt feelings. She suffered from qualms of conscience and sought the advice of one whose business it is to deal with such things. No doubt it was also a case for the psychiatrist, but the rabbi failed to carry out his part in the cooperative program.

So powerful is the adolescent's sexual drive that it is rarely possible for him to wholly sublimate it in nonsexual activities. He commonly resorts to masturbation. In the conditions of modern society he has practically no other resort for the direct release of his sexual tensions. For this reason masturbation is almost universally a part of the normal growth process. The absence of masturbation during adolescence is not only the exception but may indeed be symptomatic of a serious disturbance in emotional development. The psychiatrist may permit and even actively encourage masturbation in the treatment of certain patients suffering from unusually intense sexual inhibition or from enfeeblement of the sexual impulse. But masturbation is almost always followed by feelings of guilt, and it is a widespread but mistaken belief that the moral injunctions of the religious leader are responsible for these feelings. For reassurances about masturbation, even when they are given by a person in authority like the family doctor, usually fail to assuage the guilt of the adolescent. And they fail because they overlook the fact that masturbation is almost invariably associated with fantasies which have their origin in early childhood. It is not the mechanical act of masturbation that generates guilt, but rather the infantile fantasies associated with it. The fantasies themselves are usually highly disguised and for the most part not accessible to the conscious thinking of the masturbating teenager. It takes the special techniques of analysis to uncover and decipher them and so deprive them of their guilt-generating impact. At all events, masturbation is regarded by the psychiatrist as an immature expression of the sexual impulse. He hopes that his patient will liberate himself from the incestuous attachments of early childhood and find sexual satisfaction within the framework of marriage and normal family life.

It is in this sense that the traditional religious view that masturbation is wrong may be defended on purely psychological grounds. The normal adolescent should be given every encouragement to curb his masturbatory impulses and to aspire to adult sexual fulfillment. Naturally, such encouragement should not take a negative form—for example, threats of hellfire—but consist rather in the inculcation of the ideals of adult sexuality, including marriage, children, and family life. Everything should be done, too, to further the possibilities of sublimation through individual and group skills and activities. Values are involved here that fall within the province of the religious leader. Not threats of dire punishment, but invocation of adult ideals, should set the tone of sexual instruction administered to the adolescent by the religious leader. Thus, while the religious leader has to take into account the biological and psychological fact that masturbation is a normal and even necessary component of emotional growth, he should avoid the error of slavishly imitating the psychiatrist who encourages masturbation as a technical device in the treatment of certain selected patients. On the other hand, in dealing with the pathologically guilt-ridden parishioner who masturbates uncontrollably as part of a mental illness, the religious leader will use his authority to assuage the excess of sinful feelings and will encourage him to accept psychiatric help.

Nor will the religious leader turn his back upon that type of deviant behavior represented by the sexual perversions. Long ago Freud pointed out that sexually deviant patterns of behavior in the adolescent as well as the adult are the same as those that normally occur at certain stages in the emotional development of the child. Characteristic of these early patterns is a preoccupation with the mouth and anus, with pleasure in touching and smelling, with exhibitionism and peeping. Indeed, these patterns exist in the normal adult as part of the so-called forepleasure of sexual play that commonly precedes sexual intercourse. It is only when these preliminary patterns represent the exclusive expression of sexual pleasure that we may speak of an arrested sexual development. Such arrested development probably never occurs in isolation, but is symptomatic of arrested emotional development generally. Persons so afflicted are almost invariably passive, dependent, and incapable of gratification in normal sexual relationships. Typically, they lack adult control over their impulses in general, so that common among them, besides sexual offenses, are alcoholism, stealing, and assault. Behind these sexual and other offenses there is usually a history of severe emotional deprivations in childhood.

With this background of psychological understanding, we turn to the case of a young man who consulted a minister because of homosexual tendencies. Baffled by the problem, the minister asked advice of an older colleague, who, forgetting that he was a minister and not a doctor, responded with a detailed psychoanalytic discourse on the dynamics of homosexuality. In thus abdicating his role as a moral teacher, he failed to see that the young man was suffering from feelings of guilt about his behavior and was in search of religious counsel. It is true, of course, that a minister's guidance could not by itself have cured the homosexuality. The point is, though, that the minister should not only have advised his colleague to refer the young man to a psychiatrist, but advised him to perform the duty proper to his office, which was to assist the young man in carrying out the religious commandments. Nor is this all. The minister, if he had been better informed, would further have pointed out to his colleague that the not uncommon transient adolescent homosexuality is not to be identified out of hand with the relatively fixed patterns of adult homosexuality. The emotions and attachments of the adolescent are in a state of flux, changing almost from day to day. He is loath to relinquish the pleasures of childhood, yet he is also in a hurry to assume the responsibilities of adulthood. Moreover, the adolescent's sexual impulses are so overpowering at times that in order to protect himself from the opposite sex he will appear to be unduly attached to a member of the same sex. For example, the "crush" of a girl camper for an older female counselor does not mean that the girl is incapable of normal sexual relations. It adds greatly to the effectiveness of the religious leader if he understands that such things are part of the normal psychosexual development of adolescence.

"Going steady" is a new phenomenon. Although it will be years before they are ready for marriage, it has become common for a boy and girl to take up with each other to the exclusion of all other members of their social group. It is not clear why this has happened, although there are several factors that have obviously had some influence on the development. The loosening of family bonds in recent years has resulted in a need for closer ties. Further, there has been a relative lack of supervision of the social activities of teenagers; in order to free themselves for their own pleasures, parents are more willing to let teenagers amuse themselves as they see fit. Obscene comics and "Rock and Roll" are part of a milieu which tends to stimulate sexual interests in youngsters at a much earlier age than ever before. Besides, there is the imitative factor in steady dating. The adolescent's need to conform to the mores of his contemporaries is as conspicuous as his need to rebel against the mores of his elders. The boy or girl who does not have a "mate" feels excluded from the in-group. But rebellion plays a role too, for steady dating generates conflict between parents and children.

Aware that adolescence is above all a period of growth, parents express the fear that steady dating constricts the field of social experience of their offspring. And the danger is certainly real. In several instances in our clinical experience, an immature, clinging boy has become involved with a mature and sometimes overprotective girl. The result is an unwholesome, even neurotic relationship. The girl grows bored with the youth's dependency, and he in turn resentful of her domination, but by that time marriage and children may have occurred. A boy and a girl may cling to each other not for the happiness they experience in each other's company, but because they fear the loneliness of separation. Sometimes the socializing factor is hardly present at all, as when two youngsters in widely separated cities will announce that they are going steady, although they may see each other no oftener than once or twice a month. In these instances the claim to going steady may be nothing but a cloak for the adolescent's retreat from the normal activities of his social group. In steady dating in which physical propinquity is the rule, the result is almost invariably sexual overstimulation, and this in a setting in which normal marital gratification will not be possible for years. More important still is the fact that the skills and interests which represent forms of sublimation fail to develop as a result of this premature stimulation of the sexual drive. When going steady has these undesirable effects and parents find difficulty in coping with it, the guidance and authority of the religious leader can be helpful.

However, there is another side to the story. The boy and girl can get to know each other as human beings, and the relationship between them then suffers from none of the anxiety and superficiality characteristic of sporadic dating. When the young people involved are mature and are members of a wholesome social group—so that they contribute to each other's growth in a positive way—the parents should sanction the relationship, although within the limits of appropriate supervision. For until the younger people have matured to the point where their own controls and judgments are dependable, they need adults to help set such limits for them. The frequency of dates, dating during the school week, the hour of return from a date, keeping parents informed, points of behavior in and out of a group —these things raise questions that call for parental answer, preferably with the participation of the youngsters themselves. Unfortunately, the parents' approach to the problems of steady dating is likely to be merely negative. They are against steady dating but they offer little in place of it. It is here that the religious leader has an important role to play. He is in a position to offer guidance, pastoral and spiritual, and to foster in the religious center a rich social program for adolescents under the auspices of a competent group leader; in other words, to provide a setting desirable not only for the steady daters but for those who are unattached.

Concerning the steadiness of the steady date, it is well to bear in mind that the adolescent's emotional attachments are highly unstable. As in everything else, the inconstancy of mood so characteristic of him expresses itself in his love relationships. It is the exception for the "steady" pair of early adolescence to become marital partners in later years. The adolescent's goals and values are in flux and so are his ideals for a marital partner. For this reason the anxiety of parents over a steady date is more often than not needless. Frequently the youngsters themselves are aware of the fact. Thus a thirteen-year-old girl said in a teenage discussion group: "I like a boy of different faith. He is fifteen. I like him very much even though I can't say I love him. He has a lot of respect for me and has taken me to the movies and to parties several times. My parents tell me I must never see him again and threaten to deprive me of all my liberties if I disobey. I try talking to them and they refuse to listen. I know they are afraid of my marrying him but I never would. I feel so sad I'd like to run away from home." Here the fears of the parents overrode their judgment. If they had paid more attention to the girl's reassurances, they would have seen that her mind was far from closed to other possibilities, possibilities they should have been at pains to further.

Although time is on the side of the adolescent, and most adolescents resolve their emotional problems successfully, it is still possible for a youngster to succumb to one or another mental illness as he copes with the problems arising out of his struggle for independence and maturity, or his conflict with authority, or his growing sexuality. And it is to religion that the foundering adolescent commonly turns in his desperate search for stability. The clinical picture here is often misunderstood. It is not the excessive preoccupation with religion at this time that is to blame for mental illness, rather it is the illness that accounts for the preoccupation. The adolescent may clutch at religion to save his sanity in the face of an otherwise insoluble conflict.

One day in the spring of 1957, the tabloid newspapers announced in lurid headlines that a "religious" eighteen-year-old boy had murdered a fifteen-year-old girl after a sexual assault. None of the newspaper accounts failed to mention that the boy always carried a Bible in his hand, that he presided over a young people's group in his church, that he was a substitute Sunday school teacher, that he sang in the choir, that he was a follower of Billy Graham, the evangelist, and something of an evangelist in his own right. Did not this prove, it was argued or implied, the futility of religious training? As if to clinch the argument, the young man had attended a religious rally on the very night of the murder. Nor was this all. In the week following the murder the young man's religious fervor became even greater. And when he announced calmly to the police that "God will forgive me for my sins," the announcement was taken as the perfect reductio ad absurdum of the contemporary spate of books on "peace of mind," "the power of positive thinking," and "giving yourself to God." One distinguished journalist was moved to quote from Ecclesiastes, "Wherefore I praise the dead that are already dead more than the living that are yet alive; but better than both is he that hath not yet been, who hath not seen the evil that is done under the sun."

Let us look at this case more closely, especially in its religious aspects. At the age of three this boy was not like other boys. He was abnormally obsessed with a dread of dirt. When sent out to play in a spotless white suit and shoes, he would return hours later immaculate. At the age of nine he set several fires in the house. The parents now realized that they were in for trouble, and consulted the pastor of their church. The pastor realized that the boy's excessive self-control was breaking down, and that destructive impulses were coming through. Informing the parents that the boy needed specialized care, he arranged for a psychiatric consultation in a nearby city. Unfortunately, the boy was seen only once, and for some reason that is not clear, no treatment was instituted. The next warning came two years later. One day his mother found that he had cut up her underclothes and dresses with a razor. He denied all memory of the act, but there was no question of his guilt, and his mother spanked him severely. The punishment had no deterrent effect. On the contrary his behavior became uncontrolled, and he took to slashing women's underclothing on clotheslines in the neighborhood. When he broke into a neighbor's house and wrecked several rooms, it was regarded by the community as "just a wild teenage act by a boy with a good family background." Nothing was done by the police or the juvenile authorities. His parents, now desperate, had him committed to a psychiatric institution for adolescents. According to the report a month later, the boy displayed "a schizophrenic paranoid pattern . . . a passive personality [with] a tendency to show eruptive, aggressive and sometimes homicidal behavior . . . Such an individual warrants grave concern and should have continued psychiatric treatment . . . His bold outward actions are significant. He has deep-rooted tendencies that are definitely dangerous." Treatment was recommended for both the boy and his mother. Again, nothing happened. Hardly released, he was charged with sexually molesting two little girls. Despite a history of two previous mental examinations and clear warnings from the psychiatrists, the charges were dismissed and the boy not only set free but not even required to undergo treatment.

It was at this time, about four years before the murder, that the boy's religious preoccupation began. Excessive as it obviously was, the parents were grateful at this development. It inaugurated a period of relative peace for the family and the community. The boy became well behaved, although conspicuous for his religious fanaticism and his tendency to withdraw from the normal social activities of his equals. It would appear that his obsession with ritual helped him to reestablish for a few years the self-control which had first been shattered at the age of nine. Just how this worked and why it ceased to work are questions we are not in a position to answer. But the intensification of the boy's fervor after the murder may be construed as an attempt to reestablish once more the controls that had so heinously broken down.

What are the religious bearings of this case? Certainly religious observances by themselves are no safeguard against the sort of mental illness that afflicted this boy. But the case warrants no adverse conclusions with regard to the role of religion in normal life. What it shows, rather, is that the mentally afflicted, as we have observed before, may turn to religion as an aid to self-control. And in fact where the mental illness is not of the major kind, religious devices often suffice to bolster up crumbling defenses and make possible some degree of adjustment. Further, religion as it appears in abnormal people provides us with a clue to its role in the psychological development of normal people. It helps establish the self-control which is a necessary accompaniment of emotional growth. Of course, the religion that is centered in personal psychological needs is still the undeveloped religion of childhood. It is when religion has transcended this limitation that it becomes the religion of maturity.

We cannot conclude this section without saying something about the differences between the sexes in their patterns of religious expression. Women are more observant, as the records of church and synagogue attendance show, and as we should expect on psychological grounds, since their role is so frequently that of suffering and waiting. Perhaps it is for this reason that so few women have initiated new religious movements, though as followers of such movements they have been in the majority. But apart from this, it may be that religion's capacity to encourage an attitude of passive dependence is of greater import for the girl's achievement of a normal sexual identification than it is for the boy's. And the importance of such identification, for the one sex as for the other, is that one of the chief factors involved in the formation of the concept of self is the acceptance of one's biological role in society. Only so can man and woman play their respective roles. Religious observances contribute to this acceptance, and whether or not the bias of religion in general is patriarchal, it is worth emphasizing that rituals which dignify the specific role of each sex are psychologically of great use.

Religious Conversion

T H E reason why religious conversions occur most commonly during adolescence is not far to seek. Severe mental conflict is the seed bed of conversion, and such conflict is the hallmark of adolscence. When conversion occurs, whether religious or not, it does so usually with climactic impact. For the conflict proceeds like an underground fire that spreads and mounts in its fury and yet remains hidden from view. Suddenly it finds an opening and in a catastrophic flash makes its presence known. It is preceded by a period of intense search for a way out, in which unacceptable wishes are locked in mortal combat with cherished ideals. When the way out takes the form of religious conversion, its effect may be to preserve the sanity of the subject, indeed his very life. He is invaded by a new energy, by feelings of ecstatic fulfillment that defy verbal description, by visions of rebirth and cosmic vistas of sublime beauty. Sometimes the experience results in great achievements in art and science as well as religion.

Whatever touches off the conversion, whether it be something personal or the mass hysteria of an evangelical meeting, the chief psychological component—intense emotional conflict in the convert's mind—is always recognizable. Let us consider the case of an eighteen-year-old Protestant who told his minister that he was determined to convert to Catholicism. The young man was depressed, slept poorly, lost weight, and was unable to study. As the young man was unwilling to go into his sexual problems with the minister, the latter suggested that he see a psychiatrist, and he agreed to do so. In treatment it became clear that his rejection of the parental religion was bound up with his rejection of both his father and his mother, the one being a drunkard and the other emotionally cold. With regard to his desire to become a Catholic, he explained that he had a neighbor, a kindly man, who was a devout Catholic, and that this man's devotion to his little daughters was in painful contrast to the suffering he had experienced at the hands of his own parents. He would put himself in the place of these children and so enjoy the love of their Catholic father. Further, the Catholic view of celibacy as a higher form of life provided him with a perfect rationale for his sexual impotence. His sexual urge towards little girls, which no doubt stemmed from his identification with his neighbor's children, was a disguised expression of his wish not only to be a little girl himself, but to be embraced by a loving father. In the kindly priest and the Virgin Mary he found parents whose purity, constancy, and warmth were in contrast with his unfortunate experiences of family life as a child.

Psychiatric treatment made him conscious of these various infantile strivings and the way in which they were affecting his religious interests. The way was thus open for further emotional growth, and in time he developed a capacity for normal sexual relations. As a corollary of this improvement, he gave up his previous determination to convert to Catholicism, and returned to the religion of his family. A warm relationship developed between him and his minister, who incidentally helped him over many emotional crises in subsequent years.

The emotional eruptions of adolescence occur with a suddenness that takes everyone involved off his guard. To family and friends they may appear as if from the blue. Yet they are preceded, as we have said, by a period of profound inner turmoil. All this is vividly brought out in Peter Putnam's *Cast Off the Darkness*. To all appearances a normal, intelligent youth, Putnam was brought up in a well-to-do, happy home and was a success among friends and fellow students at Princeton. Inwardly, however, he suffered such disillusion and conflict that he shot himself in a suicide attempt. He lived, but the shot blinded him permanently. The act was beyond his comprehension and incredible to his family. In the course of convalescence, Putnam underwent a conversion which was nonreligious but which stimulated moral and intellectual power of uncommon quality. Despite his handicap, he became a scholar and a writer.

But conversion commonly follows a religious pattern, as in the case of a girl, a freshman in college, in whom the sudden awakening of intense religious feelings occurred in altogether unexpected circumstances. In high school the girl had been an excellent student, the recipient of prizes for her work. Excellent in athletics, a leader in extracurricular activities, popular socially, she had every reason to be happy, yet her success did nothing to allay her nagging doubts. At college her excellent record continued, but her anxiety deepened. Brought up in a moderately observant Jewish home, she broke with Judaism, becoming for a while a militant atheist. Then with the assistance of non-Jewish friends she turned to a serious study of Christianity, and started attending church services regularly. At church one Sunday, during prayer, she was suddenly seized with a feeling of ecstasy; she became aware, in her own words, "that the way to salvation is through the Lord Jesus Christ." The minister urged her to be baptized, but she decided to write to her parents first, telling them she felt she had no alternative except to embrace Christianity. The mother telephoned her daughter to say that she was coming to see her. Before leaving, she consulted her rabbi, who pointed out that the girl's decision to postpone baptism until she had informed her parents was the best proof that she had not come to a final decision. He advised the mother to meet with the minister in her daughter's presence and to avoid theological disputation with him. Instead, she was to ask the minister two questions: First, did he believe that it was impossible for her daughter to find spiritual solace within the framework of Judaism? Second, did he not think that the girl ought to accompany her mother back home for consultation with the rabbi? In view of the girl's experience, the minister felt that she had been ordained by God to embrace Christianity, but he agreed, and so did the girl, to the suggestion that she return home with her mother. Consultations with the rabbi took place, in the course of which he dwelt upon the broad range of religious experience possible within Judaism, and expressed complete confidence that whatever the girl's spiritual needs, Judaism was able to fulfill them. He told her he was uneasy about the ecstatic nature of her change, saying that such experiences were sometimes the reaction to an intense emotional conflict. "If your experience is valid," he said, "no human intervention can affect it. On the other hand, if it is somehow an expression of emotional conflict, why not deal with that properly? It might turn out, for example, that it is really unnecessary to forsake Judaism if you have proper psychological assistance." Aware that she was in need of help, the girl agreed to take a leave of absence from college and start a psychoanalysis. In the treatment that followed, an intense sexual conflict was uncovered, involving infantile attachments to both her parents, as well as guilt concerning masturbation. Her religious conversion represented an attempt to break these infantile attachments and to control her masturbation. As she became conscious of these factors, it became possible for her to deal with them more realistically. Although the resolution of her emotional problems took a long time, her compulsive drive to leave Judaism and convert to Christianity disappeared in the course of the analysis.

There is another type of case in which an attitude of indifference gives way to a sudden eruption of religiosity. Such an awakening of religious feelings is often the result of a reawakening of the oedipal wishes of the adolescent. Typical here is the case of a young man, overattached to his mother, who regarded his father as a rival for her affections and unconsciously harbored death wishes against him. As the years went by, father and son became strangers to each other. One day the son, then a student at an out-of-town college, received a telephone call from his father, suggesting that they visit together that weekend on the campus, which they did. It was the only time within the boy's recollection that his father had tried to be a friend. The father spoke of the years they had wasted and said it was time they got to know each other. Their parting was warm and affectionate, but in the small hours of the following morning the son woke up with a start, in the grip of a premonition that something dreadful had happened to his father. Just as dawn broke he heard the shuffling of feet outside his door and the voice of his landlord calling his name. It was a telegram announcing that his father had died during the night.

Convinced that God had awakened him on that terrible night, the young man was seized with a religious fervor. He now took up the prayer book he had not read in many years, prayed several times daily, attended church every morning. The intensity of his observance became fanatical. Several years later, suffering from great anxiety, depression, and inability to decide on a career, he began psychoanalysis. Quite early in the analysis he discussed the frustrations he had suffered at the hands of his father. An energetic, overbearing man, the father had made his son feel inadequate on many occasions, especially in his mother's presence. The patient recalled the happiness he had experienced with his mother when his father was away on business trips. In the course of all this he became conscious of his intense rivalry towards his father. He now recalled that his father did not look well on the occasion of his fateful visit, that he had been intermittently conscious that his father was a sick man. Yet because of his unconscious death wishes towards his parent, he could not allow this awareness to crystallize. In neurotic fashion he was compelled to suppress the thought that his father needed a doctor. But just this crystallization took place during sleep, and the thought burst into the boy's consciousness, not as a thought of his own but as a message from the Almighty. Since the thought seemed to come from without, he could assure himself, albeit unconsciously, that his own death wishes had nothing to do with his father's death. As for the fervent religiosity that followed, it helped maintain this state of repression. Prayer enabled him to insist that his father's death was not his wish, but God's. As the analysis proceeded and the patient became aware of the true state of affairs, the religiosity that stemmed from the anxiety and guilt of unconsciously revived oedipal death wishes towards his father gave way to calmer and better balanced religious observances.

In this case, as in others we have cited, the clinical evidence shows that acute religious conversion is often the product of mental conflicts that are themselves essentially nonreligious and that are often associated with impending or actual mental illness. The occurrence of such a conversion, especially in the adolescent, raises problems in the resolution of which the psychiatrist and the religious leader can fruitfully collaborate.

The Transition to Mature Religion

THE passage from adolescence to adulthood sees the subsidence of previous conflicts, and increasing stability, together with physical, social, and moral growth generally. As a result of his more sophisticated knowledge of the world, the individual, except in rare instances, finds it impossible to conceive of God and Scripture in strictly fundamentalist terms. Since his capacity for abstract thinking has developed, however, he is able to translate cherished childhood notions into such symbolic and figurative terms as are in keeping with his intellectual growth and emotional maturity. At this time he is apt to be concerned with the meaning of life, with the definition of his goals and ambitions. If his religious training has taught him to value compassion, that teaching is now likely to be translated into social activities that are of benefit to the community, or even mankind at large. He begins to act as a citizen of the world with a sense of obligation to his fellow men. In short, there is a transition to mature religion. The particular time when the individual makes this transition depends on his cultural background, his intellectual equipment, and most of all his emotional maturity.

THE BASIC PRINCIPLES OF

RELIGIOUS COUNSELING

4.

PEOPLE IN TROUBLE THROUGHOUT THE AGES HAVE
sought the help of religious leaders. Today, however,
in a world dominated by science, the role of the religious leader
as a counselor has become blurred in some respects and greatly
augmented and complicated in others. In previous chapters we
were concerned with religious counseling as it is practiced in
connection with the problems of children and adolescents. Here,
before we turn to a similar consideration in connection with the
problems of adulthood, we should like to set out as far as possible the basic principles of religious counseling. In this way we
hope to bring the role of the religious leader, both by himself
and as a member of a psychosocial team, into sharper focus.

Psychological Aspects of Leadership

THE nature of religion and the needs of human beings
dictate the role of the religious leader. As we see it, his
first and most important social task is the inculcation of a religiously based moral code. To this end he will avail himself
of every religious resource at his command. He will be inspired
by the faith that the universe has a purpose whose source is
God, the organizing principle of all that exists. It is upon this
basis that he will carry out his task of inspiring courage in
people in times of stress and giving them comfort in times of
sorrow. The context of the religious leader is always the psychological and social needs of the individual and his family.
There is the need to distinguish between right and wrong, good

and evil. There is the need of support in times of crisis, the need of a bulwark against the threat of chaos. There is the need to believe that life has a purpose, that human goals and ambitions are meaningful. Most important of all, perhaps, is the need for some final court of appeal. All these needs, and others, find their fulfillment in religion.

The religious leader today finds himself, as we have said, in a world dominated by science, and this may lead him to try to be a scientist himself, above all a psychiatrist. Now it is true that a knowledge of the principles of psychiatry is a great aid in his work, but the task of the religious leader is to be a religious leader. It is a role that he must never abdicate or allow to be obscured. To think of himself as a therapist, for example, is simply wrongheaded. He stands for a moral and spiritual tradition, and it is in this symbolic role that he exercises his greatest influence. The methods and language of psychiatry or social work are outside his province, and when he resorts to them he betrays his calling. He is giving to those who look to him for spiritual guidance not bread but a stone. True, many of his activities are of a concrete and practical kind, but underlying them all is a scheme of religious values. It is precisely because of this that he has a unique contribution to make to the psychosocial team which we envisage.

How this team may be employed and how the religious leader contributes to its work is illustrated by the following case. A twenty-seven-year-old woman with three children was trying to establish herself in a new and strange community, and turned for help to a social agency. She had been separated from her husband for a year and was in the process of getting a divorce. She had a chaotic family background and was emotionally unstable. As a child she had been unhappy, her only pleasant memory being that of a minister who comforted her when he found her alone and crying in church. The social life in which she participated as the result of her church affiliations came to represent for her the only real "family" experience she had ever known. In her teens she would wear a cross to keep from "doing wild things." As naïve, superficial, and even neurotic as this woman's use of religion was, it undoubtedly helped to bolster up her weak ego, and thus performed a function of inestimable importance. At her own request the social agency to which she applied for help referred her to their chaplain, who paved the way to her affiliation with a church. Since there seemed little likelihood of undoing the ill effects of her early life, she was not referred to a psychiatrist. But without family and friends, in a new community, this woman was provided by the church with human contacts and recreational outlets, and the guidance of a religious leader who represented a parent figure to her.

The religious leader today functions in a variety of roles. As a business administrator he is responsible for the financial upkeep of his congregation. As a group worker he is the moving spirit behind the special events and club activities sponsored by his congregation or parish. In his priestly role he carries out the specific rituals of his religion; he conducts worship, weddings, and funerals; he is a spiritual adviser. He is called upon for counsel, as for example in family disputes. He is the conscience of his congregation and community, stirring them to moral indignation and social action when occasion demands it. And he is a teacher.

Now it is obvious that time alone prevents the religious leader from doing justice to all these functions. Though the religious leader himself would have the emphasis placed upon his role as teacher, priest, and prophet, unfortunately, church and synagogue have come to place more and more emphasis on the business, administrative, and social group work activities. The result is that in many communities there has been a deterioration of the goals which the religious leader sets for himself because he has given in, as he often must, to relentless social pressures. The situation is not one which makes for either the physical or the emotional health of the religious leader. In these circumstances, it is not uncommon for a curious reversal of roles to take place. Just as the congregant who seeks his aid may unrealistically overestimate the powers of the religious leader, so the latter may underestimate his own powers. In the one case we have what in the language of psychoanalysis is called transference, the reawakening in an adult of his childish attitudes towards his parents and his transferring these attitudes to contemporary parent figures. In the other case we have what in the same language is known as countertransference, in which the religious leader, because his own long-forgotten feelings are stirred up, is unable to control his own reactions. In the grip of countertransference the religious leader feels unsure of himself, so that instead of acting like a parent towards the person seeking his help, he feels and often behaves childishly himself. He may have appropriate words of comfort for the sufferer facing him, yet fear to speak these words lest he be rebuffed. Even his faith may waver and his attitude become irreverent and cynical.

It is only too obvious that the religious leader thus afflicted will be especially unfitted to deal with the not uncommon case of the person who covertly needs and wants his help, but who in his overt expressions seems to reject it with hostility. Such behavior very often represents the sufferer's first attempt to cope with his misery. He may rail against God or against the religious leader. The clergyman able to recognize the anguish which the angry words conceal will not be too disturbed by them, but if he himself is in any doubt about his role he is likely to retreat before an angry outburst of this sort and so deprive the sufferer of the only help available to him.

In the following case history, mental disease enables us to look at the problem of countertransference as if through a magnifying glass. The patient was a student in a theological seminary. During the nine months of the school year his work was preeminent, not only for brilliance but for spiritual fervor. What his teachers did not know was that the close of the school year initiated a Jekyll-Hyde transformation in him. He spent his summer vacations in dissolute living, alcoholic and sexual. This went on for three years. At the beginning of his fourth and last year he confessed his double life to his teachers and spiritual advisers and handed in his resignation as a student, which he refused to retract despite the urgings of the faculty. He became an unskilled laborer, worked hard and conscientiously, and continued to harbor the ambition to save people from sin. He found a young woman, an alcoholic, who was in the late stages of deterioration. He nursed her back to health, married her, and embarked on her spiritual salvation. She became a fresh, wholesome person with an entirely new outlook on life. Yet as she improved, he reverted to his alcoholic excesses and began to indulge in marital infidelities.

He became irresponsible on his job and withdrew from social contacts. When his wife could no longer overlook his strange behavior at home, as for example his conversations with imaginary voices, she arranged an appointment with a psychiatrist, who, diagnosing schizophrenia, arranged for hospitalization and treatment.

The inner conflict responsible for this breakdown had manifested itself in the patient's Jekyll-Hyde career, as it manifested itself in his relationship with his wife, towards whom he played the role of savior. His urge in this direction alternated with an equally unwholesome need to degrade himself. It may be said that the urge to be a savior had at least one good consequence in this case, and that the degrading behavior with which it alternated was the only unwholesomeness. But the danger is precisely the likelihood of such an alternation, even when the urge to be a savior exists in a more normally constituted personality. It is simply that in the abnormal case we are considering, the danger is writ large. When the urge exists in more subtle forms, the result may still be a loss of the humility which is indispensable to the proper discharge of religious responsibilities. So the religious leader must never lose sight of the fact that he is a mortal human being who is at best a teacher of his faith. And viewing himself thus, he is not likely to be crushed by feelings of guilt or depression when tragedy has overtaken one of his congregants or parishioners. He is not likely to feel that he has failed or that God has failed, but rather that he too, like the grieving congregant or parishioner, is only human and cannot hope to understand God's ways.

The fact that countertransference of even a mild sort may interfere with religious counseling is exemplified in the minister consulted by a parishioner who was deeply depressed because his married daughter was about to move out of town. She was his only child, and he was overattached to her and her children. The move promised many advantages, not the least of which was escape from the father, whose overdependence was interfering with his daughter's marital happiness. Unfortunately, the minister was in much the same case as this father. He too, overdependent on his children, was depressed at their having moved to another city, and instead of encouraging his troubled parishioner to accept a change that was clearly advantageous to his daughter, he railed against it as an example of the "modern disrespect of children for their parents." He took it upon himself to visit the daughter and to warn her that if she moved it might break her father's heart, and even cause death. Her consternation and guilt may be imagined. There followed a period of great turmoil in the family, which ended only when the father came to accept his daughter's decision to move.

There are other individual problems—some more common than the problem of overattachment to his children—that may have an adverse effect upon the religious leader's work. One of these arises from the fact that he often functions as a surrogate father, so that if he is married the wife gets caught up in complicated emotional cross-currents. This is a serious problem, one that may affect the relationship not only between the leader and his wife, but between her and the women of his congregation. In the former case, such a complication is all the more likely if the family background of either partner or both was marked by neurotic problems. In the latter case, women may overestimate the religious leader, as they overestimated their father as little girls; in other words, the oedipal situation of early childhood is repeated, with the result that the leader's wife is regarded as a rival. When such a transference occurs, the attitude towards her is excessively critical and hostile. If she is a woman of great maturity, unthreatened by such neurotic behavior, she is in a position to offer her rivals a new kind of relationship, that with a mother figure. Unshaken by their importunities, warm and accepting, she can help them control their unresolved infantile attitudes. In this way the wife of a religious leader may contribute to the emotional growth of his congregants or parishioners.

But it often happens that the wife comes to grief in this situation. The tensions and pressures are too much for her, and she becomes depressed or hostile. In consequence she not only fails to fulfill her responsibilities to the congregation, but hampers her husband in his work. Indeed, the unhappiness of his wife may be so great as to cause the religious leader to give up an otherwise satisfactory pulpit, or even, if he has other emotional difficulties, to leave the ministry altogether. Thus the young wife of a minister assigned to a pulpit in a small Western town soon found herself the victim of a campaign of disparagement carried on by women in the church. Already neurotically disposed, she now felt more than ever inadequate, and her feelings of depression deepened still further with the birth of a baby. This, together with her need to be near her mother, as well as her need of psychiatric help, caused her husband to give up his pulpit, and finally, in an embittered frame of mind, the ministry itself.

Perhaps some training for the role of a clergyman's wife would not be a bad thing. The unfortunate consequences in this particular case might have been obviated if the woman had been instructed in the hazards and responsibilities of her position. In any case, it is clear that the clergyman should have done a better job in handling his parishioners and his wife. Himself the victim of countertransference reactions, he overidentified with his wife and allowed her distorted emotional perspective to influence him. If he had understood the transference reactions of his parishioners and of his wife, both of which placed him in the position of a father rather than a husband, he might have continued to serve his church and the community. And if he had faced up to his role as a religious leader, his wife might have benefited as well.

If the religious leader plays a symbolic role, so also may his wife, though not always with beneficent effects. A clergyman's wife was in need of a secretary and she recruited for the job one of her husband's parishioners, a woman who was active in the parish and community and was also experienced in secretarial work. Her competence was beyond question, yet she experienced a curious inability to work in her employer's home. She was constantly making errors in shorthand and her typing was poor. Despite the reassurances of the minister's wife, she became obsessed by her inadequacy, had tearful spells and difficulty in sleeping, ate poorly, and lost weight. Giving up her job did no good. The psychiatrist to whom she now turned found that the woman's mother had made her feel incompetent and unlovable as a young girl. An analysis of her attitudes revealed that in her relationship to the minister's wife she was living over again her unhappy childhood experiences with her mother. As she came to separate the two women in her mind, her relationship with each of them improved. Of course the minister's wife was not the cause of this woman's breakdown, but since her position put her in the symbolic role of surrogate mother, she added the straw which upset a precarious emotional balance.

It should be emphasized again that the relationship between the religious leader and those who seek his help is frequently unintelligible unless one takes into account the unrealistic attitudes that appear on one side or the other; that is, the intrusion of transference and countertransference. They may dominate thought and action to such an extent as to call for psychiatric treatment.

Confusion of Roles

O N C E primarily theological and humanistic, the role of the religious leader, in the conditions of the modern world and under the impact of the social sciences, has come to be thought of in psychotherapeutic terms. Under labels like "pastoral psychiatry," "spiritual psychiatry," and "religiopsychiatry," psychotherapy is being substituted for religious counseling. The trend is evident in counseling clinics conducted under the auspices of religious organizations,[1] and even in theological seminaries. Only the best intentions are behind the trend, but yet its result, we believe, is to lessen the effectiveness of the religious leader and to make his position on the psychosocial team ambiguous. It is only as each member of that team confines himself to exercising the technique peculiar to his profession that it is a team at all. So it is just as mistaken for the psychiatrist to assume the role of moralist as for the religious leader to assume the role of psychotherapist.

Yet it is precisely this role that is being advocated for the religious leader. Thus we find Carroll A. Wise in his *Pastoral Counseling,* one of the many works of its kind, describing the minister's role as that of an analytically oriented or "nondirective" psychotherapist. Emphasis is placed on the permissive character of such a role, which is thus able to dispense with a moral code. Conflict and guilt are described as undesirable, pathological states of mind. In Wise's view, all emotional disturbances fall within the province of religious counseling, provided only that the minister has the skill and training to deal with them. No consistent effort is made to distinguish between emotional disturbances that are realistically related to the circumstances of life, such as illness, death, or natural catastrophe, and those that are irrational and unrelated to reality, such as the various mental illnesses. In effect, it is denied that the one is the peculiar business of the religious leader, while the other is the business of the psychiatrist or the social caseworker.

It is not surprising to find that Wise underestimates the symbolic role of the religious leader. He writes that "religious resources," based on the quality of the relationship which the religious leader is able to offer to another person because of the inner quality of his own life, "are far more significant in the counseling relationship than are external forms or activities," by which he means Scriptures, prayers, religious rites, and religious writings of various kinds. "This is not to minimize the value of prayer or Scripture," he goes on to say, "but rather to indicate that their value depends greatly upon the kind of relationship which has been previously established, and upon the attitude of the pastor." [2] In this view, prayer and Scripture derive their efficacy from the minister as an individual. In our view, on the contrary, they derive their efficacy, not from the minister as an individual, but from the minister in his symbolic role, a role that is itself rooted in Scripture and scriptural tradition. And because he disparages the old-time role of the minister, Wise tends to see him as essentially in business for himself, rather than as a member of a group with a history and tradition.

The conception of the religious leader as a psychotherapist is not only wrong in principle, but may have unfortunate consequences in practice, as in the following case. A young woman who was having trouble with her husband consulted a minister. She confessed that her marital unhappiness was owing largely to sexual frustration. Regarding himself as a psychotherapist, the minister maintained a permissive attitude, which the woman contrasted with the puritanical attitude of her sexually inhibited husband. The result was that her sexual desires began to be focused on the minister, a development that was facilitated by the fact that transference figured prominently in the relationship. The woman idealized the minister. In this situation, if he were to cope with it effectively, the minister would have needed the special training of a psychiatrist. Only so could he have utilized this woman's transference to promote her emotional growth. Instead, as a result of his inexperience and countertransference reactions, he allowed the relationship to develop into a love affair which wrecked the woman's marriage and his own career.

A permissive attitude is part of the technique of the psychiatrist, but it has no place in the work of the religious leader. In the foregoing case, it was not by abdicating his role as a moralist, but by asserting it very positively, that the minister could have hoped to benefit his congregant. Beyond that it was his duty to refer her to a psychiatrist. Certainly he should not have encouraged and stimulated her in her emotional revelations but should have helped to limit them. Such revelations are for the psychiatrist, who is equipped to handle them as the religious leader is not.

Another, similar case involves a young man who unburdened himself to his minister, confessing to marital infidelity and dishonesty in his business dealings. Here again the permissive attitude of the minister allowed the relationship to assume an intimacy that was, so to speak, out of bounds. Unconscious feelings that the young man had experienced toward his father in early childhood now sprang up once more in relation to the minister. As commonly happens when such attitudes reappear in adulthood, the young man defended himself by becoming bitterly antagonistic to the minister. As dealt with by a psychiatrist, such a hostile expression of transference can be turned into a springboard for emotional growth. But the minister took his congregant's hostility at its face value, and the relationship ended in the young man's becoming an implacable foe of the minister and of religion.

In assuming the attitudes, if not the techniques, of the psychiatrist, the religious leader is trespassing upon a domain that is not his. And in so doing, he may not only fail to give the guidance and comfort which lie within his province, but alienate his congregant from religion and also place him beyond the help of the other members of the treatment team. None of this is to say that the religious leader will not avail himself of the insights of psychiatry, or of any other knowledge that will help him fulfill his role more effectively. But first and last he must remain true to his role.

The Religious Leader and the Social Caseworker

CONTRARY to the views of some religious leaders, and the programs inspired by these views, religious counseling is no more a form of social casework than it is a form of psychotherapy. At the same time it is true that religious institutions have pioneered in ministering to the needs of the poor, the orphaned, and the distressed. Enshrined in the traditions of Christianity and Judaism, the ideal of charity finds its practical embodiment today in the numerous hospitals and social and welfare agencies that are conducted under the auspices of religious institutions. But it is important not to overlook the fact that many of the social-work personnel employed in these institutions and agencies are themselves professionally trained and their roles defined. That is to say, their tasks are distinct from those of the religious counselor, even when these tasks are performed under the sponsorship of a religious institution. The majority of social agencies and welfare institutions in the United States are now nonsectarian—social work, like medicine, has shifted from religious to nonreligious administration, and in the course of this shift it has developed into a recognized profession with special techniques of its own. Since the problems with which it is concerned, arising as they do out of individual and family needs, are of concern also to the religious leader, we shall try in what follows to show how the concern differs in the two cases.

The aims and methods of social casework, whatever their resemblance to those of psychiatry and religion, are distinct from them. Underlying social casework is a philosophy which affirms the uniqueness and importance of the individual.[3] It holds that the welfare of the individual goes hand in hand with the welfare of the family and the community; that the purpose of social institutions is to enable the individual to achieve material and emotional security, as well as to provide him with increasing opportunity for the fulfillment of his creative capacities, irrespective of his race, creed, or color; and following from this, that state and government exist for the individual and his family, not the other way round. So the National Association of Social Workers takes it as a professional duty "to play its part in modifying or reshaping social and economic institutions which are inimical to the attainment of these broad democratic goals."

Among the technical tenets underlying social casework is the belief that individual and group behavior, although infinitely complex, is not accidental but shaped by social and psychological laws. As for the individual's behavior, it is molded by an interplay of forces, arising from his environment on the one hand and from his previous life experiences and his natural endowments on the other. Never for a moment denying that the person who seeks his help has the right to make his own decisions and shape his own destiny, the caseworker believes that by the application of his skills he can often aid the individual to a clearer understanding of himself, and by reducing the inner and outer pressures involved in his distress, further his emotional and social stability.

What is the nature of the caseworker-client relationship? The first thing to notice here is the word client. It emphasizes the fact that the relationship is not that of patient to doctor or congregant to religious leader. The client is not seeking medical care or spiritual guidance. But he is seeking help and expects the professional skills of the caseworker to provide it, skills that are neither those of the psychiatrist nor of the religious counselor. What are those skills and to what kind of problems are they addressed?

Let us begin with the problems, for it is in dealing with these that the skills have developed. The problems range from the economic to the emotional, with no clean-cut divisions between them. The caseworker deals with problem children in homes, schools, and on the streets; the placement of children and youth in foster homes; the provision of institutional care; delinquency and maladjustment among adolescents; marital troubles of nearly every sort; the care of unmarried mothers and out-of-wedlock children; family counseling of the sick, the unemployed, the invalided, the handicapped; guidance in schools, courts, prisons, hospitals, colleges, industrial plants, and labor unions; assistance to the aging and aged. The list is by no means exhaustive, and owing to the increasing stress and tempo of our industrial society, new problems are constantly arising and old ones multiplying. Thus in 1956 more than six million clients sought the help of social agencies in the United States. Adequate training of personnel and the reevaluation of techniques have never been more urgently needed.

For our purposes we may designate the two chief methods of social casework as the supportive and the reeducational. Supportive techniques are employed in cases in which the client is able to carry on, yet needs help, though not in the form of intensive psychological treatment. Here the skills of the caseworker are directed to decreasing conflict and tension and to mobilizing the client's personal strengths so as to increase his capacity to cope with his problems. In utilizing supportive techniques, although they may result in heightening self-awareness, the caseworker is not attempting to lead the client into self-examination or to manipulate the structure of his psychological patterns of adaptation. Instead, he relies on such things as direct guidance, reassurance, discussion, persuasion, at the same time that he exercises his professional authority to change those factors in the environment that are causing or complicating his client's problem. The caseworker can draw upon all the resources of the community—doctor, psychiatrist, nurse, teacher, home economist, and religious leader—that are concerned with the physical, social, and emotional adjustment of the client. One or all of these professions may play the part of consultant or collaborator, either inside or outside the casework agency.

The reeducative method, however much it leans on analytic psychotherapy, is not to be confused with it. It is applied when the client is beset with problems whose solution depends upon a change in his fundamental patterns of behavior. To accomplish this change the client needs to be made aware of his inner conflicts and motives, and of the ways in which they are affecting his behavior. Unlike the supportive method, reeducation aims to induce in the client an understanding of himself and his problem so that he may be better able to accept himself, together with his social milieu. The reeducative method is indicated only when the client is psychologically strong enough to withstand the stress of self-examination and capable of making the requisite changes of attitude and behavior. The special technique involved here is known as "clarification."

In the light of the foregoing it should be evident that the social caseworker is engaged in tasks that call for skills which only professional training can provide. And it should be equally evident that the religious counselor, however dedicated he may be to the alleviation of human distress, does not possess, and cannot be expected to possess, such skills. Not that he will remain in ignorance of these skills, but if a cooperative relationship is to exist between him and the caseworker, it is essential that he should recognize the latter's professional status, just as it is essential for the caseworker to recognize the spiritual status of the religious counselor.

Yet it is repeatedly charged by religious leaders that the social-work profession generally is indifferent, even antagonistic, to religious belief and practice. It may be that the effort to provide social work with a scientific basis has brought about, as Philip Klein explains, "a displacement of theological, religious and ethical principles." In any event, social-work literature for the most part contains little discussion of the caseworker-clergy relationship. Nor do casework records refer, except scantily, to such things as religious background and religious associations, or to religion as it figures in pathological conditions. It is not only religious leaders who have charged the social-work profession with failure to recognize the positive contribution religion can make to the resolution of personal and family problems; the failure has been underscored in numerous theses written by students in graduate schools of social work during the last decade. Yet we know of no attempt to meet this deficiency in the curricula of these schools. Still, there are signs of a change in this respect, especially among caseworkers employed on experimental working teams.

That a negative or indifferent attitude to religion on the part of the social caseworker may negate his or her usefulness in the treatment situation is illustrated by the story of a Catholic girl, aged nine, who was referred to a social agency because of stomach pains which were without physical basis, a fear of darkness, nail-biting, and feelings of sadness. Underlying her problem was a bitter rivalry with her mother for the attentions and affection of the father. In acting out this familiar family drama the girl took up an intensely religious attitude which found favor with her similarly religious father. She thus joined him against her mother, who was indifferent to religion. The caseworker, in allowing her own unconscious hostility towards religion to influence her technique, unwittingly re-created in her relationship with the child the identical religious conflict that existed between the girl and her mother. She became in effect a partisan in the conflict without influence on either child or parent. Further still, this partisanship led her to over-look the neurotic way in which religion was functioning in the life of the father. For it happened that as a result of his frus-trations in an unhappy marital situation, he became overat-tached to the daughter, and the incestuous, albeit unconscious, feelings that grew up between them found devious expression in their mutual preoccupation with religion and in their antip-athy to the mother's irreligion. If the caseworker had not aroused a hostile expression of transference in father and daughter, and had not been guilty of countertransference her-self, something might have been done, especially in collabora-tion with a religious counselor, to loosen the neurotic ties that existed between parent and child. And in general it may be said that such collaboration, when it is consistent, and leads to no confusion of roles, holds the key to the solution of many problems, individual and familial, which either worker by him-self would be incapable of solving.

What Religious Counseling Is

GRANTED that religious counseling is neither psycho-therapy nor social casework, what is it? Has it a con-tent and method peculiar to itself? We have already said that the religious counselor will avail himself of every insight into human behavior that psychiatry and social casework are able to provide, but that he is animated by principles and methods that are peculiarly his own. These principles and methods de-rive their special nature from the fact that the religious coun-selor operates within a moral and spiritual framework. His knowledge is transcendental and his authority symbolic, and both are exercised in behalf of the needs of those who come to him for help. His role is both priestly and pastoral. In the one he functions as teacher of a moral code and minister of sacramental rituals; in the other he stands as father to the lonely and physician to the wounded in spirit.

As a teacher he is called upon for instruction in problems of a most specific and concrete kind. Or he may be asked to lay down general principles or to explain allowable exceptions to them. What is the attitude of the church to artificial insemination? May religious dietary restrictions be abrogated in the interests of health? What religious tenets apply to the sexual education of children? No problem but what it has a religious bearing, so that the religious counselor's scope runs the gamut of human life itself. Illustrative of this is the following case history. A mother turned to her priest, upset at her adolescent son's sudden refusal to go to church. The boy, hitherto devoutly religious and planning to become a priest, was undergoing intensive medical treatment the nature of which the mother did not understand, but which seemed to have something to do with his increasing withdrawal from family and friends, and now the cessation of his formerly devout religious activities. From the physician the priest learned that the boy was being treated with hormones, and, discomfited by the frequent erections this was causing, the boy had to rearrange his clothing and in so doing touch his penis. The doctor did not know why this troubled the boy until the priest told him that the action was probably related in the boy's mind to masturbation, which Catholicism regards as a venial sin. Physician and priest joined forces, the one explaining to the boy why the medicine was having the effect it did, the other reassuring him that he was not, in the circumstances, committing a sin. Indeed, as the result of his consultation with the priest, the doctor decided that the biological benefits of his treatment were not great enough to offset its psychological disadvantages. And the priest urged the boy to come to him whenever he thought his conduct violated the teachings of religion. As a result of this collaboration, the boy was soon himself again. The case shows how priest and physician, each clarifying his role to the other, can cooperate to good advantage.

It is of the first importance for the religious counselor to be on his guard against taking a request for religious advice at its face meaning. Far more important than the request itself may be the unconscious motives behind it. The discovery of such motives is the great contribution of psychoanalytic psychology to the understanding of human behavior. That a request for advice is not always what it seems to be is well illustrated in the following case. Two months after the birth of her out-of-wedlock baby, a woman came to a minister saying that she wanted to join a church but couldn't decide which church to join. It was soon clear to the minister that the woman was overwhelmed by feelings of guilt and personal unworthiness. Her question, "Which church shall I join?" was put hesitantly, her intonation and attitude indicating that a more fundamental question was at the back of her mind: "Which church would want to have as unworthy a person as myself?" Along with this went another unexpressed question, "Am I fit to be a mother?" The situation, as the minister recognized, called for the help of a caseworker, rather than a decision concerning church affiliation. Such help was arranged for, while the answer to the woman's overt question was postponed until the time when improvement in her emotional state would allow her to make her own religious decision.[4]

There are many situations in which a request for religious advice is really a request for easy absolution. In such cases there is an insufficiency of conscience, and the task of the religious counselor is to supply the necessary conscience by unmistakable moral and spiritual advice. For example, a twenty-seven-year-old woman, a Roman Catholic, presented herself to a Protestant social agency for help. She had a cousin who was a priest and she avoided all Catholic agencies lest the "shame" of her predicament should get back to him. Her predicament lay in the fact that she had separated from her husband after a few months, with the marriage still unconsummated. She wanted to know what her marital status was according to church law, and whether the marriage could be annulled. The woman was referred to the agency minister, to whom she spoke of a long period of loneliness broken by episodes of sexual promiscuity. She displayed no feelings of guilt. The minister minced no words and urged her to start assuming some responsibility for her actions by taking up her questions with a priest, who, he assured her, would certainly help her. Impressed by the straightforwardness of this advice, the woman, with the help of her caseworker, got in touch with a

Catholic priest. If the minister was able to help this woman, though her faith was different from his, it was because in his symbolic role his authority cut across church boundaries.

We repeat, then, that the religious counselor who is on the alert will detect more in a request for advice than lies on the surface. It may conceal a mental illness. Thus a man of twenty-eight, an Episcopalian married to a Roman Catholic, applied to a sectarian social agency for advice about the use of contraceptives. Although his wife had no objections, he was uneasy in his conscience. He said that he had thought of going to the parish priest first, but felt he would rather discuss the problem with someone he did not know. He had also contemplated discussing the matter with a psychiatrist, but feared that the psychiatrist would attack his religious qualms as "escapist," and deprive him of beliefs that he cherished. In the course of his interview with him, the agency minister discovered that the young man's sexual problems were part of an emotional disorder for which he had been medically discharged from the army. Further, he detected that the man's concern with contraception was in reality an evasion of more fundamental problems in his sexual life. The minister discussed the attitude of various churches toward contraception, at the same time suggesting that the young man's indecision with regard to this matter might be related to a more general indecision arising out of his emotional illness. In cooperation with the caseworker the minister succeeded in inducing the young man to see a psychiatrist, who, he assured him, would respect his religious needs and beliefs. With the permission of the patient himself, the psychiatrist was informed of all the pertinent facts in the case. Thus caseworker, minister, and psychiatrist formed a team. It was the minister's discernment that brought this about. Instead of rendering a decision with regard to contraception, he used his authority to get at the root of the young man's trouble. But placing him in the hands of a psychiatrist was not the end of the matter. The minister stood by, ready to help, in case the psychiatric treatment should give rise to religious complications.

Religious morality, rooted as it is in the transcendent, extends the frontiers of the human spirit. To act in accordance with the "will of God" is to act in accordance with principles whose scope is universal. It is these principles that are the peculiar domain of religion and it is they that give life its meaning and purpose. "Only religion," says Freud, "is able to answer the question of the purpose of life. One can hardly go wrong in concluding that the idea of a purpose in life stands and falls with the religious system." [5] Neither modern science nor humanistic philosophy has anything comparable to offer in its place. The sciences, especially the medical and social sciences, have not undermined but have added enormously to our understanding of religious values and of their role in the spiritual economy of man. Nothing has altered the fact that in times of personal crisis there is awakened in almost everyone the belief in a divine Father, together with a faith in the power of prayer to alter the course of human events. There is no dearth of examples of this phenomenon; here is a particularly poignant illustration. It was a childhood incident in the life of a rabbi, one which had a lasting influence on him and on his ministrations to those who called upon him for help in time of crisis. When he was ten, his father, himself a distinguished rabbi, lay dying of cancer. Broken-hearted over the father's suffering, mother and son went to an old and famous rabbi in their community. A white-bearded patriarch, this rabbi listened to the mother with compassion, and did his best to console her. Then he said, "And now I will say a prayer for him." The boy was never to forget the prayer, nor the feeling of being healed which he experienced. He felt a great weight off his chest, and was able to accept his father's impending death with a calm and courage impossible to him before.

No one could doubt the healing power of prayer in this instance. And prayer goes to the heart of religion.[6] It mobilizes untapped reservoirs of energy; it is an affirmation of faith, an avowal of confidence and trust. It acts, when everything else fails, as a dike against the forces of chaos. It was Abraham Lincoln who said, "I have been driven many times to my knees by the overwhelming conviction that there was nowhere else to go; my own wisdom, and that of those around us, seemed insufficient for the day." Prayer is the great beneficent instrument in the armory of the religious counselor.

In times of disaster, as recent studies have shown,[7] religious attitudes are reawakened that have been long dormant; indeed, whose very existence was hardly suspected. The chief of these is the notion of God as actively intervening in all that happens. It is impossible to believe, except in theory, that our lives are at the mercy of meaningless forces. Besides, mechanical explanation does not rule out the existence of purpose. So it is that in times of disaster we invoke the will of God. Only so do disasters make sense, and they must make sense if we are to reconcile ourselves to them. It is here, in reconciling us to life's hazards, which by no means involves the passive acceptance of them, that the religious leader performs his most humane task. The following case is typical of what the religious leader can accomplish in this respect.

A young man and his family were caught in a major flood disaster, which resulted in serious property damage and physical injury. The young man himself escaped unscathed, but began to suffer from sleeplessness and obsessional self-reproaches. There followed a period of deep soul-searching. Why, he kept asking, were he and his family destined to be caught in this disaster? More important still, why was he spared? He took his questions to the minister, who suggested that perhaps God had spared him that he might fight for flood control and soil conservation in his area. Having lived to witness the ravaging effects of flood and erosion, the young man, thus inspired by the minister, became the leader of a group organized to promote legislation in these matters. Helped by a religious belief, he utilized his anxiety and guilt for a social purpose, and achieved moreover a sense of emotional well-being and personal fulfillment.

It must not be supposed that the priestly and pastoral roles of which we have spoken exist in separation from each other. Of course they overlap, as is perhaps most clearly seen in the confessional. Confession, no less than prayer, effects a catharsis, except that in the one case the catharsis takes place in the privacy of the individual bosom, while in the other it takes place in the presence of an understanding listener. That this need for a listener may be styled a human constant is evident from the fact that the practice of confession exists in one form or another in all the religious denominations. But confession of sins is only half of the story. The assurance of forgiveness is the other. The aim of confession and penance is to achieve a feeling of "worthiness," which is referred to theologically as the state of being "in grace." Only when one is in a state of grace is he deemed eligible to join his own spirit with the spirit of God. It is this latter feeling of wholeness or completeness which the religious person seeks, ultimately, from the confessional, and many people who have experienced it testify to the inner peace and strength of spirit which it imparts. Now this absolution is possible only through an individual with religious authority. In the Catholic Church, confession is a highly formal procedure, as it is among high Episcopalians. In Judaism, confession is made publicly by the body of congregants together on the annual Day of Atonement, and individually, among orthodox Jews, on the deathbed. Among Protestants, other than high Episcopalians, confession is quite informal. Some Protestant spokesmen, however, advocate the institution of a Protestant confessional. "We Protestants have erred in some matters," writes Dr. Harry Emerson Fosdick. "Our Roman Catholic brothers have kept the confessional and thereby they have been able entirely to surpass us in the realm of welfare service. Through the institution of the confessional they have built up an amazing welfare service for treating diseased souls. A good priest can, in the confessional, help individuals in a manner which we have nothing corresponding to. In spite of the fact that I am a Baptist, I have myself had for years what I should like to call a confessional." [8]

Among people who have had no direct experience of confession there is an idea that the practice encourages sin. "One has only to go to confession," they say, "and then one can begin all over again." Nothing could be more mistaken. Although it provides relief from inner tension, confession in itself is painful, and the prospect of facing the confessional and carrying out penances inhibits rather than encourages undesirable behavior. But there is the danger of "scrupulosity," an abnormal need to confess. Actions which do not involve the conscience of a normal person become matters of grave sin. There is an ambivalence in the condition known as "scrupulosity." What the penitent regards as permissible one moment he next may regard as a sin. He is perpetually on the stretch, unable to control or explain his anxiety. So fearful is he of sinning that he has no faith in the judgment of others, even his spiritual adviser. He broods over circumstances which have nothing to do with the moral aspects of an action, and to which normal people pay no attention. He is never sure that confession has absolved him, despite his confessor's assurances to the contrary. In reciting his sins he may make use of voluminous notes and be endlessly circumstantial. That mental illness may be involved here is illustrated by the following case. The patient, a thirty-year-old office worker, was as a young man profoundly affected by the death of his father, and when shortly afterwards two of his friends and a young servant girl in the family became insane, he began to suffer from insomnia, lost his appetite, and feared that he too might go insane. Once in family conversation a religious question came up for discussion, and as the young man listened he was suddenly struck by the idea that by a more careful observation of his religious obligations, till now neglected, he could save himself from the insanity he feared. He went at once to confession, but was shortly assailed by doubts as to whether he had confessed correctly. Suppose he had committed some sin he had forgotten and so failed to mention? The question became an obsession with him. Repeated rehearsal of the pros and cons only made matters worse. His depression deepened, and he became more than ever fearful of insanity; psychiatric care was clearly indicated. Under hospital treatment his condition steadily improved till the neurasthenic symptoms and the compulsive ideas disappeared.

Not all cases of scrupulosity are as severe as this. Sometimes the reassurances of the confessor bring sufficient relief to the person suffering from obsessional doubt to make it possible for him to live in the community without further treatment. Thus a Catholic woman in her thirties was obsessed with the feeling of having committed an unpardonable sin in allowing her uterus to be removed, which was done because of a gynecologic disorder. She blamed herself for the situation that now permitted her to have sexual intercourse with no possibility of conception. Ordinarily such feelings of guilt, when they ensue upon a surgically induced menopause, are ominous, and call for emergency psychiatric consultation. However, in this case the psychiatrist felt that the woman's symptoms were not severe enough to warrant treatment, besides which her history indicated a lifetime of emotional adjustment. Instead, the woman was encouraged to return to her church. When she came to confession and expressed her doubts of herself, the priest pointed out that she could not possibly have sinned, that the operation had been unavoidable, and moreover had been performed by a Catholic doctor in a Catholic hospital. This assurance was enough, and might have been given prior to the operation. We might add that now and then a confessor, not being privy to the particular emotional disorder underlying a case of scrupulosity, may be unduly harsh and so intensify the disorder, at least temporarily.

There is nothing in the confessional which prevents it from cooperating with other secular agencies. Such collaboration can be fruitful, as the following case shows. A nine-year-old boy from a devout Catholic home was referred to a social agency because he was "incorrigibly bad." The chief trouble was his stubborn refusal to participate in any religious activities. He had already been thrown out of a parochial school and was well on his way to dismissal from a public school as well. He was assigned to a caseworker, and her efforts to establish a trusting relationship with the boy were rewarded when he confessed to her one day that he was obsessed with "dirty words" whenever he tried to say his prayers. Rather than sin in this way, he chose to stay away from church altogether. Hence his failure to get along in parochial school and his conflict with his parents. Actually religiously inclined, the boy was ashamed to tell anyone of his problem, so he dealt with it in the only way he knew how; that is, by running away from it. Turning down the caseworker's suggestion that he discuss his problem with a psychiatrist, he expressed a willingness to discuss it with a priest, especially in the confessional. The caseworker arranged the matter with a kindly priest, who had a considerable understanding of mental illness. He explained to the boy that God knew he couldn't control his thoughts, and that a doctor could help him back to his proper place in the church. The boy was now ready to see a psychiatrist. Treatment brought to light a home situation involving conflict with an overstrict and punitive father. The boy's blasphemous attitude towards God was an unconscious expression of his rebellion against his father.

As father and son came to understand the situation, the relationship between them improved, and with this improvement the boy's obsessional disorder disappeared. He was able to resume his studies in the parochial school and to attend church.

A less happy outcome of a counseling situation occurred when a seventeen-year-old girl told her confessor that she had been seduced. Already filled with shame and guilt, the girl was so harshly berated by her confessor that she left the confessional in tears, and with a feeling of such great bitterness that she abandoned the church altogether. Several years later, suffering from an emotional disorder, she applied to a family agency for help, telling the caseworker that the unfortunate experience in the confessional was her last contact with religion.

In summary, we may say that sympathetic insight into people and an understanding of their particular life situations are indispensable to effective religious counseling. Together with this, and uniquely characteristic of such counseling, is the symbolic role of the religious leader. His authority and power derive from something greater than himself. In this setting his techniques are those of moral guidance, prayer, and confession.

Techniques of Religious Counseling

T H E relationship between religious counselor and troubled congregant or parishioner is above all positive and interpersonal. Whether pastor, priest, or rabbi, he is usually approached voluntarily,* and his presence from the first moment induces an atmosphere of reverence and sympathy. The very dress of the religious leader, and the church or synagogue itself, play a part here in evoking comfort and hope. Whatever the state of mind of the congregant or parishioner, whether it be rational or irrational, whether his problem be simple or complex, economic, social, or psychological, the religious counselor's attitude towards him is one of compassion and spiritual acceptance. It bespeaks the faith that every problem has a solution and every pain can be eased. He may be a patient to the psychiatrist or a client to the caseworker, but he is a con-

* Rare exceptions are persons ordered by court officials to consult their religious leaders.

gregant or parishioner to the religious counselor, which is to say that the religious relationship is in a class apart.

In the one case the methods of the practitioners are secular and psychological. They are based upon a dynamic theory of human nature, as well as a body of social experience, and their psychotherapeutic object is to adjust the patient or client to social reality. Now the religious leader shares with the psychiatrist and the caseworker an attitude of sympathy and respect for the individual—and for his family—but his relationship to him differs from theirs in that it is based upon a religious faith and a spiritual interpretation of man and society. It differs also in that it involves moral judgment and forgiveness. And those things are not just applied at random, but require the peculiar skill or set of skills that are the outcome of a particular kind of training—training, one might say, of mind and heart. Still another difference is this: While the psychiatrist and the caseworker, when they have done all they can for the patient or client, terminate their relationship with him, the religious counselor continues to figure in the life of the person who has sought his help, even after he has succeeded in solving the problem that brought the person to him in the first place. In other words, his role is not confined to times of crisis. It is a spiritual role and as such pervasive.

Before we discuss this role in detail, we should like first to remove an obstacle that stems from terminology. We have in mind the tendency among religious writers in the field of pastoral psychology and religious counseling to substitute the technical terminology of psychiatry and casework for the traditional language of Christianity and Judaism. It is a mistaken tendency, the cause of confusion and misunderstanding. To seek to eliminate the traditional religious vocabulary is to violate a tested and hallowed heritage. It will not do to substitute "symptom" for "sin," "psyche" for "soul," "superego" for "conscience," or "cure" for "salvation." The one set of words belongs to psychological discourse; the other to theological. From the standpoint of interprofessional cooperation, the significant thing is the degree to which theological language expresses psychological truth and the degree to which traditional religious practices, of which this language is the expression, fulfill specific and universal psychological needs.

So we advocate the retention of the traditional language, for as no other language does, it serves to mark the special social and spiritual orientation of the religious counselor. In his role as pastor and priest he acts, not as an individual, but as the representative of a faith, the steward of a body of historic wisdom. The minister, priest, and rabbi are leaders of a social institution which through its beliefs and practices constitutes a fellowship, and whoever joins it becomes part of a larger whole. An extension of the family and a link with the community, mankind and the universe, this fellowship depends for its vitality upon the extent to which it is inspired by moral and spiritual truths.

Not that these moral and spiritual truths need be promulgated in the form of hard-and-fast dogmas; indeed, the religious leader, especially in his role as counselor, will adapt his approach to the degree or phase of religious development of the individual who consults him. He has something to offer every person, sick or well, and the character of his actual intervention differs from one situation to another. He may exercise his role in a case of bereavement, or he may collaborate with the doctor in the preparation of a patient for major surgery. But his role remains always that of a religious leader, whose equipment is moral and spiritual.

From the first interview with a person who seeks his help, the religious counselor tries to decide on a plan, and like the psychiatrist or caseworker, he must attempt to formulate the problem with which he is presented. He has consciously to ask himself, "Why did this person really come to me? And why just now, rather than a week, a year, or a decade ago? Is he covering up the real problem? Is it his own problem, or is he acting in behalf of someone else? Or is he pretending to act in behalf of someone else when in reality the problem is his own?" The following case, brought up for discussion by the minister involved in it, is instructive here.

"A mother came to me about her nine-year-old daughter. Robin, the young girl in question, is a bright student; personable, she looks and acts older than her years. Her mother told me that Robin has no friends at all, does not seek friends and is not sought by other children. She seems self-sufficient; goes roller-skating every Saturday and Sunday and reads six or seven books a week. She doesn't complain of lack of friends and seems happy. Her grades in public school are good, but every now and then, usually at least once every two weeks, she will bring an extremely low grade, a ten or twenty. She has one sister, age six, who is sickly and has been pampered. Her mother states that the father and mother have a good home life. Her mother drinks heavily, but is never seen intoxicated. Her mother wants to know if Robin's behavior is 'normal.' If not, she wants to correct the situation. The mother mentioned that she was like Robin as a child and has been unhappy as a result. She thinks Robin should go to Sunday school and to the recreation center of the church. She feels that she did Robin a disservice by dropping out of church herself and by refusing to go to Sunday school as a child."

The minister went on to raise the question whether Robin's lack of friends did not indicate some sort of disturbance that needed looking into. The answer is certainly yes. Children are often good psychological diagnosticians, so that they will tend to avoid the company of children in whom they sense an emotional disturbance. But the case raises still another question. Why did the mother consult the minister when she did? Why not before? Robin at the time was nine years old and her troubling behavior presumably was not a sudden occurrence. Again, when and why did the mother discontinue church membership and attendance? Pertinent too is the fact that Robin was three years old when her sister was born. No doubt there was rivalry for the mother's affection, with Robin at a distinct disadvantage because her sister was not only younger than she but sickly. It is a reasonable guess that Robin's troubles originated in this rivalry.

Perhaps the most fundamental consideration of all for the religious counselor in this case is the probability that the mother, though acting ostensibly in behalf of her child, with whom, as is usual in such circumstances, she overidentified, was actually seeking help on her own account. Here was a mother who drank heavily, which would indicate some serious emotional distress, and certainly belied her claim that she had a good home life. In saying that she and Robin were alike, the mother was using the child to proclaim her own unhappiness.

Thus the religious counselor would be making a mistake if he overlooked this woman's implicit appeal for help on her own account. Simply to have advised psychiatric treatment for the child would have amounted to rejection of the mother's plea. As for the timing of her consultation, it was precipitated, in all probability, by some crisis in her life rather than the child's. It remains to add that on the recommendation of the minister the mother joined the women's auxiliary of the church, which provided a welcome relief from the domestic grind, especially as she was overinvolved with the care of her ailing younger child. Her fellow auxiliary members helped her out, so that she was able to take an occasional afternoon off. Her drinking lessened, and, alerted to Robin's problem, the teachers in the Sunday school gave her extra attention. Through the skillful use of the resources of his religious program, and more important, his success in getting the mother as well as Robin to participate in religious services and studies, the minister obviated the need of a psychiatrist or of Alcoholics Anonymous. Finally, in encouraging religious observances in the home, to the delight of the father, himself a regular churchgoer, the minister helped to cement family bonds.

From the very first the religious counselor should seek to establish in his own mind, though with the participation of the congregant or parishioner himself, what contribution he can make to the solution of the latter's problem. Further, he will seek to ascertain what factors have precipitated the appeal for help. Although his role will remain religious throughout, his techniques will differ according to the specific needs of each applicant. If the services of another member of the treatment team seem called for, his chief task will be that of making an appropriate referral.

Methods of Referral

IN SPITE of widespread and increasing mental health publicity, people still have uneasy feelings about psychiatry, with which they associate insanity, sexual perversion, and violence. These feelings have an unconscious basis, as psychoanalytic studies have brought out. Hardly consciously, people perceive in the manifestations of mental illness psychological mechanisms of their own which were brought under control and repressed in early childhood. Paradoxically, it is not the strangeness but the familiarity of mental illness that makes it so terrifying. Control of one's infantile impulses has been hard-won, and fears of its loss are stirred by the sight of mental illness. Hostile punitive attitudes towards the mentally ill are often a reflection of the same attitudes towards these impulses in oneself.

Hence referral to a psychiatrist is usually a delicate matter, and the religious counselor will feel his way before he makes such a referral. He will try to find out what the person's response is likely to be. Timing is of the first importance. If the suggestion comes prematurely, it may be taken as a cold and peremptory dismissal. On the other hand, if it is deferred too long, the relationship between the counselor and the mentally ill person may become so charged that the suggestion is resisted altogether. In both cases the effect may be damaging to the individual and may turn him against religion. Untimely referral is also likely to make the task of the psychiatrist or caseworker all the harder.

The following is a case in point. A young married couple consulted a minister, himself unmarried, about the husband's sexual impotence and the discord between them. The minister, aware that impotence was usually traceable to some deep-seated emotional problem, planned in his initial interview to refer the couple to a social agency, but he took a liking to the man and asked him to return alone for a second interview. From then on, and indeed for two years, the minister's study became a refuge for the husband. He posed as the injured party, and the minister accepted him in this role. The wife stopped coming to church, and the situation between her and the husband worsened. She did manage to get her husband to agree to a consultation at a well-known social agency in the community. Although the minister intervened to inform the caseworker that the wife was incorrigible and divorce was in order, the caseworker insisted on looking into the matter for herself. And of course two years of questionable counseling did not make it easier for her to deal with the husband.

In contrast to this is a case in which the religious counselor recognized the need for a psychiatric referral and made it promptly. A young woman, devoutly Catholic, stopped attending church after her baby was born. She explained to friends that she "didn't believe that junk any more." When the priest heard of this he visited her at her home. Happy to see him, the woman soon acknowledged that since the birth of her baby she had been afraid of crowds, and that she went to the church only when it was empty. At such times she found it peaceful to sit by herself and pray. But if the priest or other people were around, she felt she was being watched, which made her panicky. The priest explained to her that it was not at all un- usual for a mother to feel nervous after the birth of a baby, and urged her to discuss the matter with her family doctor, in whom she had great confidence. At the suggestion of the doctor, she saw a psychiatrist, whose treatment cured her of her fear.

In this matter of referral, it is important to take cultural factors into account. For example, while belief in voodoo, magic, and spiritualism may be evidence of mental abnormality in one person, it may not be so for another—say, a newly settled Puerto Rican in New York City, or an immigrant Mexican in the southwest United States.

The help of the religious counselor is constantly being sought by people with problems that require referral elsewhere. Typical examples are: an invalid mother who needs the help of a housekeeper, or nursing care; an aged parent who requires placement in an appropriate home; financial assistance for the family whose wage earner is ill; a marital problem involving intense emotional conflict; a delinquency problem in an adoles- cent. A person may not be able to handle his external life situa- tion, and referral is properly to a social agency. Or an adolescent may need guidance in selecting a career, so that the religious counselor will refer him and his parents to a vocational advi- sory service. Again, the capacity to work may have been im- paired by a physical illness, and dealing especially with this problem are state and federal vocational rehabilitation services. When the request for a specific service comes from a person who is emotionally ill, it is desirable to refer him or his family to a casework agency, which, if it sees fit, will in turn refer the applicant to a still more specialized agency. If the case for referral involves a child of sixteen or under, nothing should be done without the participation of a parent or guardian. It is of the first importance, then, for the religious counselor to know the local agencies that exist to deal with psychological and social problems.

We may learn much that is crucial to religious counseling from the following case history. One day a man in his middle twenties knocked quietly on the door of his minister's study. The minister was not surprised at his call, for the man often dropped in like this to discuss such matters as the boys' club he led, a fellow parishioner who was in trouble, or a point in last Sunday's sermon that he had pondered over. The minister welcomed these visits, for they made him feel that the church really mattered. Yet it was too bad, he thought, that this young man's wife was seldom well enough to attend church and that her face bore such a haunted expression. On one occasion the minister had asked if there was anything he could do, but the young woman had failed to respond to this overture. Now the incident was recalled by the minister as his visitor falteringly began to talk. "No, pastor," he finally blurted out, "today it's not my club, your sermon, or somebody else who's in a jam. It's me, my wife, and my baby." He had done his best to make a go of a youthful, unhappy marriage, but not even the birth of a child had healed the gap between him and his wife, and he had now come to announce that she had suffered a mental breakdown. The minister was all sympathy, and in the months that followed stood by his parishioner through the crisis of his wife's hospitalization. He found a foster home for the baby and encouraged the young man to maintain normal contacts with people. Then war broke out and the man was drafted into the army. The minister was overwhelmed by the realization that the child was now practically parentless. Although well enough to leave the hospital and to be responsible for herself, with supervision, the mother neither wished nor was able to take care of the child. The foster parents were devoted, but they were aging. What was the minister to do now? He had performed his role as a man of religion; he had established a relationship of confidence with his parishioner; he had acted with sympathy and charity. But his good will, admirable in all other respects, had led him astray in that he had assumed the role of a social caseworker. The case had aspects that called for a kind of knowledge and a set of techniques that he did not possess. For example, the placement and supervision of children in foster homes is a skill that requires years of training and experience. From the beginning the minister should have laid the ground for consultation with a responsible children's agency. It would have chosen a foster home only after a particular study of the needs of the child, and the home moreover would have been visited regularly by a caseworker experienced with children and appreciative of what separation from parents means. The agency, too, could have helped to insure the father's rights and in some sort maintain his relationship with the child. Dedicated as the minister in this case was, he complicated rather than resolved the problem it presented.[9]

Once the religious counselor has decided to refer his congregant or parishioner to a social agency, he will get in touch with the latter, preferably through personal conference with one of its members. He will acquaint the caseworker with the nature of the problem and what his own ideas are about the way the agency might help. At the same time he will find out all he can about the agency and the social worker's point of view, learn how best to interpret the referral to his charge, and ascertain how he and the caseworker can work together to the best advantage. Having assured himself about the agency in all possible ways, the religious counselor's next step is to assist his charge to accept its help. The following is an instance of this process. A minister consulted a family agency about referral of a parishioner and his children. The story he told was of a widower who was having trouble managing his two offspring, a boy of twelve and a younger girl. The mother, who was a Jew, had become an active member of a Christian church. She had been baptized and had the children given a religious training. Though both parents had shown warmth and understanding towards the children, they were never well managed and the home was not well kept. Now, two years after the mother's death, the children were out of hand altogether and the father did not know what to do with them, with the boy especially. The minister, with the father's consent, had got in touch with a placement agency but had been told it would probably be a mistake to place the boy without the girl. The minister saw the point and turned to the family agency. After talking with the family-agency caseworker, he explained to his parishioner that such an agency specialized in precisely the problems that were confronting him and would help him think things through. At the same time he assured the father that the church would do all in its power to serve him in any way that he or the agency might suggest. The parishioner accepted the plan with relief.

This case illustrates the steps that go to make up the process of referral, though it also illustrates an error. In keeping with his religious role, the minister succeeded in establishing a warm relationship between himself and his parishioner. Further, aware of the kind of problem with which he was confronted, he saw the necessity of calling upon a caseworker. What he did not see was the specialized roles of various social work agencies, so that he was led into the mistake of first approaching a placement agency instead of an agency able to manage the whole family problem. Fortunately, he received the right advice from the placement agency. If he had simply directed the father there, the man would have undergone the disheartening experience of an unnecessary "run-around." In consulting a family agency without the knowledge of his parishioner, the minister was acting in this instance quite appropriately, for if it had turned out that he was once more applying in the wrong quarter it was just as well the parishioner should not know about it. But it did not turn out so, and the referral was handled in a way acceptable to the beleaguered parent. The outcome was a satisfactory one for both father and children. Because he was aware that the problem fell strictly outside his domain, the minister avoided the pitfall of becoming overinvolved with the parishioner, but he did not withdraw his religious support.

It is not uncommon for the religious leader to be called upon to make a decision in an emergency, to shift abruptly from a priestly to a pastoral role. Thus a rabbi, at the conclusion of Sabbath services, was approached by a young woman whom he had never seen before. "Rabbi," she said, "I'm going to kill myself. I am a worthless person. My mother and I lived together. We had only each other, yet we quarreled all the time. Many times I said, 'I wish you would drop dead!' Well, I got my wish. She died two weeks ago. Now I'm all alone and I don't want to live any more." When he had regained his composure, the rabbi said to her, "Come back to my study on Monday. In the meantime I will try to find a psychiatrist for you and he will take care of you." The woman turned away silently, walked out of the synagogue, and did not come back. The rabbi, it is clear, was too shocked to fulfill his role properly. He should not have allowed the woman to leave the synagogue with what must have seemed to her a peremptory dismissal. He should have given her every assurance of help. If he was unable to take her to his study at the moment, he ought at least to have urged her to come back that evening or the next morning, and to feel free to telephone him in the interim. It was his duty, too, to find out all he could about her, whether she had friends or relatives whose aid could be recruited. In a psychiatric emergency of this sort, it is especially important for the counselor to be in full possession of himself, since he may have to grasp the problem and think of the proper referral at the first encounter.

According to popular lore, a person who threatens to commit suicide hardly ever does. This is not true. Every threat of suicide should be taken seriously. Even a person who is obviously indulging in dramatics to gain attention needs to be watched. The suicidal person should be placed in the hands of a psychiatrist at the earliest possible moment. But it is not only the person who gives verbal expression to suicidal ideas that needs emergency psychiatric care. Just as serious are such signs as excessive weeping, restless pacing, wringing of the hands, loss of appetite and weight, and insomnia. In any case the religious counselor, confronted with a person who harbors either suicidal or homicidal impulses, is obliged to deal with the problem of referral both promptly and sensitively. But he must not underestimate the help he can give on the spot. Despite appearances, people are often overwhelmed by feelings of helplessness and crave the guidance of someone with authority. If the religious counselor manages to communicate the special symbolic character of his position, he can often influence the behavior of even a violently irrational person.

Obviously, not all referrals, whether they involve religious counselors, caseworkers, or psychiatrists, are automatically productive of good. Religious counselors make mistakes, and the quality of casework and psychiatric treatment is extremely uneven. Although the treatment of illness is in general carefully regulated by law, the treatment of mental illness and the practice of social casework are not always subject to similar licensing, nor are there the same professional controls. In consequence, unqualified people—at any rate, people who do not meet the highest professional standards—are permitted to administer psychological treatment. When the religious counselor is in doubt he can secure guidance from the local county medical society or from a qualified social agency in his community. Moreover, he should use his influence and prestige to raise existing standards, either by assisting the groups in his community that are interested in such matters, or if no such group exists, by helping to organize one.

Nothing could better illustrate the dangers of a hasty or mistaken referral than this case, from the files of a social agency in a small Western community. A woman with three small children applied without an appointment to a private family agency. She said that a minister had referred her to the agency and that she was in immediate need of food and rent. Her husband having disappeared two months before, the woman had been evicted and now lived in a single furnished room with her children and her mother, who was on public welfare. The landlord was asking them to move. She said that the Department of Welfare investigator had refused her financial aid, saying she should go to work while her mother cared for the children. She professed her willingness to work, but until she found a job, she needed an apartment and food for her family. Unfortunately, the caseworker already had an appointment and asked the woman to come back. Meanwhile, she offered to get in touch with the public welfare agency. Put out by all this, the woman refused the offer of a later appointment. Poor referral technique was to blame for this unhappy situation. The minister had failed to discuss the case beforehand with the private agency and he had also failed to communicate with the public welfare agency. If he had done the first the woman would have been spared the frustrations of going to a private family agency where emergency basic financial needs could not be met; if he had done the second he might have procured the needed assistance for her.

Of course, in such crises as threatened eviction, lack of

food, or a marriage breakup, misunderstandings tend to occur on all sides. But the religious counselor can often do much to prevent them. In this case the minister later confessed to the caseworker that his usual practice, when a parishioner of his own was involved, was to contact the agency before making a referral, but that the woman here was not a member of his church. This amounted to confessing that he was not fulfilling his role as a religious leader. His duty towards the woman who had consulted him was exactly the same as that towards his parishioners. It is a duty that embraces all mankind.

Psychiatry and Religious Institutions

I T I S natural, in view of the historic traditions of Christianity and Judaism, that the church and synagogue should participate in services which are the province of the social service agency. Some religious leaders have set up social services within the framework of the religious center itself, so that the congregant is not referred to a community agency, but rather to an agency which is associated with the church or synagogue. In the case of the Free Synagogue in New York City, the synagogue social-service agency has even set up a specialized sub-agency which confines itself to the problem of adoption. In New York City, the Marble Collegiate Church and other religious centers have established psychiatric clinics, complete with psychiatrists, social workers, and psychologists. Various advantages are claimed for these arrangements. It is said that people who are mistrustful of psychiatry and social work as being hostile to religion are ready to accept the services they provide if such services are sponsored by their own church, but not otherwise. Or it is felt that psychiatrists and social workers should be not only favorably disposed to religion, but members of a church. It is claimed, too, that since people seeking the advice of religious counselors are in need of psychiatric and social-service care, it is desirable to administer this care on the spot, so to speak, in a physical environment that is already familiar.

All these arguments have a measure of validity, but they are also open to objection. What happens in actual practice is that the specific and irreplaceable contribution of the religious leader often undergoes a subtle distortion. Before long the religious leader is utilizing psychological techniques, or even giving psychological tests. Sometimes he goes so far as to hide the fact that he is a religious leader by deliberately wearing ordinary street clothes and avoiding the use of a title that might reveal his calling. Staff psychiatrists, in their turn, practice something called "religio-therapy." And there are other objections. An emotional disorder may be such that it is best treated in a nonsectarian setting. For example, a mental imbalance which leads to a constant change of church affiliation may be worsened, even given a definitely antireligious turn, when treatment takes place in a sectarian setting. Even people with strong religious convictions may prefer to turn to a nonsectarian agency for help with a nonreligious problem. Further, there is the danger that the agencies set up by a religious center will be geared, not to the community at large, but to the interests and needs of the particular church or synagogue. Unnecessary duplication of services and consequent waste of money is another danger, and a serious one in view of the actual shortage of social and psychiatric services in most communities. No doubt there are special social problems indigenous to each faith, but would not the desirable course of action here be to train caseworkers to understand the religious needs of their clientele? Moreover, there exist in most communities centralized Protestant, Catholic, and Jewish agencies equipped to deal with these problems, which seems more desirable than an agency for each church or synagogue.

We have seen in this chapter something of the armory at the disposal of the religious leader engaged in grappling with the emotional and moral problems. In both its general principles and its specific practices religious counseling is different from all other counseling, and it is this difference that constitutes its peculiar effectiveness. At the same time the religious counselor will collaborate with the other helping professions, and relate his own insights and method of treatment to theirs. It is in this way that he contributes most to the emotional and moral growth of his charges, and enlarges their capacity for religious ideals.

RELIGION IN SEX AND MARRIAGE

5.

IN THE MIDST OF ALL THE CHANGES OF OUR TIME, RE-
ligion is still a primary influence in marriage and
family life. The marriage ceremony and the rites of baptism
and circumcision are there to testify to the fact. Religious
leaders, it is true, are constantly being urged to revise their
attitudes towards sex and marriage, but the fact remains that
people continue to feel a deep need for the sanction that religion alone is able to provide. Behind this sanction is the ages-
long tradition of church and synagogue, which, if they differ in
some respects, share in common the principle of the sanctity of
wedlock.

On the other hand, economic demands, social conventions,
and psychological needs are today placing a great strain upon
the cohesiveness of the family. Our society is unstable, and this
instability is reflected in marriage. The breakdown of the old
prohibitions has resulted in altered sexual practices and moral
indecision. So it is not surprising that the majority of problems
that come before religious leaders, as before caseworkers and
psychiatrists, have to do with marital conflict and marital unhappiness. What, then, can religious leaders and institutions do
to stem the corrosive forces in our environment? More concretely, what can religious counseling contribute to the resolution of present-day problems of sex and marriage? What can it
do to strengthen the unity and stability of the family?

There can be little doubt that religion, by making physical
union a sacrament and love central in human relations, acts as
a binding factor in marriage. Further, by conceiving of home

and community as part of a broader fellowship, religion has been a unifying force in both. A growing recognition of the need to cope with the psychosocial forces that are weakening familial ties is indicated by the fact that marriage counseling has come to be accepted as a function of the religious leader. Not that the religious leader is replacing the psychiatrist; he is cooperating with him. Psychiatry has conscientiously studied marital behavior and laid bare the complexity and subtlety of the psychological factors in marital failures, so that no one can hope to deal with the predicament of the modern family unless he recognizes the existence of unconscious as well as conscious factors. But our aim here is to explore the extent to which religious leaders and religious practices can prepare children and youth for monogamous marriage and for social stability after marriage.

First, a few general observations. It is clear from the case material that the family is the proving ground of marriage. The behavior of parents to children, and to each other, provides the clue to the values and practices that promote or impair family stability. The basic personality patterns established in childhood and adolescence—for example, the desire to resemble or be different from parents—assert themselves during courtship and make it possible in some measure to predict the likelihood of marital conflict or stability. It is during this courtship period, which may be long or short, calm or stormy, that these subtle but powerful unconscious forces often come into play. The role of the religious leader as a marriage counselor is unique. Not uncommonly he knows both partners premaritally and consequently can estimate their future compatibility. If he has known one or both partners in childhood or adolescence—as well as their family backgrounds—he can sometimes evaluate what childhood attachments have not been resolved. In his pastoral role he acquires an intimate knowledge of the members of the family and their achievements and vicissitudes. In his priestly role he is the recognized guardian of spiritual and moral values, the representative of a hallowed tradition. He is the guide and counselor at the critical times of birth, sickness, disaster, separation, and death. Through religious counseling, he offers emotional support quickly and directly in the crises of life. And he also paves the way to psychiatric and casework help. Accordingly, in that most complex and challenging of fields, premarital and marital counseling, the religious leader has an unusual responsibility and a matchless opportunity.

Premarital Counseling

SINCE four out of five couples are married by a minister, priest, or rabbi, the religious leader is frequently called upon for premarital counseling. Indeed, he will encourage premarital interviews, not only because they give him an opportunity to stress the importance of such things as compatibility, mutual affection, children, and family life, but because he may be able to detect some abnormality that makes marriage inadvisable. In such instances the religious counselor, by a nice application of his skills, may manage to forestall what could become a complicated personal, family, and community problem. He may not only forestall pathological marriages, but by making premarital referrals for psychological help he may prevent problems that would be created by the arrival of children. Referral at this time is often easier. Individuals are often more receptive to treatment before marriage, when the decision is more tentative. Thus, a young couple about to be married presented themselves to a minister. All the arrangements for the wedding, three weeks away, had been made. Invitations had been sent out to friends and relatives. Wedding presents had started to arrive. Although he was twenty-three and she was nineteen, their decision to be married had been made a few years before. They were childhood sweethearts, neighbors in a small suburban community. The families were friends. It had all the appearances of being an ideal match, so that when the minister asked what interests they had in common he was shocked to see the girl burst into tears. Between sobs she explained that they had little in common, that her fiancé found fault with everything she did, had no pride in her, and was always trying to make her over. The young man admitted her charges, but felt that her outburst was just a case of "prenuptial nerves," not to be taken too seriously. The minister was inclined to take a more serious view, scenting the possibility of incompatibility between the couple. Although his suggestion that they see a psychiatrist was met with an indignant refusal by the man, the young woman accepted it eagerly, and a consultation was arranged. The psychiatrist discovered that the girl suffered from a variety of neurotic symptoms, the most serious of which was a fear of vomiting in public places, a fear that occurred primarily in the company of her fiancé. On the advice of the psychiatrist the wedding was postponed and the young woman started a course of treatment. The minister, working in collaboration with the psychiatrist, prepared the couple for a probable breakup of their engagement. Actually, their relationship had been an unhappy one all along, owing partly to the overbearing character of the young man, but chiefly to the fact that the young woman in not too unusual manner was substituting the young man for her father, who was a carping critic. It was precisely this unamiable quality in her father that was the basis of her attachment to him. As the psychiatrist helped free her from her infantile attachment to her overcritical father, he simultaneously freed her from her attachment to the young man, and after a few months she decided that she would not marry him. The analysis went on for two more years, during which she grew considerably in emotional maturity. At the end of that time she met another young man, emotionally more suitable, and with the blessings of the same minister they married. Throughout the entire period of the young woman's treatment, minister and psychiatrist had collaborated, the one in a moral, the other in a medical capacity.

It often happens that the religious counselor is approached by distraught parents who want to prevent a marriage that seems to them doomed to failure. Here he will come to no conclusion without giving all concerned an impartial hearing. Frequently the parental judgment is based upon material considerations or anxieties of their own, although on objective view the projected marriage gives every promise of success. It is this objective view that the counselor will seek to inculcate in the family through precepts as well as practical guidance. He will explain how difficult it is for parents to adjust themselves to the fact that their children have embarked upon adulthood, and how ready parents are to criticize the children's marital choices, even when these are based on good sense. Or he may try to lead the parents to see that their judgment is based on wrong values. Or it may be the other way about; he may agree that the parents' misgivings are well founded. There may be a gross disparity in the ages of the couple, in their cultural backgrounds, or in their religious loyalties. The choice of a prospective partner may be dictated by a sense of guilt or a spirit of rebellion. Such choices are usually invested with considerable emotion and are not easily influenced by advice, however logical. Indeed, such advice often has an effect opposite to the one intended. The best method is to help one or both persons to accept casework or psychiatric assistance. When neurotic factors are involved, one or the other of the couple with the assistance of the minister can become sufficiently aware of them to welcome such referral. To put off referral may be to invite serious consequences, as may be seen from the following. A young woman and a man fifteen years her senior applied to her minister for premarital counseling. The man had a history of three previous marriages, each of which ended in divorce. The situation was further complicated by the fact that he and his fiancée were of different faiths. The minister expressed his misgivings and asked the man if he did not think that psychiatric consultation might help him understand the basis of his repeated failures in marriage. The man answered that he did indeed have nervous symptoms and had at times considered psychiatric help, but felt that this had nothing to do with his present marital plans. After a discussion the minister stated that he could not carry out the marriage ceremony unless the opinion of a psychiatric consultant was obtained. The couple left, presumably to think the matter over. Instead they went directly to another, less cautious minister, who married them at once. Three years later the marriage ended in divorce, leaving the young woman with two small children. It was only at this late date that the man went into analysis. It transpired that he had lost his father at the age of four and been placed in an orphanage by his mother. From the orphanage he went to several foster homes, and he was thirteen before he finally rejoined his mother and his brothers and sisters. Understandably embittered by what he felt was an act of desertion by his mother, he often ran away from home as if to show that he could desert her just as she had deserted him. When he grew up he achieved financial success and became the main support of the family. No less cynical than embittered, he chose wives in the image of his mother, and ran away from them as he had run away from her. But the awareness of all this came too late to remedy the complications of his fourth marriage. As events proved, the first minister was well advised in acting as he did.

What line ought the religious leader to take when the question is asked him, "Shall I tell him or her of sex experiences that I have had in the past?" Sexual intercourse prior to marriage is no longer rare. Whether to confide in each other on this score is a matter that the young couple have to decide for themselves. But the religious counselor can help them arrive at a decision, especially if he has intimate knowledge of the personality and life situations of each partner, and can thus estimate their reactions. Excessive guilt feelings may lead to disclosures which are ill advised, particularly if the partner is rigid and overrepressed in sexual matters. In such instances the religious leader can reassure the guilt-ridden partner and sanction waiting until they know each other better, when the need to share this information may be lessened. If the person continues to be preoccupied with a need to reveal such youthful indiscretions, regardless of the circumstances, this may be an indication of pathological guilt and may express a need for psychiatric treatment. Thus a woman related to her minister that things had reached an impasse between her and her husband owing to the fact that she had confessed to him just before their marriage that she had been sexually promiscuous. The husband, a hard and unforgiving man, used this to punish her constantly, and the woman was now convinced that he was trying to drive her crazy in order to get rid of her. The minister reassured her, but, cognizant that she needed psychological help, arranged an appointment with a caseworker. The caseworker, after consultation with the minister, utilized the woman's religious beliefs to allay her feelings of guilt, and her self-esteem was bolstered when she was selected by the parent-teachers association of the church to attend a national conference. During an interview with the caseworker following a Palm Sunday, she looked unusually composed and happy, and spoke of an experience at church which had done much to ameliorate her guilt. Listening to the minister's Palm Sunday sermon on "the Maker's forgiveness of the fallen one," she felt that she herself had been forgiven her sins. Her husband's attitude, she said, no longer wounded her, for "if a prostitute could be forgiven by the Maker, then I can likewise be forgiven." There followed a gradual improvement in her capacity to function as a wife and mother.

The premarital interview provides the religious leader with an opportunity to foster mutual trust and a shared interest in religion and religious activities. He can impress upon the couple the importance of an exchange of thoughts, feelings, and experiences and so lay the groundwork for a similar exchange in marriage. Such intercommunication contributes to emotional stability and to the growth of a mature marital relationship. By means of the premarital interview the religious leader can also create a bond between himself and the young couple, one which will establish him in their lives as a helping person to whom they can always turn in times of stress.

Marital Counseling

THE religious leader who has succeeded in establishing a relationship with one or both partners premaritally, or early in marriage, is able, as people in the other professions are not, to proffer help in cases of marital discord before such discord becomes chronic. But even more important, he can be a factor in reinforcing marital health. With his access to people and their easy access to him, his advantages both in forestalling trouble and in dealing with it from the start are great. People do not like to expose their personal problems before strangers, for these are often associated with feelings of shame, guilt, or failure; so they may do nothing, or resort to superficial solutions, until things have reached a critical pass, when remedial work is unlikely to be effective or is very long and costly. And further, in a marriage there are other members of the family to be considered; indeed, delay in resolving a marital problem may involve a whole family in disaster. The great advantage of the religious leader is that he is on the scene when discord is in the offing. Unlike the psychiatrist, whose round is usually limited to his office or the hospital ward and who must wait until he is consulted for help, the religious leader in his pastoral role enters into the routine of the home, and is thus able to observe the couple in their relationship to each other and to their children, as well as their adjustment to the outside community and to the church group itself. From his peculiarly intimate vantage point, he can take stock of the factors in the life of a family which threaten trouble, and against these he can mobilize the factors which are positive or healthy.

A woman of thirty-five, the mother of four children, came to her minister in tears, complaining that her husband did not give her enough money to run the household. And the husband accused her of being improvident, she said, so that bickering between them was incessant. The minister asked if he might come to the house some evening when the husband had returned from work, and the wife readily agreed. When he got there, the minister observed an unhappy household. The children were all subdued and frightened by the constant strife between the parents. The father sat sullenly before the television set, scarcely taking notice of the minister's entrance. When the minister expressed his concern for the welfare of the family, the man snapped angrily that there was no cause for concern, everything was all right except that his wife was a spendthrift. The minister withdrew, realizing that he would have to know more if he were to accomplish anything. He assured the couple that he wanted to help, and invited the woman to return to his study the next day, which she did with the consent of her husband. As a result of this second interview it became clear to the minister that, far from being extravagant, the wife accomplished miracles with the budget at her disposal. The minister told her that the church had a fund for families in need, but the woman refused the offer of financial help, pointing out that her predicament was chronic and that such a stopgap measure would solve nothing. She suggested, however, that since her husband was extremely receptive to inquiries about his health, the minister might try approaching him on this ground. The minister agreed to this and finally persuaded the man to see the family doctor, which he had delayed doing for years. It turned out that the husband was suffering from a form of mental illness characterized by delusions that his wife and others in the community were mistreating him. The woman accepted the minister's referral to a family agency, where she was helped to accept the fact that her husband was ill. The bickering in the home now ceased. Since the husband's work was deteriorating and he was about to be fired, the caseworker arranged for his hospitalization in a sanitarium for the mentally ill. Likewise she arranged for sick leave and for home relief for the wife and children. Here then was a case which seemed merely to involve a question of finance and homemaking but in fact involved much more complex factors. Through his observation of the family, gained by personal visits and interviews, the minister was able to get at the root of the trouble.

Even when a couple informs a religious leader that they can no longer live together, his desire as well as responsibility is to save the marriage if possible. He will acquaint himself as thoroughly as possible with the wishes and needs of each partner in order to determine how deep the contradiction between them is. He will want to know whether there have been any previous separations, and if so, how many and how long; what their quarrels were about; who provoked them; how they were settled. All such information is vital to determining what factors might be invoked to save the marriage, and whether referral is in order, and to what agency. Of course, not all cases of marital pathology need or can benefit from psychotherapy. One partner, for instance, may derive pleasure, often unconscious, from pain while the other partner may enjoy inflicting it. Such persons may complain continually about the behavior of their partners, but they would resist any change in their marital relationships. If a religious leader is in doubt about how chronic the difficulties of such a marriage are, he would do well to consult a caseworker or psychiatrist about the couple. More than one consultation may be needed, and it may turn out that referral is inappropriate. However, where pathological factors causing conflict are clearly involved, the religious leader will of course refer one or both parties to a caseworker or a psychiatrist.

A religious leader was consulted by a couple in their middle thirties, the husband determined on a divorce. The couple had four children, many friends, and interests in common. It was the husband's third marriage and the wife's first. He admitted that he had loved her dearly when they were first married, but that he had lost all feeling for her. Although their sexual life had once been happy, it was now many months since she had aroused any desire in him. Meanwhile he had fallen in love with another woman, with whom he was more adequate sexually. In response to the minister's questions, he said that he had not yet moved out, that this was their first separation after ten years of marriage. His two previous marriages had been of brief duration, both ending in divorce. Both partners expressed feeling for and interest in the children. The minister summed up the reasons against separation, suggested that they do nothing rash, and arranged for another meeting with the husband. At this meeting the minister, speaking gently and making clear his determination to do what was right for all concerned, elicited the fact that the man's marriages had all followed the same pattern. That is to say, there had been an initial period of intense romantic love associated with deep sexual satisfaction, followed by a loss of interest and a loss of sexual desire, and finally rekindling of sexual desire with another woman. The husband had to agree that there was every reason to expect that his new liaison would run a similar course and end in unhappiness for all concerned. Having got this far, the man was ready to accept the minister's suggestion that he see a psychiatrist. Analysis revealed that the man's pattern of behavior was set by certain experiences of his as a child. His mother had run a private school for girls, and since they preempted so much of her time the boy was extremely jealous of them. The result was that he wished he had been born a girl so that he too might qualify for his mother's attention. On the other hand, bitterly resentful of his mother, he also wished to abandon her as she had abandoned him. As this childhood situation was brought to light, the patient came to accept his masculine role with less conflict, feeling a diminishing need to "prove" his sexual prowess in extramarital relations. As he succeeded in separating his wife from the image he entertained of his mother, his sexual desire for her reawakened. Meanwhile, the minister was guiding the healthier of the two, the wife, in order to sustain her belief in the sanctity of the marriage, helping her to have patience with her husband's irritability and impotence and to maintain her interest in homemaking and church affairs. In the process the marriage was salvaged.

Whatever the marital problem that arises, one partner cannot be considered in isolation from the other, nor from the other members of the family or the community. This becomes especially plain when the problem is the dissolution of a marriage. The spiritual impoverishment of a family that is torn by marital strife has lasting effects upon the children and the partners themselves. It may activate immature patterns of behavior that continue with increased intensity even after the breakup of the marriage. The result is recurring unhappiness that is usually not solved by separation or divorce. The religious leader's traditional concern to preserve the marriage tie and to do battle against the forces that disrupt it thus has much to commend it. This is not to say that he wishes to encourage a mechanical acceptance of the principle "for better or for worse." Certainly not today. Instead, he is concerned to understand by every means at his disposal, which includes casework and psychiatry, the forces that threaten marriage and the family, and so work all the more effectively to their elimination. So it is that here as elsewhere the religious leader finds himself engaged in a joint undertaking with other professions, and he does well to familiarize himself with their methods, goals, and even vocabulary. But if the religious leader needs the psychiatrist and the caseworker, they also need him, and it is a mistake to suppose that they do not. For example, a young man of orthodox Jewish background, himself observant, married a woman who was less so. In premarital discussions with the couple, the rabbi failed to go into the details of a religious wife's marital duties, but from his own discussions with her the husband-to-be assumed that she would instruct herself in these, especially as they bore upon the requirement of the monthly ritual bath. But she did not, nor did she attach any importance to the matter. The marriage turned out to be stormy, and the young man developed emotional difficulties which necessitated psychiatric treatment. In the course of his treatment it became clear that the sexual life of the couple was not satisfactory. The wife as well as the husband had deep-rooted sexual inhibitions, and each rationalized avoidance of sexual intercourse, the wife ascribing it to her distaste for the bath ritual, the husband to her failure to observe this ritual, which he claimed set up a sexual taboo in him. It was plain to the psychiatrist that nonreligious emotional factors were at work here, but in discussing the matter with the rabbi, which he did with the permission of the young man, and in his presence, it also became plain to him that the religious factor could not be omitted from his plan of treating this devout young man, nor could it be separated from the problem of his wife. With both factors in mind, the psychiatrist worked with the young man and a caseworker with the young woman. The caseworker helped the wife to understand the neurotic basis for her refusal to accept the religious practices of her husband. When she cooperated in this religious matter, her husband for the first time had to face up to the nonreligious elements in his sexual inhibition. This opened the way to further progress in his treatment, and gradually an unhappy marriage was transformed into a more congenial one. Thus it was only after consultation with the religious leader that the psychiatrist and caseworker were able to work out a successful plan of treatment.

It has been pointed out that children form attachments to the parents which must in time be transformed if normal emotional development is to take place, and that if childish attachments continue into adult life, emotional disturbances are likely to play an unwholesome role in the choice of a marital partner and to interfere with normal sexual fulfillment. It sometimes happens that while one marital partner is undergoing psychiatric treatment, marital difficulties may, for a time at least, become intensified. The neuroses of the two partners may have originally complemented each other, even though bickering between them was incessant, as with a long-suffering wife and an abusive alcoholic husband. There may have been circumstances at a particular time in a marriage which now create intense feelings, thereby precipitating conflict. For these reasons, while one partner is receiving psychotherapy, the religious leader may have to lend encouragement and spiritual support to the other. Here too it is important for the minister to know the day-to-day lives of the couple.

A religious leader attending a seminar at a divinity school told the story of a man who telephoned him in a panic, stating that his wife was walking out on him. The minister prevailed upon the wife to come to his study with her husband. The couple were in their late thirties and had two children just starting school, the older of whom had a crippled leg because of polio. The woman unburdened herself at great length about her husband's failings. They had been married for eight years and the husband, an accountant, went from one job to another, never able to earn a satisfactory living. Recently he had got a job as a postal clerk. He was in the probationary period and fearful of being fired, and he talked about nothing else to his wife. He was particularly concerned about his inability to tie knots properly. The religious leader noted that the wife felt herself to be a martyr and seemed to enjoy the role. She complained that her husband never went out of the house without her, had no friends, and that she could do with an occasional evening away from him. The woman agreed to return home with her husband, but not before the minister had fulfilled her bidding to get the husband to attend the men's Bible class. He attended two meetings, and in spite of every effort to make him feel at home, he mingled with no one, took no active part in the proceedings, and dropped out. A month later the religious leader received another frantic call, this time from the wife. She told the following story. Her husband had come home from work saying he had been fired. When she became hysterical, he burst out laughing and said he was only joking. This was the last straw. The woman related that her husband's stories of trouble, recounted at the dinner table, upset her so that she would have to vomit. She had put up with enough and was finished—once and for all. With great difficulty the religious leader quieted her and persuaded her to return home. And so things stood when the religious leader related his story before the seminar and asked for advice concerning the further management of the case.

One member of the group felt that saving this marriage was not worth the effort; the couple were better off divorced. After some debate, it was agreed that a religious leader should utilize every resource at his command before writing off a marriage as a hopeless failure. But it was felt that the factors which precipitated the marital crisis had not been delineated with sufficient clarity. The marriage, of eight years' standing, had survived financial adversity and a severe illness in one of the children. What had changed? The most conspicuous change was the husband's new job, which at once promised greater security and had the effect of intensifying his fear of failure. It appeared that his physical awkwardness, together with a speech disorder, called for a proper medical diagnosis. Both his nagging behavior and his wife's hysteria at the dinner table suggested infantility and a need for psychological treatment. It was pointed out also that the crippled child, who had just started public school, might be having difficulty adjusting to her schoolmates. All these considerations were pertinent to the case in hand, and the religious leader had not taken them into account sufficiently. Since the man suffered from a speech impediment, having him join the Bible class had been a mistake which only intensified his sense of failure.

At the suggestion of the religious leader, the husband consulted his family doctor, who referred him to a neurologist. An incurable neurological disorder was found which, although fortunately mild, constituted a real handicap at his job and in social situations. With the patient's consent his superior at the post office was notified and he was reassigned to a task more in keeping with his physical handicap. In addition, the case called for a strategically timed referral to a family agency, and when referral was finally made, the religious leader cooperated closely with the caseworker. He was to find that it was the wife, rather than the husband, who would profit most from participation in organized church activities. What she needed was an opportunity to expend some of her energies outside the family circle. In this way she would gain a sense of achievement and be led to exert less pressure upon her handicapped husband. The caseworker guided the troubled woman with her many domestic problems and her own "martyr complex." By this joint approach the marriage was salvaged and the children provided with a more wholesome home environment.

While marital fulfillment is hardly possible without procreation and the raising of a family, there are couples who, happy enough while they had only each other, find their relationship beginning to suffer with the appearance of children. A wife may discover her emotional unfitness for motherhood, or a newborn child may reawaken long dormant sibling rivalry problems in a husband or wife. Emotional disturbances in both parents and offspring are the result. So it is necessary to be on the lookout when a parent ostensibly requests help for a disturbed child, for the request may be a cloak for his own more serious disturbance. But if the applicant has emotional difficulties, injudicious questioning may increase anxiety and guilt, or even cause him to withdraw entirely. The helper, whether religious leader, caseworker, or psychiatrist, will best start by taking the request at its face value and inquiring into the nature of the child's difficulties and how they have been handled. The exploration should proceed at the applicant's pace, for the real nature of the request is bound to emerge sooner or later.

The problems that arise in family life are of the extremest diversity. A physically or mentally handicapped child may be placing such a strain on the marriage as to threaten to disrupt it. Or the problem may be one of birth control, or infertility with its attendant problems of adoption or artificial insemination. Or a state of "emotional divorce" may exist, with spiritual and intellectual communication no longer taking place between the parents, and with the children torn by feelings of divided loyalty as they try to relate to the silent or aggressively warring parents. Here it may be the task of the religious leader to help the parents resolve their indecision. At the same time he will do everything he can to mobilize adult feelings of responsibility and positive aspirations in the couple. He will see to it also that his church provides an auxiliary family experience for the children, fostering in them a sense of belonging to a group and instilling a clear understanding of the meaning of life in terms of religious values.

In spite of the heated debates that rage around contraception, bringing about conception in childless couples is an equally pressing social, psychological, and medical problem. Clinics that were once called birth control centers are now called maternal health clinics, to emphasize the fact that the techniques for overcoming the obstacles to parenthood are as important as those aiming to make parenthood a planned and rational choice.

One of the techniques employed to overcome sterility is that of artificial insemination. In this procedure the physician introduces seminal fluid directly into the cervical canal by means of a syringe. In actual practice the semen of the husband and the donor are often mingled so that the possibility is not excluded, if conception occurs, that it was due to the former. We are not concerned in this book to debate the legal and moral implications of artificial insemination. The attitude of the religious leader is usually one that has been handed down to him by higher ecclesiastical authorities who have examined the matter and have come to a decision which they feel is most in keeping with the moral code of their faith. From our point of view, the religious leader who is approached in the matter and is prepared to sanction the procedure should attempt to ascertain what facts and feelings have motivated the inquiry. By way of illustration we cite the case of a young couple who after ten years were still childless. The marriage was not a happy one. Vain and emotionally immature, the wife was consumed with jealousy whenever one of her friends became pregnant. The husband, on the other hand, owing to the incompatibility that existed between him and his wife, regarded their childlessness as a blessing, feeling that a child could not be happily brought up in their home. Medical examination, insisted upon by the woman, had revealed that the husband was sterile. Regarding her husband with contempt, she decided upon a pregnancy by artificial insemination. For complex reasons, among which religious scruples played a role, this was deeply objectionable to the husband. The minister's first impulse was simply to try to allay the husband's scruples, and to give the venture his blessing, but as he went into the case more thoroughly he came to see that other factors besides sterility were involved. In separate interviews with each of the pair he arrived at a detailed picture of their unhappiness. What impressed him most of all was that the woman appeared to be moved not by maternal impulses but by envy and a desire for social prestige. The minister consulted with a psychiatrist, who doubted whether so self-centered a woman could survive the emotional strains of motherhood. With this and their marital strife in mind, the minister urged the couple to postpone deciding about artificial insemination until they had had the benefit of psychiatric help.

When it is adoption that is at issue, the religious leader needs to be wary, especially of all informal arrangements. Adoption raises many problems whose solution calls for training and experience. Careful consideration has to be given to such things as the physical and psychological health of the child; the emo-

tional maturity and physical well-being of the adoptive parents
as well as the material comforts they are able to provide; the
state of health and the emotional problems of the real parents;
and the legal problems involved. The religious leader's chief responsibility here is to insist upon the use of a licensed adoption
agency, and to discourage, forcefully, any informal arrangements, however sensible they may appear at the time. If he does
not know of a licensed agency, he can obtain the information
through another social agency or through a directory of social
agencies. Interfaith marriage complicates the problem still further. In many states a child can be adopted only by a couple
whose religious faith is the same as that of the mother. As taking precedence over human issues, this enactment often results
in hardships.

To illustrate some of the complications that may arise over
adoption we cite the following case history. A thirty-year-old unmarried woman was referred to a caseworker by a private hospital where she had registered at the prenatal clinic. The father
of the baby she was expecting, unwilling to marry her, advised
her to place the baby for adoption. During the initial interview
with the caseworker she said that she would like to keep the
baby, but because her parents might find out about it, she was
considering giving the infant to her married sister, who was
childless. The next day the minister of a nearby church telephoned the caseworker, informing her that he was calling at the
request of this young woman. Several years back, he had seen
her on a weekly basis for about a year. Her troubles were emotional, and took the form of falling in love with men with whom
there was no hope of marriage. The minister went on to say that
the church's consulting psychiatrist had suggested psychotherapy, a suggestion which he seconded but which the woman
turned down for reasons that were obviously rationalizations.
In short, she was a "very mixed up girl," unable to decide what
she wanted, switching from one religion to another and from
one job to another. Recently she had come to the minister again,
stating that she wanted to talk about religion but felt that her
interest in religion was "pretty neurotic." All this the minister
passed on to the caseworker so that they might work together
without duplicating each other's services; he was concerned also
that the woman might try to pit one against the other. He had

advised her to write to her parents, which she had done by the time she next saw the caseworker. The latter informed her of the minister's call, and she said that she had consulted the minister mainly about "some religious questions of her own," relating to her decision to transfer from her former church to his. In subsequent interviews she could not make up her mind whether to have the baby adopted or keep it herself, then again she was fearful that no one would adopt the baby. She spoke of her previous religious affiliations. At times she wanted assurances that her baby would not be placed in a Catholic home; at others she expressed friendly feelings toward the Catholic Church. In the last few years she had alternated between that church and the Episcopalian, and for a time had joined a Puerto Rican Catholic group; she "could not stomach white Protestants." Just before going to the hospital for delivery she went to see the minister about entering a convent. He told her that he could not recommend such a course and urged her to continue working with the social agency. After a prolonged and stormy period of indecision, the problem was settled in favor of adoption. This woman was obviously suffering from a mental illness, but she could not be prevailed upon to accept urgently needed psychiatric treatment. The minister, however, encouraged her to participate in group activities of the church, and succeeded in establishing a relationship with her that was warm, yet also restraining whenever she threatened to become involved in undesirable relationships as a result of her mental illness.

We have dwelt here upon the emotional problems of the mother, but add to this the complications that arise when the adoptive parents are emotionally, physically, or materially unfit for that role, together with the dangers to which the child is thus exposed, and one will readily understand why adoption arrangements are the province of the expert.

While almost all married people want children, they are often concerned to limit their number, and so choose to practice birth control.[1] Many medical leaders recognize birth control as an essential part of public health, and so do innumerable religious leaders, who refer their congregants and parishioners to physicians and planned parenthood clinics for this purpose. If an interval between pregnancies is indicated for health or economic reasons, the mother should be given instruction in the latest, the most effective, and for her most suitable contraceptive methods. If she is a Catholic, for example, she should be instructed in the "rhythm method," which is sanctioned by the Catholic Church. On the other hand, there are religious leaders who are opposed to birth control recommendations under all circumstances, feeling that contraception is always an evasion of the responsibilities of parenthood and hence a degradation of the sacrament of marriage.

When parishioners or congregants practice contraception against the regulations of their church, the conflict often results in psychological disturbances which need the specialized treatment of a psychiatrist or of a caseworker. The following is an example. A twenty-three-year-old Catholic woman, married a year and a half, was finding it less and less possible to communicate with her husband, who though himself a Catholic entertained views different from hers. They were practicing birth control, but she was profoundly troubled about it, feeling that it was sinful. At the same time she felt that it would be unwise to have a child till the tensions between her and her husband had been resolved. From the first her husband had insisted on practicing birth control, and she was unable to see what else she could do. Religion had always played a part in her life and she still went to confession, but could not expect to receive absolution unless she gave up birth control. Obsessed by the consciousness of wrongdoing, she felt herself gradually being estranged from her religion, and this frightened her. In this distraught mental state she consulted a social agency. The caseworker agreed that her position was difficult, but reassured her that it was not she but her husband who insisted upon it, besides which she herself had said she believed it might be necessary under the circumstances. The woman remarked that she wished she could talk to her husband as she talked to the caseworker. The latter did not reassure her that her action was right or wrong, but encouraged her to tell her husband of her contact with the social agency and to ask him to join her there in search of a solution to their personal problems. To the wife's surprise, the husband confessed that he, too, felt the need for help and willingly accompanied her on her next appointment. The caseworker concluded that both were in need of psychiatric help and made the appropriate referrals. It became evident that the religious conflict over birth control concealed more deeply rooted nonreligious emotional problems in their relationship. Under therapy both partners developed a normal impulse to raise a family and gave up the use of contraceptives. When communication between them had improved, an understanding priest helped further with religious counsel and so assisted them in their marital readjustment.

The desire to limit the size of a family raises the question not only of birth control but of abortion. To interrupt a pregnancy simply because there is no desire for offspring is morally condemned and legally prohibited in our society, but when pregnancy is a threat to the life of the pregnant woman, and the fact is certified medically, doctors can legally perform an abortion. What attitude the religious leader takes towards this situation depends of course upon the official teaching of his church. By acquainting himself with all the particulars of a case, he may find that other therapeutic measures besides abortion are possible and preferable. In the following case the intervention of a religious leader prevented an unnecessary abortion. A young woman in an agitated state of depression was referred to a psychiatrist. Twenty-three years old, she had been married for a year, was in love with her husband and he with her. Until she became pregnant, the marriage had been a happy one. Between them they earned enough to get along on, but not enough to support a family, so that the prospect of a baby disturbed the woman, but more profoundly than the objective circumstances would seem to warrant. In a state of despair, she even contemplated suicide. Her family doctor told the psychiatrist that she suffered from a metabolic disease which had begun at the age of four. The condition required daily injections of medicine and a highly restricted diet, which forbade her the things children ordinarily enjoy eating. A congenital deformity of one of her legs had required prolonged hospitalization and extensive surgery that had been only partially successful. Nor were her troubles lightened by an overstrict home environment. In her teens she developed an emotional disorder which took the form of antisocial behavior. Psychiatric treatment helped only a little. But in her eighteenth year she seemed suddenly to have changed from an emotionally unstable into a cheerful, friendly, and responsible person. She got a job as a saleswoman, was highly respected at her work, and received several raises. It was at this job that she met the young man she married. To the doctor who had seen her through her stormy as well as her calmer years, her present state was reminiscent of her former illness, and because of her unstable emotional background he was afraid she might carry out her threat to commit suicide. It was at this point that he referred his patient to the psychiatrist, asking him whether under the circumstances a therapeutic abortion might not be advisable. The first thing that impressed the psychiatrist was that the young woman wanted a baby. "Can you blame me?" she said. "I am happily married and of course we want to raise a family, and I would gladly do it if only someone would tell me how. I have thought about it over and over. I see no way out. We just haven't enough money. I'll be sorry to give up the baby but I'll be more sorry if I don't, I know it!" In response to the psychiatrist's inquiry about other members of her family, she said, "I have thought of all of them. There is no one who can help us, no one!" "What about your father?" asked the psychiatrist. Here the patient burst into tears. Her father, a stern Protestant, had disowned her when she married a Catholic. Not a wealthy man, he could nevertheless help them, but he made his help conditional on the husband's becoming a Protestant and going through the appropriate wedding ceremony. The husband, having broken with his own church and being indifferent to religion, felt it would be dishonest to join another. The psychiatrist offered to call the woman's father, but she refused to allow this. Instead, she allowed him to call a minister in whom the father had confidence. The minister knew the situation in detail, but had not known till now that the wife was pregnant. He had tried repeatedly but without success to prevail upon the father to become reconciled with his daughter, and he told the psychiatrist that he would try again. When the father heard that a medical abortion was being discussed he exclaimed at once that this was out of the question, but again refused to help unless his conditions were met. "Then," said the minister, "you want me to inform your daughter that you, supposedly a man of God, will abandon her to her predicament unless her husband accepts your ultimatum? What will you do if her husband refuses? I must know this for sure before I speak to her."

There was a pause, and then the father burst into tears and said, "I will help her. Tell her I will help her." The minister assured him it was the only decision he could make as a religious man. By this intervention a potentially disastrous step was averted, and the birth of a baby enriched the spiritual life of the family. There were other crises, naturally, but the minister, working cooperatively with the family doctor, helped the family through each of them, and in response to their new happiness and responsibilities, the young couple matured.

The foregoing involved not only a request for an abortion but also an interfaith marriage, with both elements the expression of unresolved parental conflict. We turn now to the topic of interfaith marriage.

Interfaith Marriages

INTERFAITH marriages are looked upon with disfavor by the leaders of all organized church bodies. The Central Conference of American Rabbis has declared that mixed marriages "are contrary to the tradition of the Jewish religion and should therefore be discouraged by the American rabbinate." The Roman Catholic church refuses to accept the validity of any marriage involving a Catholic which has not been solemnized in a religious ceremony under prescribed conditions. The stand of Protestant denominations has become increasingly firm.

It is unfair to argue, as is sometimes done, that the concern of the church stems purely from its fear of losing members. While it is true that persons contracting mixed marriages tend to drop away from their respective churches and are more or less indifferent to the religious rearing of their children, there is another and more important reason for the church's stand in the matter. It is that interfaith marriages are likely to be unstable. Religious leaders have long known this and recent sociological studies have borne them out. Unfortunately, the young are impatient of the verdict. "We are broad-minded," they say. "We are quite willing to respect each other's religious beliefs. Besides, religion is not as important as it used to be." What these young people overlook is the real nature of religion and its role in life. Religion is not merely a set of beliefs; it is a way of living and thinking. Roman Catholicism is a culture pattern, as sociologists put it; so is Judaism, or Methodism, or Episcopalianism. Each has a distinctive set of values and particular forms of worship which enter into the warp and woof of the adherent's daily life. Eating fish on Friday, for example, is a dietary institution; and the observance of church holidays involves the organization of a family's leisure time.

Now it is true that when the partners to a marriage are emotionally mature they can work out a modus vivendi in spite of differences in their religious backgrounds. Usually the details of this are worked out long before the marriage itself. It is when emotional immaturity is a factor that trouble arises. And of course this is the case whether the marriage is between persons of the same or of different faith. But the point is that an interfaith marital choice is itself often a symptom of emotional instability. It was pointed out in the discussion of adolescent conversion that the flight from one's religion is often a flight from infantile attachments in the home, and that what seems on the surface to be a religious problem is often the product of mental conflicts which are essentially nonreligious in character and are frequently associated with actual or impending mental illness. Much the same situation is evident in interfaith marriages, so that their frequent failure is not so much a result of the religious differences as of the emotional unfitness of the parties concerned. This is why religious counselors scrutinize with particular care the interfaith couples who come to them for premarital counseling. To exercise his role to the best advantage, the counselor must be alert to the possibility that the interfaith choice may be symptomatic of a psychiatric problem.

In one case, a young woman, an only child, was a member of a Catholic family in a small Western community that was almost entirely Protestant. Her father was a successful businessman and one of the leading citizens in the community. Although the family was esteemed socially, the young woman had always felt herself a stranger to her non-Catholic neighbors. She had gone to a parochial school attended largely by youngsters from "the other side of the tracks" whom her family looked down upon. Lacking normal outlets for play, she became overdependent on her parents, particularly her father, a big man, highspirited and much admired. At college the girl was extremely

shy, but finally made friends with a Protestant boy who differed
from her father not only in religion but in every other respect.
The boy was called up for military service and the pair decided
on an impulse to get married. But the minister urged circum-
spection in view of the religious difference between them, with
the result that the wedding was postponed. Shortly thereafter
the young man was sent overseas and the girl returned home.
Her parents noticed that she was depressed, but they avoided
all discussions of the marriage that was scheduled to take
place when her fiancé came back, which he did after a year.
Almost at once the young woman, now twenty years old, began
to drink to excess. And with this apparently sudden addiction
to alcohol the girl developed peculiarities of speech and action
that made hospitalization necessary. In the course of psychiatric treatment, it became apparent that her attitude towards religion was ambivalent. On the one hand she blamed her church
for her unhappy childhood, on the other admired it since her
father was an observant Catholic. Because she was unduly attached to him, her marital choice represented an attempt to
escape from this attachment. As she came to understand these
matters she decided to cancel the marriage. Her interest in
Catholicism reawakened, and she began going out with young
men of her own faith. Yet after several years of treatment she
was still unable to make a marital choice or to assume the responsibilities of married life.

Although it is certainly true that many interfaith marriages
represent a flight based on anxiety rather than a choice based
on mature love, it is nevertheless true that when such love
exists the marriage can be expected to be a happy and stable
one. Furthermore, the spiritual life of one partner may supply
a deficiency in that of the other. The religious leader who performs the marriage ceremony can be of inestimable assistance
in helping the young couple to work out their religious problems.

Thus we may mention the case of a young woman of Christian
background who became a successful singer, and after two unsuccessful attempts at marriage, entered upon a happy marriage
with a Jewish doctor. The woman never knew her parents, for
their marriage broke up when she was a baby. She was boarded
in a series of homes, in all of which she felt like a stranger. Deprived of normal parental relationships, she of course grew up

possessed by loneliness and feelings of unworthiness. One of her "foster fathers" inculcated her with a deep sense of sin and convinced her that she was a "bad" girl, that God watched her ceaselessly, knew her every thought, and was merciless and unforgiving. Religion, as she knew it, only intensified her self-hate; it is no wonder that she concluded that while God might be a friend to others, He was forever a stranger to her. In her quest for some anchorage in the world, she entered upon a brief and ill-advised marriage at the age of sixteen with a youngster as immature as herself. Divorced several years later, she married again, and this marriage too was short-lived. The man, himself lonely, with no deep ties to his family or his community, was unable to provide her with the emotional sustenance she needed. Of her third marriage, one significant thing is the impact her husband's family had upon her. Relatively nonobservant, theirs was nevertheless an unequivocally religious home. It was here that she encountered a scheme of values for which she had always longed, a way of life based on moral and spiritual aspirations. She insisted on a religious wedding, and eagerly undertook the study of Judaism. The family's participation in the wedding ceremony, their acceptance of her as a member of the Jewish community, and their affirmation of the commandments of Judaism, all impressed her deeply.

Like all conversions with deep emotional reverberations, hers drew its power from profound personal needs, which because of the homelessness and lovelessness of her life had till now remained unfulfilled. And this brings us back to the importance of religious affiliation in the process of establishing personal identity. Religious disunity and conflict in the home intensifies, sometimes dangerously, the difficulties of its younger members. A harmonious religious environment is a factor in normal emotional development, just as disharmony may hamper such development.

Let us recapitulate a few points already made. As we have seen, interfaith marriages are less stable than those between partners of the same faith. In trying to account for this instability we suggested that the choice of a partner of different faith may be a neurotic symptom in its own right, a flight based on fear or rebellion rather than a choice based on love. It is for this reason that the religious leader should adopt an especially cautious and critical attitude towards interfaith unions, and think twice before sanctioning them. At the same time it would be folly not to recognize that an interfaith choice may rest upon quite unexceptionable grounds, in which case the marriage is likely to be as stable as any other, especially if the religious leader is in a position to help the couple work out a modus vivendi in matters of religion. More than this, the spiritual life of one partner may enrich the life of the other, and so bring about his or her conversion, and a greater than ordinary harmony between the two people.

Problems of the Unmarried

THE religious leader is so interested in premarriage counseling that he tends to forget the "pre-bachelor" or "pre-spinster" in his congregation. But he should do all he can to understand and help those members of his teenage and young adult groups who are too shy to have free, happy relationships with the opposite sex; who are unable to break their emotional ties to one or both parents; whose interests run predominantly to members of the same sex; or whose attitude towards the opposite sex is hostile or critical. Programs under the direction of properly trained social group leaders may be of help here, or, where it seems desirable, psychiatric or casework treatment. The latter should be provided early, while the prognosis is still relatively favorable. As the unmarried move through their late twenties and thirties they become increasingly a problem both to themselves and to others, owing partly to the complications of their own inner state, and partly to the fact that neither the family nor society makes a place for them. Even the religious center, organized as it is on the basis of families, has the effect of making the single person feel unwanted. These people should be provided with opportunities for adult education and emotional growth.

Since remaining single is for some people a necessary condition of emotional adaptation, it is always ill-advised to bring pressure upon them to get married. Such pressures are already great, and their result is only to intensify in them an insoluble emotional conflict. If left alone they may at least be able to function in an unmarried state. Let us take as an example the case of an intelligent, attractive woman in her early thirties courted by a man who appeared to have all the qualities that go into the making of an excellent husband. She steadily refused him, but was subjected to mounting pressure from friends, which she resisted until they invoked the aid of the minister, who after much argument prevailed upon her to accept the man. In the honeymoon period she became depressed, anxious, and sleepless. She was of two minds about her physical revulsion for her husband, describing it on the one hand as illogical and on the other as simply due to the fact that she was not in love with him. She blamed her friends and the minister for having urged her into a loveless liaison. For months the marriage remained unconsummated and the husband decided to sue for annulment. After another round of urging by her well-intentioned friends she went to a psychiatrist, who found that the woman was extremely retarded in her emotional development. The most important relationship in her life was an infantile and unwholesome attachment to her mother, an emotionally unstable person who constantly quarreled with her daughter. Outsiders could not understand how they managed to live with each other, but the psychiatrist saw that they were even less able to live without each other. Along with this attachment went a great fear of adult sexuality on the part of the younger woman. An eccentric and opinionated person, she still had older women friends and was able to hold a good job; that is to say, she was able to function in the community. Marriage only brought her to the brink of a mental breakdown. She rejected the advice of the psychiatrist to go into treatment at once, and instead avoided the breakdown by going back to live with her mother. She was ill-advised to get married in the first place, and unfortunately was probably beyond the help of a psychiatrist in the second.

Advice to older single people to uninhibit themselves through sexual intercourse is equally unwise.[2] Sexual intercourse is but one item in a total human relationship, and it provides emotional fulfillment only as it is an expression of mature love between a man and a woman in marriage. Advice that overlooks this is likely to have dangerous results. Thus we have the case of a thirty-six-year-old woman who was extremely devout and an active leader in the various social activities of her church. Unmarried, an only child of aging parents, she held a responsible job and the church seemed to provide her with an auxiliary family experience which rounded out her life quite happily. One day she came into the study of her minister and told him that she had fallen in love with a man who belonged to a different denomination, and had decided to marry him. So much of her happiness had been tied up with her life in the church that the minister should have been especially on the alert, all the more as the step involved leaving her old friends and converting to her husband's denomination. But instead of raising questions he congratulated her warmly. Even in subsequent interviews, when she spoke of the growing physical intimacies between her and the man, the minister chose to listen passively and in a seemingly permissive manner. It seems probable that the woman recounted these intimacies, which were threatening to get out of her control, in the hope that the minister would lend the weight of his moral authority to putting a stop to them. This did not happen, and she wound up by having intercourse. It occurred only once, but was followed by a deep depression and feelings of personal unworthiness. The quality of her work deteriorated seriously, and it soon became obvious that the woman was mentally ill. It would of course be wrong to ascribe this breakdown to the single sexual act. As marking a change in the woman's usual behavior, it was itself a symptom of the impending illness. But if the religious leader had shown more concern with the motives of her sexual disclosures, he might have forestalled the woman's action, and might even have seen that the case called for psychiatric help to prevent the breakdown.

The unmarried do not constitute a fixed and unchangeable group. Circumstances in their personal lives may so change as to foster maturation and so complete the delayed process of emotional growth. Or psychiatric treatment may bring about the alteration which fortuitous circumstances sometimes effect. Thus a thirty-four-year-old woman suffered an aftermath of depression when she terminated a highly frustrating sexual affair, of many years' duration, with a married man considerably older than herself. Her personal history was one of unhappiness; it included placement in an orphanage at the age of five following the death of her mother, and unhappy experiences with a foster mother and with a stern, rejecting stepmother. Religious for a period in her teens, she became more and more cynical as the frustrations of her life piled up. At the time she began psychiatric treatment she had given up religion entirely. In her psychiatric treatment she was made conscious of the fact that she had identified God with her own father, despite the fact that her father had failed her in many ways. As she became aware of her continued childhood attachment to her father, she was able to put her former lover out of her mind, and thus overcome her depression. It is interesting to note that by way of emphasizing the separateness of God from her own father, the woman abandoned her old religion and converted to another. She entered upon a happy marriage with a man whose religion was the one she had newly adopted.

UNDERSTANDING ILLNESS

6.

CHRISTIANITY AND JUDAISM ARE PECULIARLY COGNI-zant of the toll in suffering inflicted upon mankind by sickness and injury, just as both religions feel the need to alleviate the pain and grief that are its consequences. To tend and comfort the sick is an obligation enjoined upon everyone, but above all upon the religious leader. His responsibilities here are manifold and complex. On a community level he will have opportunities to initiate and support educational programs and social action designed to improve medical facilities when such facilities are inadequate. He may work within the framework of the public-health service, or through government- and church-supported hospitals and clinics, or community chests and welfare councils. Or his efforts may be directed to promoting equal medical services for all, regardless of race, creed, or material circumstances. The community volunteer program may engage his attention, especially as an increasing number of the services in our hospitals today are being provided by volunteer workers. This is the case at all levels of hospital care, from the reception desk to the patient's bedside. Without these workers, hospital services would often have to be seriously curtailed, so that the religious leader engaged in explaining to the community the need for volunteer workers, in recruiting the volunteer force and maintaining their morale, is performing a task of critical importance. In some communities the interest and energies of older people are mobilized, and they visit the sick and take gifts to chronic shut-ins without family or friends. All such activities have a deeply religious content and are appropriately included among the responsibilities of the religious leader to the sick in his community. There are few church activities that evoke more intense support than programs to promote the welfare of the sick, but their success depends upon expert and inspiring leadership.

In addition to the services which in many communities are provided by secular agencies, there are services which the religious leader alone is best able to render. No one is more concerned than he with ascertaining the hospital chaplaincy services, voluntary and paid, available in the community, or more ready to make great efforts to increase them, not only for his denomination, but for all. And he will see to it that younger chaplains have opportunities for consultation with more experienced colleagues.

It is hardly possible to consider with any profit the role of the religious leader in his ministrations to the sick unless we first say something about the psychological characteristics of the physically ill.

Psychological Aspects of Physical Illness

IN ORDER to understand the behavior of a person who is seriously ill, one must bear in mind that nothing concerns him so much as his illness and the restoration of his health. The result of this is a preoccupation with the psychological mechanisms that reduce the fears normally generated by illness. All of which is to say that sick people tend to be self-centered. When active, self-sufficient people find themselves in a hospital, helpless and inactive, confined to bed, deprived of clothing and freedom, they are likely to undergo fundamental psychological changes. Immature behavior patterns which may have been repressed, or otherwise held in check, may reappear at this time. Strange smells, ominous-looking instruments, whispered conversations among grave-looking consultants, and undeniable evidences of physical disability combine to reawaken attitudes of foreboding reminiscent of early childhood. Along with this reawakened, anxiety-ridden attitude of helplessness, childlike wishes for magical help from doctors and nurses come into play. This kind of regression occurs to some degree in all sick people, especially if the illness is severe or prolonged.

As the patient's anxiety mounts, psychological devices automatically act to keep the level of anxiety within endurable limits. Regression itself is one such device, and there are many others; indeed, there are as many ways of reacting psychologically to illness as there are personality types. Long ago a distinguished physician said that it is more important to know what manner of man has the disease than to know what disease he has. This is a maxim which the religious leader, if not the diagnostician, may take as a guiding principle. For example, there are people who regard illness as something shameful, and are apt to blind themselves to it until they are so incapacitated that they have to ask for help. Secretive about the nature of their illness, they do not welcome visitors. In the hospital, surrounded by every evidence of illness, they behave as if they were not sick. Naturally, they have difficulty in adjusting to institutional routines. On the other hand, there are people who freely acknowledge that they are ill but make light of the matter. Such patients tend to be uncooperative, especially when absolute bed rest and disciplined adherence to specific regimens of medication and diet are called for. And when their cheerful attitude is belied by facts they can no longer ignore, the result is likely to be a serious depression. At the opposite pole are patients who feel they must dramatize the fact that they are ill. They are often terrified people, fearful of not receiving proper attention unless they complain loudly and bitterly. It was probably in this way that they compelled an indifferent parent to do her duty, for these patients commonly give a history of neglect in childhood. As patients they will clamor about some relatively minor discomfort in order to force their minds away from a terrifying major disorder. Still another type of patient is the one who seeks a scapegoat. Close at hand for this purpose are the doctors and nurses. Half in anger and half in guilt, the patient is ever ready to cry out, "Why did this happen to me?" Like the previous type of patient, he too tends to reveal a characteristic life history in which a feeling of being the victim of long series of injustices predominates. Patients who complain that they do not get enough treatment or insist that they are getting the wrong treatment are of course a great trial to the hospital staff and their physicians. In this situation the religious leader is often able to smooth things out by seeing to the correction of some minor neglect or by maintaining a sympathetic and an un-threatened attitude in the face of the patient's angry complaints. It is of the first importance to recognize with regard to this group that the hostile façade is a cover for fright.

Less trouble to the hospital staff but not less desperately in need of emotional support are those patients who react to illness by withdrawal into an unresponsive apathy. It is easy for the nurse in her hurried rounds through the ward to overlook these silent sufferers. Equally likely to be overlooked by an overworked staff is the patient who is not desperately ill himself but is in a ward among those sicker than he. The loneliness and fright of such patients can be very great, even though their illness is not serious, and the religious leader will certainly include them in his bedside ministrations.

The plaintive "Why did this happen to me?" is a common psychological reaction to physical illness, expressive of a guilty feeling that one's moral lapses have somehow brought the illness about. And associated with this feeling is a melancholy sense of personal unworthiness that often affects the patient enough to hamper his recovery. The religious leader can combat this guilty reaction to physical illness by his attitude of compassion.

Such are some of the patterns of behavior that accompany physical illness. The illness sets them off, but their character is determined by the way the individual has reacted to emotional stress throughout his life. While the "jolly" patient who laughs off a manifestly serious disorder may be less emotionally threatening to those who tend him than the patient who whines or rails bitterly at all who come to his bedside, both may be equally frightened and equally in need of the comfort of the religious leader. The strategy of giving that comfort will differ as the psychological needs of each patient differ.

The Religious Leader on the Hospital Team

N O T a few patients react to a visit from the religious leader with the terrifying thought that they must be critically ill; in fact, at death's door. To obviate such misunderstandings, the religious leader, the doctor, and the nursing staff should have some idea of each other's role, and of the way in which they can collaborate for the common good of the patient.

The doctor plays a very special role in the psychological life of the patient. The dependency that characterizes the earliest years becomes all the greater during periods of childhood illness, when the patient's fears are augmented by the, to him, obvious fears of his parents. Into this atmosphere of anxiety, where even his parents seem to have failed him, comes the doctor. He understands what is wrong and knows what to do. His prestige, already great, becomes still greater with the child's recovery. The child comes to look upon him as an unusually good parent, superior in power even to his own parents. This attitude is one that persists more or less in all people, and illness renews it. Once again the doctor appears upon the scene, the all-good and all-powerful parent. Unfortunately the doctor, like other people in the helping professions, may be beguiled into taking this view of himself, so that when his merely human efforts to save a patient's life or restore him to health prove insufficient, he may be ridden with feelings of guilt, and his communications to the patient less frank than they ought to be. In taking cognizance of all this, the religious leader can be a source of reassurance to the doctor and a help to him in giving the patient the best care possible.

The nurse who bathes and feeds the patient stands to him in the relation of a mother or an older sister; indeed, "Sister" is one of her titles. Given the closeness of her relationship to the patient, and the symbolism inherent in her office and uniform, it is not surprising that her work should pose a variety of psychological problems. True, she is trained to meet these, but only experience can enable her to carry the heavy burden which a patient's illness thrusts upon her. For example, a young nurse was called in to care for a man dying of heart disease. Every day when she entered his room, she felt a strange upsurge of guilt. She was going to live, while he, also young, was about to die. "I know he wanted to talk to me," she said, "but I always turned it into something light, a little joke or evasive reassurance which failed to reassure. The patient knew and I knew. But as he saw my desperate attempts to escape and felt my anxiety, he took pity on me and kept to himself what he wanted to share with another human being. And so he died." [1] In situations of this sort the religious leader, alert to the problem, can inspire confidence in the young nurse, or himself act as confidant to the patient. In any event, by understanding the nurse's role and the problems that go with it he can enrich his contribution to the care of the sick.

A crisis has arisen with regard to the provision of adequate nursing care. The shortage grows more acute as the population increases, and overcrowded schedules and inadequate pay scales do not foster patience and gentleness. Moreover, our time has witnessed a general deterioration of human values, with the result that people dedicated to an ideal of self-sacrifice are uncommonly hard to find. More than ever the religious leader is obliged to take the patient's complaints about inadequate nursing care seriously. He will of course ascertain the facts and, when he finds good grounds for complaint, do what he can to rectify the situation. For example, he may arrange for relatives, friends, or even other parishioners to supplement the hospital nursing care, if such an arrangement is acceptable to the medical personnel.

If he is to play an effective role on the treatment team, the religious leader must begin by acquainting himself with the nature of the patient's illness in consultation with the physician. Often the patient himself is ignorant of what ails him and he may be allowed to brood morbidly over his condition; and this at a time when laboratory reports have all come back "negative." The religious leader is in a position in the course of his pastoral care to make up for the neglect of an overworked or insensitive physician and to reassure the patient himself. On the other hand, if the condition is really serious, the religious leader is again in a position to help the patient, this time to face his future, as the following illustrates.

A psychiatrist was called in to see a sixty-five-year-old man who was in a severe state of depression. Never ill before, he had developed a rectal bleeding, which made the physician suspicious of cancer, and had been hospitalized. He asked no questions and no information was volunteered him. Operation revealed the suspected cancer, and the affected large bowel was removed and the rest of the bowel brought to the surface of his abdomen, where a permanent new opening was established (colostomy). All this came to the knowledge of the patient only on the third postoperative day, and then only because he was alert enough to watch his dressing being changed and see the discharging fecal matter from the colostomy. His shock turned to horror when he was told that this was a permanent arrangement. Extremely agitated and weeping loudly, he expressed a determination to kill himself.

It was at this juncture that the psychiatrist was called in. The patient was given large quantities of tranquilizing drugs to tide him over the first shock, and after two days it became possible for him to speak more calmly. He expressed feelings of worthlessness, outraged dignity, and resentment against the doctors who had left him so ill-prepared. It was possible for the doctor to reassure him on medical grounds that a useful life and cleanliness, even by the man's meticulous standards, were possible with the colostomy. Knowing that religion was important to the patient, the psychiatrist arranged a conference for him with his minister. The psychiatrist explained to the minister and discussed with him the patient's need for spiritual support. In the course of daily visits with the patient the minister read psalms to him, as well as other religious writings in which the meaning of life is boldly affirmed. A leader in his church, the patient welcomed accounts of church activities, and in the ensuing discussions of long-term program planning, the minister assumed as a matter of course that the patient would resume his former role. Except for his wife, the man had no surviving relatives, and the minister arranged for various members of the parish to visit and send little presents. The man left the hospital in a considerably improved state of mind, even though his physical prognosis was poor.

As a member of the hospital treatment team, the religious leader functions in still other ways, as for example in cooperation with the medical caseworker. He may on occasion provide a housekeeper for small children from among his parishioners, or make arrangements with an employer for sick leave, or work out a plan for convalescent care after an operation.

The Pastoral Function

THE nature of the religious leader's contribution in the whole area of illness depends upon many factors. Is the illness acute or chronic; is a fatal outcome expected; is it associated with physical mutilation or crippling; is the patient

about to undergo surgery or is he post-surgical; is he con-
valescing; how old is he; what are his religious attitudes? The
answers to these and other questions determine his approach,
but throughout, the religious leader's chief role is that of spiritual healer. It is his task to help the patient face his trials,
whatever they are, with more courage, and to accept chronic
crippling or certain death with greater equanimity. It is in the
face of such problems that the most practiced physician often
feels helpless, and it is here especially that the religious leader
has most to offer.

However great the skills of the physician and the efficiency
of our best modern hospitals, the patient cannot but feel fearful.
Nor is this a sign of emotional immaturity. The fact is that an
element of uncertainty exists in all medical and surgical pro-
cedures; unforeseen complications can occur even in seemingly
minor ones. Hence the patient's fear is always based at least
in part on reality. No one in these circumstances can replace
the religious leader, for the patient's feelings about the future
depend largely upon his basic sense of security, or what may
be thought of as his capacity for optimism and faith, and religion acts to reinforce these as nothing else does, especially
in periods of crisis.

Loneliness and fear plague the sick, and the church, with its
capacity to act as a surrogate family, may perform a healing
function as vital to these people as medicine itself. The following
is a case in point. When Mary was admitted to the hospital,
her mother explained that she said her prayers every night before going to bed. But Mary refused to pray when bedtime came
each night. The nurses did not know why she refused, and Mary
was getting impatient because the adults about her could not or
would not understand why she could not say prayers. Finally,
on Sunday night, Mary said shyly to a nurse, "Please sit down
—there." The nurse dutifully sank into an armchair. Mary
promptly climbed out of bed, went over to the nurse, and knelt
before her, resting her elbows on the nurse's knees. Folding her
hands, Mary looked up into the nurse's face anxiously. "My
mother said that God would hear my prayers," she said, "but I
don't have a witness. Mother used to be my witness, but you're
my witness now." The nurse gathered the child into her arms
and hummed a lullaby, and Mary said her prayers.[2]

In the unfamiliar setting of a hospital, the family's religious leader is a welcome link with the everyday world. Nor is this all. At the bedside vigil for a dying loved one, it is he who can bring the participants together in a fellowship that transcends death. Thus a religious leader was called to the bedside of a two-year-old child dying of cancer. The grief of parents and relatives was indescribable, and in desperation the father appealed to him. "Do something. Help us," he said. Speaking words of comfort, the religious leader drew from his pocket a small book of prayers. "Here," he said, "are thoughts inscribed by great saints during their hours of suffering. They, too, suffered great personal tragedies. Let us see whether the words which comforted them do not contain some comfort for us, too." He sat by the bedside with the grief-stricken family and read aloud from the prayer book. After a half-hour, as he rose to leave, he handed the book to the father, and gave the others leaflets which contained prayers designed to comfort the sick and their loved ones. Following the clergyman's suggestion, the family, especially the father, kept up reading by the bedside until the early hours of the morning, when the child died. Great as their grief was, they had derived immense comfort from the presence of their pastor and from the prayers he had left with them. No other representatives of the helping professions could have offered consolation with greater wisdom or sensitiveness.

Desperate situations, it is said, call for desperate remedies. Whatever reservations one may have about the following case history, it illustrates the power of religious faith, which in this instance restored the will to live in a grief-stricken widowed mother and made it possible for her to nurse her daughter through a grave illness. A fifty-five-year-old woman lost her husband after an unsuccessful operation for a malignancy. She was left with an only daughter, a thirty-five-year-old mother of three youngsters. Always close to her daughter, she became more so as the result of her bereavement. Her reaction of panic and depression may be imagined when the daughter herself developed a malignancy and had to undergo an operation whose outcome was uncertain. Suffering untold anguish, not only was she unconsolable, but she was unable to discharge her responsibilities to her grandchildren and her sick daughter. She was prevailed upon to see her minister, who had officiated at her husband's funeral. Since the weather was fine he suggested that they take a drive together and talk on the way, and she was scarcely aware of their arrival at the cemetery where her husband lay buried. There, while he said a prayer, she burst into tears. He urged the woman to pray with him and encouraged her to express her grief. Nothing was said directly about her daughter, her grandchildren, her obligations to the living. But somehow this experience was a turning point in her attitude towards herself and her problems. Standing at the grave, she faced up physically to the grim reality of death, which on that lovely spring day did not seem quite so grim. She returned home with the feeling that, whatever the outcome of her daughter's illness, she would be able to face up to it. Strengthened by faith, she persisted in believing that the outlook for her daughter was not hopeless, despite the doctor's gloomy prognosis. Nor was this the only change that took place in her after that day; her relations with her daughter and grandchildren became deeper and richer. As a happy ending for this story, the daughter recovered, and the mother's crucial change at the grave was a lasting one.

In this case there was no referral to a psychiatrist, as there might easily have been. Instead the minister recognized that the woman's grief was a normal human reaction to an overwhelming hurt. Here was the first proof of his wisdom. The second was his appreciation of the fact that no ordinary attempt at comfort could console a person in such a predicament. The third was his faith in the woman's capacity to respond to the religious experience to which he exposed her.

Even if the woman had not been helped by the way the minister approached her problem, it would still have been a correct and justifiable approach. Even if her feelings towards her daughter had been rooted in an unconscious hostility and she had been unable to master them, the minister's kindly, firm wisdom would still have strengthened a relationship in which he could at the right moment refer the woman to a psychiatrist. The latter would then have dealt with her inability to nurse her sick daughter.

Earlier in this chapter a case was cited in which a patient was kept in ignorance of the kind of operation he was to undergo and of its disfiguring effects. We should like now to raise the question of whether the patient ought not to be prepared realistically when mutilating surgery is involved. Here is a case that poses this problem, though in a somewhat complicated form. A minister in a midwestern hospital approached the bed of a man who was to be operated on the next day. Whether the operation was to consist of the simple excision of a small growth on the foot or the loss of the whole leg would depend on a laboratory test to be carried out in the operating room. Since the man had a wife and children to support and his work entailed a great deal of walking, a major calamity threatened. Still, he was in remarkably good spirits, waving aside the minister's attempt to comfort him with the words, "I have no fear. I have faith and I have prayed long and hard. They say, 'God guides the hand of the surgeon.'" The worst happened, and visiting the patient the next day the minister found him depressed. A long period of invalidism and financial insecurity lay before him. To the minister's distress he asked, "What happened to God's guiding hand, pastor?" The minister came away with a sense of personal failure and a conviction that the patient was a victim of a fallacy. In the minister's words, the belief that "God guides the hand of the surgeon was after all a poetic idiom which, taken as literal theology, confounds and confuses." He felt that, to counter this sort of belief, "one must begin early and educate people to understand that God is not a personified entity."

Our own view is that the trouble lay not so much in the religious education of this patient as in the minister's failure to temper the optimism it bred. He seemed to join, if only passively, in the patient's unrealistic evasion of the facts before the operation. We have already spoken of the too sanguine patient, pointing out that such patients are easier to deal with than their opposite numbers, since they threaten us less. There is not only the danger of accepting their evasions, but of aiding and abetting them by evasions of our own. To the minister the good spirits of this patient seemed "remarkable," but he should have seen that they were also unrealistic and therefore a danger signal. It could have been predicted that a deep depression would follow if the operation did not turn out as the patient wished. It would have been far more religious to have pointed out to the patient that none of us knows God's intention and that we must be prepared to accept whatever He ordains. "Thy will be done" is the only valid attitude for a religious adult. To say that we have faith, meaning thereby that all our wishes will be fulfilled through prayer, is the naïve religiosity of a child.

With regard to the sense of failure which this minister experienced, we may repeat what was said in Chapter Four on the subject of countertransference—that the religious leader may react to the unrealistic expectations of an emotionally regressed parishioner with equally unrealistic expectations from himself. And since these are doomed to defeat he comes to feel that he and God and religion generally are on trial. But no question of theology is involved here, nor a call for reorganization of religious education; the problem is in essence that of countertransference. Unless the religious leader adopts a realistic attitude, he is in no position to give the spiritual aid which a patient about to undergo serious surgery needs, nor to be of much use to him afterwards.

After a mutilating operation, people go through a period during which they "mourn" for the part of the body they have lost and pine for their former state of physical well-being. If he is familiar with this phenomenon, as he should be, the religious leader will not be surprised at the patient's initial reaction of shocked bewilderment, and he will know that there is little he can say at this moment that will be of direct comfort to him. The patient must be given time. In an attempt to cope with his inner anguish he may in the initial phase of mourning express great bitterness. He may need a scapegoat if he is not to fall victim to a depressive reaction which might conceivably result in self-destructive behavior. At such times expressions of hostility towards God are not only understandable, but psychologically useful. In these circumstances it is only by standing firm in his own faith that the religious leader can best serve the rebellious patient. Yet it is a trying time for him. The patient's accusations cannot leave him unmoved; he may even fall in with them and believe that God, as well as he himself, has indeed failed. Feeling this way, he may become anxious and depressed and even suffer some impairment of his own faith, and the result may be abdication at the very moment when the patient needs him most. He should remember that the patient's angry outbursts, while they give an appearance of strength, are actually the facade of an inner helplessness. And it is to this helplessness that the religious leader should address himself.

While the patient is in the state we have been describing, the mere physical presence of the religious leader can be a support to him. At this juncture the symbolic character of the role may by itself exercise a therapeutic effect. When the patient has rallied, perhaps only to give expression to feelings of bitterness, the religious leader will try to create an atmosphere that is not only permissive but warmly accepting. The relationship which he will now do all he can to forge and consolidate may provide the turning point in the patient's rehabilitation. By fortifying the faith and hope of the patient, the religious leader is contributing not only to his moral but to his physical rehabilitation, for in the latter, as experts in the field are agreed, motivation is of supreme importance. God, he can assure the patient, has spared him so that he can continue to live for his family, or for some other specific concern that he knows the patient has. He will deal too with the patient's feelings of unworthiness, utilizing every resource to restore his faith and to console him. At the same time he will tell the patient about the physical and vocational resources in the community, having determined their availability in consultation with a social agency.

In short, mature religion, as we understand that phrase, while it preaches faith and optimism in the face of life's uncertainties, is not based on childish wishful thinking. It is founded on the realities of life or it is founded on nothing. Faith unquestionably plays a highly supportive role in the psychological economy of the patient, and the way in which it does this has been illuminated by the insights of psychiatry. But—and this is the crux of the matter—it is the business of religion, not that of psychiatry or any other science, to create and augment this faith.

Ministering to the Mentally Ill

MENTAL illness falls within the context of illness generally, and it is best treated so; yet it is true that the mentally ill present some special problems for the religious leader. In the first place there is the dread with which mental illness is commonly regarded. And in the extreme forms of mental illness, the psychoses, there may exist a major crisis of communication, which makes the simple exchange of ideas a practical impossibility. Such a problem rarely arises in the religious leader's ministrations to the physically ill. Yet religion may have an impact even on people so mentally ill as to be apparently out of touch with their environment. Thus a religious leader agreed to visit a patient in a state hospital for the mentally ill. He was shocked to find the patient locked away in a room by herself, mute, disheveled, and wild-eyed. She seemed to pay no attention to his greeting. He felt that he had undertaken a hopeless task, but having given his promise to the family to pray with her, he drew up a chair near her and began reading psalms. After about fifteen minutes, she gave the first sign that she was aware of his presence. She reached out slowly and touched the rim of his glasses. He smiled at her encouragingly, but at that moment the nurse walked into the room and the patient quickly withdrew her hand. Immobile as before, although the minister read to her for another half-hour, she paid no attention to him when he said good-by; and he left feeling that he had discharged his promise, but had accomplished nothing more. He was surprised to hear that the following week, when the family visited her, she spoke a few words, the first in many months. They consisted of a line or two from the psalms the minister had read to her. In other words, the minister alone had succeeded in establishing contact, however tenuous, with a sick mind.

But it is not only in hospitals that the religious leader encounters people who are mentally ill. Not uncommonly he finds them in the course of his daily routine, and at such times he may have to improvise swiftly. Nor is this as difficult as it sounds, provided he is not overcome by his own anxiety, as happened in a case previously described, in which a young woman approached the religious leader after a service and threatened to commit suicide. Very different is the following case, which was managed with the compassion and faith that are appropriate to the religious leader in the ordinary course of his work. A student rabbi was conducting High Holiday services at a resort hotel. Before the Day of Atonement, a woman of about forty-five came up to him in the lobby in a disheveled and agitated state. In her hand was a melting ice-cream cone which she disregarded, and without any preliminaries she said, "I'm cracking up. You must help me!" As the rabbi looked at this distraught woman, his first thought was, "This is not a problem for me. I must be careful not to do her more harm than good." Smiling in a friendly fashion, he encouraged her to eat her ice cream, and in order to establish some rapport with her he bought an ice-cream cone for himself and said, "Let's go somewhere where we can eat our ice cream and talk this over." He found an alcove off the lobby where they could talk with some privacy. "Do you think I'm crazy?" she began. He answered, "That's a pretty powerful word. We are all more or less nervous. Perhaps you are more nervous than others. Do you have a doctor looking after you?" "Oh, yes," she exclaimed, "I have a psychiatrist. I'm not satisfied with him. He hasn't helped me." She then plunged headlong into a detailed account of her troubles. It seems that she had always had difficulties with her domineering mother, and since her father's suicide three years ago these difficulties had become more acute than ever. "And yet," she hastened to add, "she is good to me. She is the one who insisted that I come to this hotel with her to rest my nerves. But I shouldn't be here with her. I should be home with my husband and two children." The children were of high school age and the husband was a worker in a factory. "I neglect them," she said. "I should get up in the morning and prepare breakfast for them. Instead I lie in bed all day and do nothing. When they come home, they first have to take care of me." The rabbi asked, "Why do you stay in bed all day?" Her answer was, "My father talks to me. I hear his voice and he tells me not to get up."

Throughout his discussion with the woman two thoughts were foremost in the rabbi's mind. First, it was obvious that the woman was extremely ill and that he must proceed with caution. Second, he wondered what he could do as a rabbi. He kept turning over in his mind what to say to her about God and religion, but he could find nothing that seemed appropriate. Finally he said to her, "Your father is dead. If you hear your father's voice telling you to stay in bed, I want you to say to yourself, 'I will do what is right. I will get up and take care of my family.' " As he took his leave of the woman, he said, "I'll see you at services, won't I?" She answered, "Of course. I'll be there." The talk had left her considerably relieved. True to her word, she came to the service; she was neatly dressed, sat in the front row, and was deeply attentive to all the prayers. When the long day of praying came to an end, she approached the rabbi, a dramatically changed person. "Rabbi," she said, "I feel much better. I have thought over all that you told me. My mother wants me to stay on but I am returning home to my family in the morning." He wished her well for the New Year and urged her to consult further with her doctor when she got home.

Yet the rabbi was not easy in his mind. Determined upon caution as he had been, he wondered if he had not perhaps overstepped his bounds and in some way done harm to the woman. Nor was he satisfied that from a religious point of view he had done all that was possible. Actually, though, he had carried out his counseling with great skill. Nothing could show better what may be accomplished by a religious leader who understands his role clearly and fulfills himself in that role. Quick to see that the woman was mentally ill, the rabbi was equally quick to appreciate her suffering and need for help. He gave her the solace of his friendship, aware at the same time that the case called for a doctor. The woman had come to him in his capacity as a religious leader and he did not shirk his duties in this respect, but performed them sensitively. He countered her hallucinations with a simple statement about reality, namely that she must, although her father was dead, fulfill her responsibilities to the living. And the rightness of his invitation to her to attend services next day was eloquently testified to by the alacrity of her acceptance. The day of worship brought her visible relief from her tortured mental state. Finally, the rabbi's advice that she seek further medical help was sound.

As we have seen on more than one occasion, the religious leader functions as a symbol no less than as an actual human being. In the latter capacity he may be totally unknown to the person who consults him. The following case is an illustration of this, as it is also an illustration of the supportive role the religious leader may play towards a person plagued with guilt over a mentally sick relative. One day a minister whose study looked out on the main highway leading to a large state hospital for the mentally ill, saw a car turn off the road and career up the path. An excited woman leaped from the car and ran up the steps. A moment later he could hear her frantically ringing the doorbell, and she was ushered into his study. She was a total stranger, but as soon as she saw the minister she burst into tears and cried, "Pastor, help me. I know I'm going out of my mind!" She proceeded to relate that she was on her way home from the nearby state hospital. It was her first visit there to see a younger brother recently hospitalized for a severe mental illness. She was not prepared for the strange speech and actions with which her brother greeted her, nor for the bleak surroundings in which she found him. "Oh, pastor," she cried, "he was such a good person. Why did it happen to him? Why didn't it happen to me? I deserved it more, believe me!" Perceiving her heavy burden of guilt, the minister spoke to her gently and said, "You know, truly religious people don't believe that sickness comes to a person because of the evil things that he has done. We don't know why there is sickness in the world and why it so often strikes good people. All we can say is that God in His wisdom knows why. Surely your brother's illness was none of your doing. It was God's will. Let us pray that God will impart His wisdom to the doctors and nurses who are treating him and that he will be brought back to health. To you the surroundings are perhaps bleak, but to your brother, who is engrossed in his thoughts, the environment does not appear the same way. The furnishings are often kept simple for protective reasons. I do know that we have fine doctors and hospitals in our state. I have visited them many times myself. I am sure the doctors and the others on the staff understand your brother's needs and are doing what has to be done to get him out of his present condition and back home as quickly as possible. Write letters to your brother. Send him presents. Visit him. Inquire about his condition from the doctors and the caseworker. Let him know that you love him and are concerned about him. When you go to the church pray for him. These are the things you can do for him." The woman left, considerably relieved.

We may break down the minister's contribution here into several distinct components. As symbolizing a higher authority, he was able to lighten the woman's crushing sense of personal responsibility for her brother's mental illness by invoking God's will. With his knowledge of state hospitals and their inmates, he could reassure her about the environment that so distressed her. Finally, he gave her concrete and constructive suggestions as to how she could participate in the treatment of her brother.

As a trained observer, the minister recognized in her excess of guilt a serious problem requiring psychiatric treatment, but he had the wisdom to refrain from exploring into the basis of her guilt. Such a venture into "pastoral psychiatry," as he saw, would have been inappropriate and ill-advised. Instead, he confined himself strictly to his role as religious counselor, and in this role also he encouraged the woman to consult with the caseworker, who could make the referral to a psychiatrist.

Religion and Alcoholism

THERE are many reasons why alcoholism, which is an illness, should receive separate consideration in this chapter. Perhaps the most important reason is that the religious leader is very often the first person to whom the alcoholic patient or his family turns for help. Second, the problem of alcoholism has always had strong moral overtones. The alcoholic person is guilt-ridden, and his self-degradation is part of the punishment which he feels is his due. In his quest for punishment the alcoholic provokes others into rejecting him, and frequently succeeds in doing so. For he combines a core of abject self-hatred with an outer armor of arrogant defiance. Accordingly there is nothing surprising in the sociological fact that alcoholism should be traditionally misinterpreted as an expression of moral weakness; indeed, the alcoholic patient himself is frequently the first to emphasize his moral "depravity." And the sort of relationship he seeks to establish with people in authority is one in which he plays the role of the "bad boy."

The problem of alcoholism calls for the exercise of several important functions on the part of the religious leader.[3] First of all, he must inform himself about the nature of the problem. Misinformation, prejudice, arrogance, fanaticism, and ignorance exist widely with regard to the alcoholic patient, and unfortunately religious leaders are not immune to them. But moral indignation will not cure the alcoholic any more than it will cure other patients who are gravely ill. Alcoholism is a serious disease and its treatment requires great skill. One of the chief public health problems of our time, it ranks with cancer, tuberculosis, and heart disease. Chronic alcoholism leads to intellectual and physical deterioration, impaired earning capacity, crippling organic disease, and death. A major cause of broken homes, it has a malignant effect upon family life and wreaks incalculable harm upon the emotional development of the young. The disease has far-reaching social effects as well. It is an outstanding cause of absenteeism in industry, as well as being a significant contributory factor in accidents of all kinds, especially automobile accidents, themselves a major cause of death. And it figures largely in homicide, suicide, and sexual aberration. Informed of all this—and he cannot be too thoroughly informed—the religious leader is in a position to assume a responsible role in the education of others and the mobilization of treatment resources in the community, as well as in the devising of community mental health programs aimed at prevention.

Religion has a specific role to play in the rehabilitation of the alcoholic. Its most important contribution is that of fostering an unshakable attitude of acceptance towards the alcoholic, whatever his efforts to provoke rejection. The importance of religion is perhaps best exemplified in the methods of Alcoholics Anonymous (AA), a treatment program which is instituted by alcoholics themselves. The program is one of the most successful regimens so far discovered for the control of alcoholic addiction. It originated and operates without the help of physicians, except when a physician who is himself an alcoholic becomes a member for purposes of treatment. The movement is at bottom deeply religious. The AA Program of Recovery spells out the idea that control of alcoholic addiction depends on the addict's acceptance of his own personal powerlessness to cope with his illness and of the necessity of placing his reliance on a Power ("God as we understand Him"). Prayer and meditation are a basic part of the program. The founder, and many followers, came to the AA program as a result of an experience which had the qualities of a religious revelation. The essentially religious orientation of the program is evident from its moral code, which involves "a searching and fearless moral inventory of ourselves," confessing "to God, to ourselves and to another human being the exact nature of our wrongs," and drawing up "a list of all persons we have harmed," making "direct amends to such people wherever possible, except when to do so would injure them or others." Such religious principles are at the heart of the AA program, and they are adhered to strictly. Nothing is less tolerated than the uncritical condoning of human behavior, whatever form it takes, which is indulged in by misinformed, "nondirective" religious counselors; nor is there an uncritical search for "tranquillity at any cost." Above all, the program confines itself strictly to the treatment of alcoholic addiction and does not aspire to become a generalized system of psychiatric care.

Specialists in the treatment of alcoholism have emphasized the importance of the attitude of "surrender," which is a basic element in the Alcoholics Anonymous program. Among members it is referred to as "hitting bottom," and it often has the quality of a genuine religious experience. In the process of "surrender," a patient with deep needs of dependency, who fears these needs in his relation to his fellow man, is often able to express and fulfill them fearlessly in relation to God.

Besides encouraging the alcoholic to join the AA, or take advantage of some other reputable treatment facility, the religious leader will in all likelihood want to refer the family to a social agency equipped to deal with the problems created by the alcoholism. But his greatest contribution will probably occur in the post-treatment phase, when the patient returns to work and is able once more to assume his appropriate place in the family. Nothing will consolidate his improvement so much as wholehearted acceptance into the fellowship of the religious community.

Should the Patient Know the Truth?

IT IS often difficult for the physician himself to know the "truth" about a given disease. Medical literature is full of astonishing instances of prolonged survival after an illness which is almost always rapidly fatal. Patients have often outlived the healthy doctors who predicted their imminent demise. Hence it is often possible to hold out, quite honestly, some ray of hope for a patient who is desperately ill. But aside from this, it is important to bear in mind the differences between patients in their capacity to accept painful truths. No two of them are quite alike in this respect, for each brings to his illness the basic personality which has characterized him all his life. Some fragile people survive only because they are sheltered by loved ones; others show a seemingly limitless capacity to absorb punishment. As we have said, each reacts to adversity in a characteristic way, some by unrealistically cheerful evasions, some by a quest for a scapegoat, others by apathetic withdrawal, still others by unwholesome surrender to the childlike helplessness of chronic invalidism. On the other hand, there are those who accept reality, however grim it may be, and marshal all the spiritual resources at their command in order to give as much meaning as possible to what remains of their lives.

Dying is a process in which all parts of the body participate, the brain included. Consciousness becomes blunted, and with it the awareness of change, and from the same cause that produced the change itself. It has been observed that most people die as they are born, unaware of what is happening. Within this general framework the religious leader will take into account the patient's age and mental condition. He will of course address a dying child differently from a dying adult, and a mentally ill person differently from a normal one. Nor must he overlook the life responsibilities of the individual, for they may be decisive in the question of whether to apprise him frankly of his physical state. The patient may be planning to undertake some important business enterprise, or to move to an area where proper medical facilities are lacking. Or the public interest may be involved, as in the case of a man who has it in mind to dispose of his fortune before he dies, to charity, or to science or education. And there are patients who cannot contemplate death without the last rites of their religious denomination.

Just as there are differences among patients, so are there differences among doctors. A surgeon may be skillful and fearless at the operating table, yet lack the courage to tell a patient what the operation has in store for him. An anxiety-ridden physician may deny the truth to a patient who is quite able to tolerate it, while a callous physician may blurt out the truth to one who is utterly unprepared for it.*

* It sometimes happens that a doctor prescribes "sugar pills" or some other inactive substance to a patient who thinks he is getting a potent medication. Such inactive ingredients administered in this deceptive way are called placebos. There are specific medical indications for such substances, such as emotional states in which the medication achieves its curative effect because it is a symbolic gift from a kindly parent in the person of the physician.

It is clear that the problem is a complex one and involves a great many variables, yet certain basic principles emerge. In the first place, it is up to the physician to give information which is of grave import to the patient. Equipped with the clinical knowledge and experience to deal with the patient's questions, he alone can give answers that inspire the patient's confidence. Not infrequently the surgeon feels incapable of telling the patient of a mutilating procedure he is about to carry out. Yet this is what he ought to do and be encouraged to do. Victor Rosen cites instances in which severe mental illness set in when the patient understood that a grave surgical situation existed and was terrified because the surgeon in the case lacked the courage to disclose the truth.[4] It is a task that calls for tact and delicacy, and if the surgeon feels unequal to it, he should turn it over to his assistant or to the family doctor. When the recipient of the bad news is a mentally ill patient, the psychiatrist may be the one best able to deliver it. In any case, the patient should be told by a doctor. When the matter has been neglected by the doctors, as not infrequently happens, the religious leader, aware of the emotional needs of the patient, can do something to prepare him for the truth. But he cannot venture upon a diagnosis, however persistent the patient may be in asking him for it. He can only refer him to the doctor, though he himself will also consult with the latter about the patient's need to know the truth.

More important than the information itself is the way in which it is conveyed to the patient. Of prime importance is the establishment of a positive relationship between patient, physician, and religious leader. And this takes time and patience, certainly several visits. The goal is to make the patient feel that those helping him know him as an individual and are genuinely concerned about him. The initial disclosure should be made in such

---

The healing agent is the human relationship between doctor and patient. For certain neurotic patients this "magical" gift is indispensable to their well-being. The modern physician is fully aware of the psychological issues involved, so that when he prescribes placebos he is not in fact practicing a deception but utilizing a specific form of "suggestive therapy." Some religious leaders and moral philosophers have spoken of this practice as a "wicked and deceitful lie and a shameful abuse, betraying the unworthiness of the physician for his noble calling." In view of the fact that the procedure is employed effectively to maintain the emotional well-being of a specific group of patients, it cannot be called immoral.

a way as to leave it to the patient to determine the extent to which he will grasp the nettle of truth. After the first facts have been cautiously imparted, the patient's inquiries and reactions will guide the physician and the religious leader as they determine together the amount of detail he is prepared to tolerate at any given time, and the strategy to be used in communicating it. Some patients will show in their actions and attitudes that they are prepared to move at once to the heart of the matter and drastically reorganize their lives in accordance with the grim realities which confront them. But caution is in order here, for a brave invitation to tell the whole truth may mask an unrealistic tendency to reject the disagreeable. One such case involved a physician who, breezily assured by the patient that he could "take it," informed him that he had cancer. A few minutes after he was given the information which he himself had requested, the patient plunged to his death from the window of his hospital room. Actually the patient's prospects were fairly good, and he could have looked forward, in any case, to several years of productive life. Never allowing himself to forget that sadness, loneliness, and fear are normal reactions to news of a crippling or fatal disease, the religious leader will be a pillar of support in a period of crisis, and he will be quick to see through the façade of false cheer.

The primary role is the physician's, but the religious leader has an important role of his own to play, both before an operation, when he will seek to buoy up the patient's hopes with prayer, and afterwards, when he will assist him to accept his lot. We could hardly have a better example of the religious leader's unique role in meeting the emotional needs of the desperately ill than the following. A chaplain in a veterans' hospital called on a young man who had just learned that he was the victim of a fatal disease. The patient was hostile to the chaplain's efforts to comfort him, asking simply that he be left alone in his misery. Unshaken by this rejection, the chaplain stated that he would visit him again soon. Subsequent visits proved equally unrewarding, until one day the chaplain suddenly asked, "Tell me, Joe, when are you going to die?" The question jolted the patient out of his self-pitying lethargy, but before he could answer the chaplain continued, "Tell me, Joe, when am I going to die? And who in your opinion will die first, you or me?" By this time, Joe was actively interested. "I'm asking you these questions," said the chaplain, "because both you and I are going to die. That much is certain. Who first and who last only God knows. Since we are both doomed, what shall we do, Joe? Shall we sit and weep until that fateful moment arrives? Do you know, Joe, I believe that He who gives life to all watches over us. If we try to give meaning to our life, He will see to it that we complete our mission on earth." This conversation was a turning point for the patient. Abruptly he gave up his attitude of self-pity, and his efforts to encourage other patients were a source of joy to himself and inspiration to them. The chaplain's handling of this case is noteworthy in more than one respect. For one thing, he remained completely unthreatened by the patient's hostile, rejecting attitude. Devoid of guilt and anxiety, never losing sight of the desperate emotional straits of the sick man, he returned to him, and succeeded finally in reaching him. Further, he depended solely on a simple affirmation of his own faith and the fellowship of a shared belief. In emphasizing the religious necessity for living out one's life here on earth as perfectly as possible, and in appealing to faith, the chaplain brought into play, as only a religious leader could have done, the deepest resources of the patient.

In a study of dying patients, a psychiatrist acknowledged his failure to break through the loneliness of one of his patients, who had only a few months to live. In spite of his best efforts he was unable in this case to overcome the sense of isolation from which the dying so often suffer acutely. "It would have helped," said this physician, "if I could have told the patient that I, too, was suffering from a disease bringing me slowly closer to death. In this moment a community spirit would have been established which would have permitted an identification on her side." [5] What the doctor failed to grasp here, and what our chaplain in the foregoing case grasped perfectly, is that all of us, well or ill, belong to the community of the dying. If he had been more deeply sensible of this he might have succeeded in overcoming the gulf between himself and his patient. That we do not know when death will come to any of us is an ever present fact to the religious person, and it is a reason for trying to make each day of one's life as perfect as possible. "And therefore never send to know for whom the bell tolls; It tolls for thee," wrote John Donne, the Dean of St. Paul's, during a serious illness. Such realization of the precariousness of life draws loved ones together and creates a sense of fellowship with all of mankind. But for religion death is not the end, and in holding out the hope of immortality, it provides the dying with the infinitely comforting prospect of reunion with loved ones.

The question whether the sick should be told the truth sometimes gives rise to still another question, that of euthanasia. Psychiatrists are particularly familiar with the patient who wishes to die. He suffers from an abnormal state of melancholy and his despair of life is itself a symptom of illness. Such patients can be cured of their melancholia and their capacity for normal life fulfillment restored. Certainly it is a mistake to give in to their request to die, either allowing them to do away with themselves or facilitating their death in any other way. Still it may be asked, what of the individual with an incurable illness which is painful, crippling, or disfiguring? What if such a person asks for death? Should one comply with the request —or sanction it? There are some who would. But psychiatric experience is against them. A case in point is that of a man who was admitted to a mental hospital after an attempt at suicide. According to his family, his depression had set in about a month before, when he had had an ileostomy; that is, an artificial bowel opening in his abdomen. In the mental hospital a heated debate raged among the resident physicians, some contending that his attempt at suicide was an appropriate and rational act and that in similar circumstances they would do the same. The man had a wife and three small children and a successful business which required his active direction. He received a course of electroshock therapy, and his depression lifted. Returning to his family with a new zest for life, he resumed his work and his friendships. The hospital directed him to a club all of whose members had had an ileostomy, and in their company he learned to live with his handicap. In thus responding to treatment this man gave the lie to the people at the mental hospital who regarded his case as one that justified euthanasia.

Mention should be made, too, of those well-known figures who have risen above fearful physical handicaps, and given meaning, even greatness, to their lives, and brought joy and fulfillment to others. As good an example as any is that of Sigmund Freud, who suffered from a painful cancer of the mouth over a period of many years. During this time he continued to live a life of great creative achievement. It has been suggested that psychiatrists apply themselves to discovering how people ought to die. Orthanasia it has been called. To our mind, far more important than learning how to die is learning how to live. And in this the religious leader has his greatest responsibility.

FACING BEREAVEMENT

7.

THE DEATH OF A CLOSE FRIEND OR RELATIVE, EVEN
when it occurs late in his life, can affect us deeply, and
the loss is desolating if it is premature or unexpected. All things
combine to remind us of a loss that is irreparable, and so must
be accepted. Death tends either to stimulate or to dull religious
feeling, and for the devout, bereavement is a test of faith. The
psychiatrist, although he may play a role during the mourning
period, can never replace the religious leader, whose role here
is primary.

Normal Psychological Aspects of Bereavement

THE religious leader can profit from a knowledge of
the psychological aspects of bereavement. Human beings usually react with specific symptoms to the loss of a loved
one, and in normal circumstances these appear at once and
are of limited duration. Mourning is a dynamic process; that
is, it has a beginning stage, it undergoes a characteristic development, and it moves towards a conclusion. At the outset
there is grief. This may express itself in uncontrollable crying,
or in a shock-like state with confusion, temporary panic, and
thoughts of self-destruction. There may be physical weakness
and loss of appetite. Adult controls break down to some extent,
and there is withdrawal of attention from the surrounding
world; at first the grief-stricken person is more or less inconsolable. The intensity of these reactions depends on such
things as the degree to which the person has been prepared

for his loss, the intensity and nature of his relationship to the deceased, the dependency needs which were fulfilled by the latter, and the availability of such resources as family, friends, and work, as well as inner psychological strengths. The amount and duration of weeping, a normal expression of mourning, is determined in part by the prevailing cultural attitudes towards expressions of feeling. In our culture great importance is attached to self-control and physical tension arises from fear of its loss. Yet considering the psychological needs of the human being during bereavement, it is healthier to give way to the impulse to cry than to aim at self-control.

After an interval the process of mourning consists in an attempt to control its original intensity. The success of this depends primarily on a gradual release of feelings over a period of time, for the mourning process cannot be hurried. The tie to the loved one is represented by many different memories, and in effect each of these memories must be dealt with separately, the bonds untied one by one. Each new reminder is a hurt that must be faced and endured. In the words of Freud, "Reality passes its verdict—that the object no longer exists—upon each single one of the memories and hopes through which the libido [or love] was attached to the lost object, and the ego [or self], confronted as it were with the decision whether it will share this fate, is persuaded by the sum of its narcissistic satisfactions in being alive to sever its attachment to the non-existent object." [1] No wonder that Freud chose to call this process the "work of mourning." It is work which is difficult and unpleasant. Hence some people tend to evade, postpone, or prolong it. Take for example the death of an aged grandmother. It is not just her presence that is missed, or the fact that her rocking chair is empty, her knitting needles idle. The warm milk that had to be prepared for her is no longer needed; her advice and counsel are no longer available. Her death has brought about a whole new pattern of activities and relationships, and in adjusting to these we suffer. This is the work of mourning.

During the work of mourning, the bereaved person tends to withdraw into a shell, to cut himself off from family as well as from friends. After a few weeks of mourning, when he tries to reestablish contact with the world, everything seems different in a strange and disturbing way. This curious phenomenon is illustrated by the following. "Mrs. A. [who had lost a beloved son a few weeks earlier] went for a walk with a friend through familiar streets, in an attempt to reestablish old bonds. She suddenly realized that the number of people in the street seemed overwhelming, the houses strange, and the sunshine artificial and unreal. She had to retreat into a quiet restaurant. But there she felt as if the ceiling were coming down, and the people in the place became vague and blurred. Her own house suddenly seemed the only secure place in the world. . . . The external world was felt to be artificial and unreal, because real trust in inner goodness had temporarily gone." [2] During such times the presence of patient and loving friends and family provides a bridge to reality. The religious leader, especially if the dead person was known to him, is in a strategic position to exchange reminiscences with the survivor in an atmosphere of religious consolation and rededication to life's realities.

Along with the loneliness and sadness that accompany bereavement are feelings of rage, for the grieving person is always an angry person. Love is mingled with hate, a phenomenon known as ambivalence. The actual mixture of love and hate, and the anger that goes with it, varies quantitatively from case to case and determines the character of the mourning process. The note of anger is unmistakable in the widow's weeping complaint about her husband, "Why did he do this to me?" The resentment may be slight, but it gives rise to guilt and so to expectations of punishment. And this accounts for much of the superstitious dread that often marks the early stages of the mourning process. The longed-for return of the deceased becomes mingled with terrifying expectations of avenging ghostly visitors. If, in addition, the ambivalent feelings have a basis in reality—for example, if the deceased was indeed the victim of the mourner's neglect during life—the manifestations of these feelings are all the more intense. Further, the deceased may have played a symbolic role in the life of the mourner, without the latter's being aware of it. Thus a husband may have represented a father figure, with the result that the hostility towards the father experienced early in childhood may now reassert itself and give rise to guilt out of all proportion to any immediately observable cause. Such hidden sources of guilt may so perpetuate the emotional disturbance of bereavement as to require psychiatric treatment, as happened in the previously cited case of Mrs. A., whose grief reaction followed the death of her young son. From the analysis of a dream she had during the period of mourning, it became clear that she identified this lost son with a younger brother to whom she had been closely attached in her childhood. Further analysis revealed that with all her love and admiration for this brother she had been jealous of him, envying his mental and physical superiority, the fact that he was a boy and the favorite of the mother. Her jealousy became so intense at times that she wished he would die. Long forgotten, her malignant wishes now re-emerged in her dreams, troubling her sleep and intensifying her anguish by day. The constancy with which she dwelt on her son's wonderful qualities tried the patience of the family and friends alike.

In the attempt to fight off repugnant thoughts about the deceased, the mourner may become obsessed with the latter's good qualities. Idealization and retrospective falsification take place, with results that may be incongruously out of keeping with the actuality. But it is by means of this psychological device that the mourner deals with the emotional complications of ambivalence. He may carry the process a step further and adopt peculiarities of speech and gesture that were characteristic of the deceased, or even develop physical complaints like those which once afflicted the dead person. All this represents an attempt to deny the loss of the beloved one by identification with him.

The mourner's anger towards the deceased may result in bitter self-reproaches and more intense sadness. On the other hand, the anger may be turned upon others. A scapegoat is sought. It may be someone within the family, a business partner, the attending physician, or the religious leader. Whoever it is, he is likely to suffer discomfort, but such outwardly expressed rage is actually a constructive attempt by the mourner to cope with his guilt-generating hostility.

When death has come after a lingering illness, especially if great suffering was involved, the mourning process may start before death actually takes place, and as a result the phase of acute grief may be shorter and less intense.

The normal mourning process proceeds with ever decreasing intensity. After a time—weeks or months or longer—the world becomes a less painful place to the mourner. If, as usually happens, his self-esteem has been shaken by his loss, he now begins to recover it. There is a gradual return of the capacity to relate to other people and to work effectively. Finally the mourning process comes to an end; such reminders of the deceased as the anniversary of his death may reinstate it, but only temporarily.

If he has carried the work of mourning out to its conclusion, the bereaved may emerge from it a stronger person than ever. The degree to which the mourner remains unable to accept the irrevocable reality is a measure of the incompleteness or abnormality of the mourning process. It is only by eliminating from conscious awareness much of the reality which surrounds him that the mourner can maintain a belief in the continued earthly existence of the deceased. And to do this is to fall into a psychological state which is incompatible with mental health.

Distorted Mourning Reactions

T H E inability to carry out the work of mourning may usher in a process of personal disintegration, the upshot of which is mental illness. Among the factors that may precipitate a distorted mourning reaction is an untimely loss. A death for which one is completely unprepared will usually have a more devastating impact than death from a chronic disease. A sudden tragedy may freeze the mourning process in its initial state of shock.

Vividly illustrative of this is the following case history. A man of thirty-eight, happily married and the father of two fine children, went on a fishing trip with his family. Caught in a storm, their boat capsized, and all except the father were drowned. When he alone was brought safely to shore by the Coast Guard, his anguish was unspeakable. For a week he refused to eat. He attempted suicide but was forestalled. During the ensuing months he walked the streets in a daze, and made more attempts at suicide. He would spend his nights at the cemetery sleeping by the graves of his family. He spent hours with a revered theologian, who was a student of religious mysticism, pleading with him to find a way of communicating with his dead family. The theologian listened to his expressions of grief, tried to console him, and urged him to seek solace in prayer. There was no letup in his distraught state. The religious leader urged him to consult a psychiatrist, but to no avail. Years after the tragedy the man's physical and emotional deterioration continued.

Another distorted reaction to death is one in which the individual is unable to feel or show grief. A striking example is that presented by the case of a man in his thirties who started psychiatric treatment because of a variety of physical complaints which were without apparent organic basis. In addition, for years he had undergone periods of uncontrollable weeping that would descend upon him suddenly and unaccountably. An only child, attentive and devoted, he had been a student at a distant university when his mother died. When the news of her death reached him, he departed at once for the funeral. On the way, and at the funeral itself, he found himself incapable of any feelings of sadness. Despite all his efforts to mobilize emotions appropriate to the occasion, such as forcing himself to recall the most treasured memories of his mother, her goodness and devotion, he could not feel anything but indifference. Unable to free himself from the torments of self-reproach, he would time and again conjure up the memory of his beloved mother in the hope that he might weep.

The death of this young man's mother had come at a time in his life when he was severely beset with neurotic problems, among them difficulty in concentrating on his school work, sexual impotence, and generalized feelings of inadequacy. Treatment brought out that underneath his show of extreme filial devotion there existed a state of marked conflict. In early childhood he had developed an intense hatred for his mother because of her frequent absences from home. Controlled during the latency period, this hatred flared up for a time at puberty. The boy's excessive display of affection for his mother, his dependence upon her, and indeed his tendency to mold himself after her rather than his father were all the result of a struggle to control his hostile feelings. Accordingly, it became clear that the mother's death met with the bitter response of early childhood "She has left me again!" Once more full of hatred for his mother, as he had been in childhood, he was incapable of feeling grief at her death. And his guilt towards her continued to express itself not only in conscious self-reproaches, but in physical symptoms similar to those from which she had suffered. The outbursts of weeping represented a release of the childhood anguish caused by her absences, anguish which he had repressed behind a façade of indifference.[3]

The mimicry of physical symptoms, as exemplified in this case, is a rather common expression of a distorted grief reaction. People will react to the loss of a loved one with fears or even symptoms of the disease, whatever it may be—cancer or heart disease, for example—that the departed had. Such fears or symptoms may set in directly after the death and recur over a period of years at the anniversary of the death. Or the mourner may remain in perfect health until he approaches the age at which the loved one, usually a parent, died, when he will be overcome by a morbid fear. It is also not unusual for a mourner to develop symptoms or actual physical disorders different from those of the deceased. Such serious diseases as ulcerative colitis, arthritis, asthma, abnormal uterine bleeding, hyperthyroidism, and leukemia may occur upon the death of a loved one.

A temporary manifestation of normal grief, such as the tendency to withdraw from friends and relatives, may become permanent. In some cases, social withdrawal is clearly related to an attempt to control the angry feelings which rage within the mourner. It may happen too that guilty feelings touch off a pattern of indirectly self-destructive behavior. For example, he may indulge in acts of such ill-considered generosity as to pauperize himself. When intense rage is involved, it may erupt in the form of a mental breakdown with delusions of persecution, or the rage may be turned inward, causing a state of agitated depression, a feeling that one is beyond forgiveness, which may turn to suicide.

With proper psychiatric treatment these distorted expressions of grief gradually disappear, to be replaced by the true, undisguised mourning process. Such mourning can occur years after the actual bereavement. For example, we have the case of a patient in his early forties who was referred to a psychiatrist by his family physician because of a groundless fear that he would die suddenly of heart disease. At one point in his treatment his symptoms became suddenly worse, for no reason which the patient or his psychiatrist could fathom at first. It turned out, however, that at this time a member of his family had telephoned to remind him that the anniversary of his father's death was approaching and that he should arrange time off from work to attend the Jewish memorial services. When he had put the two things together, the patient's fear of sudden cardiac failure abated but in its place he experienced great anger. During the religious services blasphemous thoughts kept interrupting his recitation of the mourner's prayers, and his irreverent behavior involved him in a quarrel with the sexton.

As treatment continued, this sequence of events repeated itself at each anniversary with lessening intensity. The patient became more and more aware of his feelings of irreverence and resentment towards his father, whose sudden death from a heart attack had occurred when the patient was five years old. On growing up he had taken his father's place in the household, becoming a successful businessman and providing well for his mother and sisters. While the patriarchal role he played in the family won him their gratitude and affection, it also had the effect of intensifying his feelings of guilt towards his father. As his problems were worked through in analysis he began to feel an affection for his father which had hitherto been lacking. The result was that forty years after his father's death he underwent for the space of a few days a true reaction of mourning.*

---

* An interesting illustration of a mourning reaction which was protracted far beyond the outer limits of normal is provided by W. Somerset Maugham in his autobiographical essay, *The Summing Up* (Mentor, New York, 1951, p. 190). After his mother's death, Maugham, at the age of eight, was sent to a boarding school. He says of this period, "When I was a small boy and unhappy I used to dream night after night that my life at school was all a dream and that I should wake to find myself at home again with my mother. Her death was a wound that fifty years have not entirely healed. I have long ceased to have that dream; but I have never quite lost the sense that my living life was a mirage in which I did this and that because that was how it fell out, but which, even while I was playing my part in it, I could look at from a distance and know for the mirage it was. When I look back on my life, with its successes and its failures, its endless errors, its deceptions and its fulfilments, its joys and miseries it seems to me strangely lacking in reality. It is shadowy and unsubstantial." After this striking account of the way the uncompleted work of mourning his mother's death affected his grasp of reality, Maugham goes on to suggest that this also affected his religious life, giving rise to what he calls a "deep ancestral craving for God

In addition to sudden or untimely death, the age of the bereaved person can be a factor in causing an abnormal mourning reaction and producing ambivalence. Children of four or five often react to the death of a parent with a show of apparent callousness or indifference, and thus postpone the true mourning reaction till they are better able to cope with their loss. But when they do give way to grief in a setting of loneliness and inadequate support from parent substitutes, they may become vulnerable to mental illness with suicidal impulses that appear later in life. All this is also true of the child at puberty. However, it is not only the young who react abnormally to death. The loss of a marital partner late in life may fail to elicit any true expressions of grief, but in its place there may appear a variety of disabling physical ailments, accidents that result in broken bones and crippling, or the sudden approach of senility.

One might suppose that excessive mourning is a measure of the mourner's great attachment to the deceased, but the fact is that love by itself does not give rise to such excess. We have seen that what is involved here is the phenomenon of ambivalence, love mingled with concealed hate. Although the help of a psychiatrist is commonly needed to overcome excessive ambivalence, as well as the other manifestations of abnormal mourning, the religious leader is often the first one consulted for help. Hence it is important that he be able to recognize and understand these manifestations, and be prepared to make the appropriate referrals. In bereavement, as on all other occasions, the religious leader is acting as a member of a team and constantly working in cooperation with his fellow members.

The Role of the Religious Leader

O U R discussion of the psychological characteristics of the mourning process should help us define the specific role of the religious leader towards the bereaved. Standing out with particular significance is his role as a parent substitute.

---

and immortality," a craving which he would not permit himself to accept, however, any more than he could permit himself to accept the reality of the world around him.

The feelings of helplessness that assail the grief-stricken lead them to envisage the role of the religious leader above all in its symbolic aspect. That is to say, his powers are not judged realistically, as those of a human being, but are assumed to be almost those of the Father in heaven. The relationship between the mourner and the religious leader becomes one between the very small and the very great; in it, therefore, the mourner experiences transference and psychological regression, and expresses attitudes and expectations that date from early childhood. Still, by faith and ritual the religious leader is able to direct the mourning process into normal channels. When grief is excessive, he will take the fact into account in providing consolation, and when the work of mourning seems deficient, he will seek to mobilize the feelings of the mourner. In both interventions he is fulfilling his pastoral and priestly roles.

Countertransference, no less than transference, tends to occur in connection with bereavement. One danger is that when the mourner's grief is at its height, the anxiety-ridden religious leader may interfere with the normal course of mourning by excessive attempts at consolation. Another trap that the mourning process may pose for the religious leader is the expression of hostility by the bereaved. The following case history is typical. Heavy of heart and extremely anxious, a religious leader paid a call on a devout young woman who had lost her only child. She greeted him with a scream of rage: "Get out of my house and never come back again. Go with your God. I want no part of either of you!" The religious leader was a young man, and as he stood in anguish at the doorway the woman continued to rage at him. Discouraged, he turned away and left. In discussing his experience with a psychiatrist at a seminar he asked, "What could I have said? If she were a simpleminded illiterate I could have told her that her child is happy in heaven. I could have told her it was God's will. But this is twentieth-century America! People don't believe such things any more. I felt so helpless in the face of her anger. If I had spoken in religious terms she would surely have withered me with sarcasm and bitterness. I didn't know what to say, and I still don't know what to say. That is why I'm consulting a psychiatrist for advice." Quite properly the psychiatrist pointed out that if the religious leader himself had no answer, then no one did. Did not Freud say that the idea of a purpose in life stands or falls with religion? "And so," he continued, "you alone have it in your power to give meaning to this otherwise senseless tragedy. Furthermore, this woman hungers for an answer. All people yearn to believe that the catastrophies of life have some meaning. Otherwise many grieving people would remain forever unconsolable." He went on to speak of the helplessness and weakness of the mourner, pointing out that in a fundamental sense the person suffering from acute grief is emotionally like a child. Anger, he said, is a regular accompaniment of the normal mourning process, and it is much like the temper tantrum of a frustrated child who loses self-control in the face of an unendurable hurt. The most important fact about this anger is that it enables the sufferer to turn his misery outward and so experience it in a more bearable form. Hence the importance of the scapegoat. It is a device for escaping from a too painful reality, and in some instances it is literally a life-saving device. Yet in the end it is uneconomical, for the aftermath of venting one's rage upon another, especially a loved or revered person, is likely to be guilt and self-reproach, which only add to one's suffering. A vicious circle is thus set up, in which mental depression deepens and self-defensive outbursts of rage intensify.

In view of all this, the religious leader in this case should have allowed the woman to vent her rage against him, but in the way that would be least likely to intensify her feelings of guilt. He might have said to her, "I know how deeply hurt you are and I can't blame you if you feel bitter. When your hurt is less I want to come back and talk to you. We'll try to see then whether there is meaning to this tragedy." The psychological key to the woman's outburst lies in the fact that her rage was an expression not of strength but of helplessness. To have abandoned her at this moment amounted to abandoning her when her need was greatest. At this point our religious leader asked the psychiatrist, "What am I to say to her when I return? Let us assume that the intensity of her feelings has ameliorated and she is now willing to listen." The psychiatrist emphasized the loneliness of this bereaved woman, point-

ing out that the fellowship of another human being joined
with her in the religious bonds of love and compassion would
be a healing device. She would probably want to discuss her
beloved child, and the religious leader might tell her of the
ways in which great Biblical figures faced up to similar tragedies of their own. He could remind her that tragedy has been
the lot of man from the beginning, yet he has not turned away
from God. It is precisely in his periods of greatest suffering
that he has sought out the help of religion.

The psychiatrist then turned to the role of guilt in the mourning process. The bereaved searches his mind a thousand times
and fearfully asks, "What did I do wrong? What might I have
done to avert this loss?" It is almost a certainty that guilty
suspicions haunted the mind of this grief-stricken mother, suspicions that she failed her child somehow, or perhaps even
unwittingly contributed to his death. And it may be that these
suspicions had some basis in fact, in which case her feelings
of guilt would be all the greater. In any event, the religious
leader's simple but firm insistence that the tragedy was God's
will, that there is an Authority who takes some of this responsibility from her, could effectively counter her destructive self-
reproaches. There are many different ways in which the discussion with this distracted mother might have been carried
out, but underlying them all is the religious principle that the
death of her child was not her will but God's, and that it
served God's purposes, though we do not know how. This is
the consolation the religious leader has to offer. It is his affirmation of faith. The scientific armamentarium of the psychiatrist provides nothing better.

The dangers of countertransference are plain. In its grip
the religious leader loses contact with reality, and if the angry
mourner attacks him he reacts with guilt, as if he were indeed
responsible for the misfortune. Or he may identify too vividly
with the bereaved person, and make his loss his own loss, and
in the process experience similar feelings of spiritual annihila-
tion. At a time when he should rally with strength to the support of the mourner he permits himself to be overwhelmed,
suffering feelings of guilt and personal failure. In consequence,
he may silently join the bereaved person in his complaints

against God and undergo some loss of faith at the very moment when unswerving faith is of vital importance to the mourner.

Unfortunately it sometimes happens that the religious leader forgets that, although he symbolizes a power beyond himself, he is still human, and comes to expect of himself the very impossibilities that his suffering congregant expects of him. He is of course doomed to frustration and disappointment, attended by a sense of personal failure and guilt. It is a paradox which cannot be stated too often that the religious leader's strength lies in his humility. He makes no claim to be able to decipher all of God's purposes in the world, but his faith in an overruling plan remains steadfast. It is with this faith that he confronts the mourner.

Having enunciated some general principles concerning the mourning process, we turn now to a consideration of the specific ways in which the religious leader may apply them in practice. Since the mourning process goes through different stages, his ministrations will differ from one stage to another. Confronted with the first uncontrolled expressions of grief, he will not yield to his impulse to give comfort. For natural as this impulse is, it is open to question from a psychological point of view. Clinical case studies make it clear that the chief initial need of the bereaved is to give expression to his grief. Nothing is more ill-advised then than attempts at consolation or urgings to self-control. Such efforts are unlikely to penetrate the stunned and dejected mind of the bereaved, and if they do they may only intensify guilt feelings, with consequent distortion of the mourning process. Interventions of this sort may also arouse hostility that will set up a barrier against the religious leader and impair his effectiveness later on. And if these well-intentioned efforts should succeed, they may delay the grief reaction and thwart the healing effect of normal mourning. Nor will it do for the religious leader to suggest that the expression of grief betrays a lack of faith. For while it is often argued that a belief in immortality should enable the mourner to control his grief, still the fact is that he does experience a deep sense of loss, and there is nothing irreligious in his giving expression to it. The argument is a piece of misplaced logic. Only a pedantic formalism would make religious belief incompatible with the feelings to which loss, separation, and loneliness give rise. And so the religious leader will do nothing to discourage the free expression of grief. If anything, he will encourage it at first.

In the initial period of bereavement the mourner may be so helpless as to be unable to make the funeral arrangements, and if no member of the family is available for this purpose, the task may have to be undertaken by the religious leader. It is one of the many tasks that fall to his lot at this time. In this instance he has the opportunity, as well, to protect the guilt-ridden mourner from the financial excesses that disgrace the modern funeral. The next responsibility of the religious leader is that of conducting the funeral service, and it is at this point that his active healing role begins. Now his object will be to give comfort to the bereaved, and this in turn requires, above all else, that he do honor to the deceased. The mourner is inclined to idealize the deceased, sometimes to the point of utter incongruity, as in the instance of a woman who had suffered public humiliation for decades because of her husband's infidelities but who extolled him as a paragon of virtue during the period of mourning. Idealization plays an important part in the psychology of bereavement, so that the religious leader, anxious to guard the normal mourning process against the likelihood of distortion, will accept and, when possible, add to the mourner's good opinion of the deceased. To do otherwise is needlessly to wound the sensibilities of the living. In the nineteen fifties a notorious underworld character was murdered. His great wealth, his exotic self-indulgences, and the lurid circumstances of his death combined to make his funeral a public event. The religious leader who conducted the services denounced the evil career of the deceased. The mother was present, and was of course deeply hurt. For weeks afterward the members of this minister's congregation debated the pros and cons of his action. Yet the denunciation was unseemly. Certainly a funeral is not an occasion for dishonest encomium, but it is not an occasion either for publicly humiliating a grief-stricken mother. If the religious leader is so revolted by the career of the deceased that he cannot find it in his heart to say a good word for him, he should discuss his feelings with the family and ask permission to withdraw. At least he owes them a warning, if he plans to take up the deceased's moral character in the pulpit. For the religious leader's chief responsibility at a funeral is to do honor to the dead and to give comfort to the bereaved. Questions concerning the morality of the deceased should be postponed to a more suitable occasion, such as a private discussion with the bereaved family after they have got over the acute stage of their grief. Of course the religious leader is free to express his views on the issues raised by the character of the deceased, but he can do this without reference to a particular individual. In short, during bereavement, the religious leader should focus his function on the needs of the bereaved.

The funeral over, the religious leader has the task of reconciling the bereaved to the irrevocability of his loss, at least so far as this earthly life is concerned. What follows is a moving illustration of the point. A woman lost her only son, a fourteen-year-old boy, in an automobile accident. Her reaction was conspicuous for the absence of overt grief, but she filled the house with his mementos and kept his bedroom made up as if he were getting ready to go to school. She kept fresh underclothes, a shirt, and his best suit in constant readiness. His briefcase filled with school books stood on the floor, and his favorite gadgets were about as if he had just been tinkering with them. When company came she kept his door closed. The boy's room became a shrine which only she was permitted to enter. Her neglect of husband and daughter went so far that they appealed to their religious leader, who forbade the woman to continue her behavior. At first she bitterly refused to give it up, but finally she tearfully disassembled the "shrine." The minister prayed with her, spoke words of consolation, and got her to attend religious services. For weeks she felt deeply depressed, but it was now that she began to undergo the normal process of mourning. The minister drew her into Sunday school activities and she joined the parent-teachers association. Her interests thus mobilized, she benefited not only her surviving child but other youngsters in the community as well. In this way the religious leader was able to redirect the woman's distorted and deadlocked mourning into wholesome channels of expression.

The promise of immortality is perhaps the greatest comfort the religious leader can hold out to the bereaved. At the unconscious level, at least, the belief in immortality is deeply rooted in all of us. On this subject Freud writes: "How does our unconscious behave in relation to the problem of death? Almost exactly as does primitive man. In this respect as in many others, primitive man lives unchanged in our unconscious. Our unconscious does not believe in its own death. It behaves as if it were immortal." [4] "Primitive man" here might with greater accuracy be described as "the child." To the child there is no death, only a departure, a temporary separation. It is this idea that survives unconsciously in the adult and expresses itself in consciousness. The notion that after death we return to our former dwelling place may assume the symbolic form of unconsciously equating heaven with the mother's womb. Or the grave may be thought of as a return to mother earth, where we sleep until the resurrection. Or death may be regarded as a voyage of discovery, a journey to a land where hidden things will be revealed. The symbolism of the unconscious provides us with a clue to the genesis of this way of looking at death. It is related to the survival in adult life of childhood's gnawing curiosity about the mysteries and secrets of the adult world. In any case, at the conscious level immortality assumes a variety of forms, depending on such factors as the person's religious denomination, his intellectual and emotional development and cultural background. To one person immortality may mean a literal state of reincarnation; to another it may be a figure of speech, as when it is said that a man lives on in his children, in the books he writes, the pictures he paints, the music he composes, in his business enterprises, his good deeds, or the grateful memory of those who loved him. Whatever its psychological roots or the forms it takes, the idea of immortality is one to which the religious leader can confidently appeal in giving comfort to the bereaved.

The religious leader will tap every source of consolation available to him. For example, there is the psychological mechanism that generally comes into play at the prospect of sudden violent death. Thus a passenger in a jet plane which went into what seemed a fatal nosedive experienced a great feeling of calm and contentment in the split second that passed before the pilot regained control. In reporting the experience afterwards he said it was as if he were at home in bed, cozy and warm under the covers, congratulating himself that it was not yet time to get up for work. It was only later, on the ground and out of danger, that he was seized with fear and trembling. Now if this man had lost his life, it might have provided some measure of relief to the mourners to know that in all probability the few seconds of awareness left him were not filled with unimaginable terror.

For the religious leader, the governing psychological principle here is that the work of mourning takes time. In the days and weeks following the funeral, he will realize that it is in this period especially that the mourner looks to him in his symbolic status, as one who is conversant with the mystery of death, who knows the written record of sorrow and suffering as recorded in the Scriptures. To the bereaved he is wise and strong, and his mere physical presence is a support and comfort. Accordingly he need feel no embarrassment in walking into a house of mourners, whom he will greet with a few words of religious consolation, taking his place quietly among them and following their lead in the discussion. For example, the mourners may choose to reminisce about the departed and the religious leader will contribute what he can; certainly he will not try to divert them from the subject. Ill-advised attempts at consolation may only give rise to embarrassing small talk at a time when the mourner's greatest need is to recall the beloved. On the other hand, the mourner exhausted from weeping may want to be diverted from his sorrow. Here, too, lugubrious words of condolence are out of place. In short, if the religious leader's sensitivity is not blunted by anxiety, he will be able to gear the tone of his conversation to the emotional needs of the mourners. If conversation is out of the question, as it may be in a household struck dumb with sorrow, he will read the Scriptures and conduct religious services.

Only unfortunate complications can ensue when the religious leader deviates from his role as a man of God, as is illustrated by the young melancholiac woman who was referred for analysis. Her illness arose with the death of her father, which

occurred under peculiarly unhappy circumstances. He suffered
from a chronic illness for which a relatively minor surgical procedure had been recommended. Extremely fearful of surgery,
he kept postponing the operation. Finally, when all others had
failed, his daughter, to whom he was very close, prevailed
upon him to enter the hospital. A surgical error during the
operation and a lapse of nursing attention afterwards resulted
in the father's sudden and utterly unexpected death. The
daughter was appalled. Panic-stricken, she rushed to the minister's house only to find that he was out of town for two days.
She left word for him to call as soon as he returned and went
back home, where she remained secluded and inconsolable.
When the minister later appeared at her door, she refused to
allow him to enter, but cried out to him in anguish, "Tell me,
please, tell me, was the death of my father destined by God?"
To the woman's profound disappointment, all the minister
could find to say was that her father's doctors had been irresponsible and inept and that she ought to bring suit against
them. In consultation with a psychiatrist several months later,
the woman expressed the opinion that if the minister had met
her outburst with some genuinely religious reply she might
have avoided her present predicament. Actually, her emotional problems antedated her father's death, yet she had good
grounds for complaining against the minister. What she had
a right to expect of him was a response to her agonized wish to
believe that her tragedy, seemingly so senseless, had a meaning, that it was indeed God's doing, not her own. As she said,
"If I wanted to know if I had a good case against the doctors
I would have consulted a lawyer!" The religious leader must
never lose sight of the fact that the person who consults him
wants religious help, not legal or psychiatric advice.

We might add as a postscript to this case that psychiatry, in
resolving the woman's emotional conflict, did away not with
her religion but with the neurotic expression of it. She wrote
to her doctor, "I feel more profoundly religious now than ever
before in my life, religious in the sense that I believe that
good deeds are rewarded and that God does watch over us. If
some misfortune occurs I am sustained in the firm conviction
that it is all part of a larger, meaningful pattern which is not
given to me to understand, but which will ultimately justify

our continued struggle to live with love, respect and dignity. And yet, curiously, the old ways in which I used to express my religious feelings have practically disappeared. For instance, my frequent visits to my father's grave have dwindled to an annual pilgrimage which I make more out of respect for my mother, who asks me to accompany her, than for any other reason. The last time she asked me to go, I begged off because I was busy. My refusal to accompany her did not occasion the panic and self-reproach that it formerly would have. For our yearly Christmas dinner I used to set a place for my father. This year I finally concluded that this was a measure of enslavement to superstition and neurotic guilt which was out of place on such a joyous occasion."

Bereavement in Childhood

IN OUR earlier discussion of childhood attitudes towards death, we pointed out that these attitudes change as the child develops. For example, in his understanding of death, as well as in his ability to carry out the work of mourning, the child of four differs from the child of ten. To the younger child, death is an abandonment, with consequent loneliness, fear, and resentment, and he may shy away from this painful and complicated situation by a show of callous indifference. Yet if he is to mature normally, he must be guided into taking account of the reality of his loss, and encouraged, now and later, to envisage the truth to the fullest extent of his capacity. When the normal work of mourning fails to take place in early childhood the consequences may be serious, as the following case illustrates.

A five-year-old child reacted to his mother's death without feeling. In later life he repressed not only the memory of his mother, but of everything that occurred before her death. In his early thirties he consulted a psychoanalyst. He now had no love relationships, friendships, or real interests of any sort; his reactions to all that had happened to him since his mother's death were dull and apathetic. He had no ambitions, expressed neither the joy of success nor the hurt of failure, and the death of relatives left him unconcerned. His feelings were not unfriendly, nor were his impulses aggressive. The analysis was slow and difficult. The patient's recollections of childhood were meager and consisted primarily of negative and aggressive attitudes towards his mother. These attitudes were in force especially during the "forgotten" period, which was marked by the birth of a young brother. The only reaction of longing for his dead mother betrayed itself in a fantasy which had persisted for several years in his childhood. In this fantasy he left his bedroom door open in the hope that a large dog would come to him, be very kind to him, and fulfill all his wishes. Associated with this was a vivid childhood memory of a bitch that had left her puppies alone and helpless, having been killed shortly after their birth. Nothing else that he recalled revealed any trace of longing or mourning for his mother. He had protected himself only too well, and in the process had become proof not only against unendurably painful emotions, but against all emotions.[5]

Numerous cases could be cited in which children who were showered with affection to the point of overindulgence, yet reacted to the loss of a mother with no overt manifestations of grief. In one such case the family was so shocked by what they felt was the "heartless" unconcern of an adored only child of five that they consulted their religious leader. He was able to reassure the family that they were not rearing an unfeeling "monster" by explaining that the reaction is a common one in childhood, and is the result of an excess of feeling rather than a lack. This excess is sometimes so great that the child feels that, like Humpty-Dumpty, he will never be able to put himself together again if he gives way to it. The religious leader advised the family to keep pictures and mementos of the mother in evidence about the house, to discuss her in the youngster's presence and draw him into these discussions whenever possible. In keeping with the minister's suggestion, the family also made a point of taking the youngster to visit his mother's grave on Memorial Day. Not until two years later did the youngster react at the cemetery with sobbing grief and expressions of loneliness for her, and envy of other youngsters who had "mommies." He had finally come to grips with the fact of death and so launched towards normal emotional growth.

Excessive concern to protect children from the knowledge of

the realities of death is psychologically unsound. Proper instruction here depends upon quantity, timing, and the use of language intelligible to a child. How much at a time is the child to be told and when is he to be told? As we remarked in a previous chapter, small children should not be exposed to the spectacle of uncontrolled grief on the part of elders on whom they depend, but this does not mean that all expressions of grief should be concealed. Provided the child is not too young or emotionally insecure, he may attend the funeral, in which case the religious leader will address special words of consolation and reassurance to him. If the child has not reacted with appropriate sadness at the time of his loss, good psychological reasons exist for taking him annually to the cemetery—in other words, for reopening the mourning process—so that he is given repeated opportunities to cope with his loss under circumstances of gradually increasing emotional control.

In order to foster a normal mourning reaction, the religious leader has to deal with unrealistic attempts to evade the fact of death. Thus a young widower came to a religious leader in a state of despair several weeks after the death of his wife. He had two young children, a girl of seven and a boy of four, and was unable to tell them that their mother was dead. He kept evading their questions, but less and less plausibly, and the children were becoming visibly disturbed. Neither child was eating well. The boy began to suffer from severe recurrent nightmares and the girl was afraid to go to school in the morning. Aware finally that things would go from bad to worse if he did not tell his offspring the truth, he asked the minister to break the news to them, which the minister declined to do, helping him instead to talk to the children himself. He encouraged the father to express his own grief and pointed out that everyone, children no less than adults, had to face up to reality. Evasions could only have the effect of convincing the children that death was impossible to contemplate, even for an adult. Nothing was better calculated to undermine the children's faith in the world and to do them lasting psychological harm. Thus fortified, the father undertook the painful task and with his children now properly mourned the mother's death.

In lending comfort and assurance to the bereaved child at the funeral service, the religious leader performs a task which may be of critical importance for steering the child's subsequent mourning reaction into wholesome channels. As an illustration, a five-year-old girl was inconsolable on being told that her mother had died. Her grief was especially poignant since the death occurred after several months of intense suffering. The family pastor, in attempting to comfort the girl, said that "her mother was taken because God needed her more than the child did." The child's reaction was one of long-lasting hostility towards God. When her father discussed the matter with him, the minister said that there was no intellectual answer to the problem of death. This is no doubt true, but in the circumstances it betrayed a lack of understanding of the psychology of childhood. For the problem here was not to find an intellectual answer, but one which, while religiously valid, was also emotionally satisfying. Uppermost in the mind of a child of five is loneliness and anxiety about his future. "Who will take care of me now?" is the paramount question; reassurance that he will be taken care of is the paramount need. And complicating the psychological problem involved in grief is guilt. In the case of a girl who is at the height of her oedipal attachment to her father, it is not unlikely that she feels that her hostile wishes contributed to her mother's death. The effect upon her of being told that God needs her mother more than she does is to intensify rather than assuage her feelings of guilt. Plainly God's need could not be greater than hers, and she can only interpret the statement as meaning that God takes mothers away from little girls because they have bad thoughts about them. Yet it remains true that, if there is an answer that can be given to a little girl who has lost her mother, it is one couched in religious terms. In the above case it would have been especially easy to explain to the child that her mother, who had suffered so much pain, was now happy, because God had relieved her of her suffering.[6]

It is important to remember the young child's inability to handle abstractions. He can think only in concrete terms and understand only concrete language. For instance, the explanation that someone who dies is now "with God" is very vague to a small child, who tends to identify God with his own father. Even more important than the matter is the manner of telling it. The explanations offered are largely determined by the religion of the parents, but one thing that all explanations should emphasize, without threatening or causing fright, because of the child's dependency on his parents, is that if the parents—or the remaining parent—should die, there are always parent substitutes at hand who will provide for his needs. It is because of this dependence that the parents should not give way to expressions of uncontrolled grief in the presence of their young children, and that children should not be allowed to attend funerals when they are likely to be overwhelmed by the emotional disorganization of their parents, who at this time are their sole source of security.

More important than all else, perhaps, is that the child should be helped to grasp what the death of a loved one involves. To this end it may be necessary to bring up the subject at a time when the child himself prefers to avoid it, and also to bring it up at intervals in the future. In this way he may be spared the serious complications that result from omission of the work of mourning.

In our culture, religious institutions, for one reason or another, almost invariably take part in the rites of burial and mourning. To some people burial ceremonies represent a simple compliance with social custom, while to others they are rooted in the superstitious fear that takes hold of us when we are confronted with the mystery of death. Yet it is safe to say that the majority of men and women are moved to engage in such ceremonies by genuine religious feeling; by a need to reaffirm the belief that life has purpose and meaning; and by a need for the solace that religious faith offers. Whatever the motive—tradition or custom, superstition or fear, or genuine religious faith—the religious leader plays a prominent role in the experience of bereavement.

RELIGIOUS CONVERSION AND

MYSTICISM

8.

THE PHENOMENON OF RELIGIOUS CONVERSION—THAT is, the acute awakening of religious feeling—has been referred to several times in previous chapters, with examples involving children as young as four and others involving adolescents, among whom it is a particularly common occurrence. In the light of these, it seemed apparent that conversion was the outcome of mental conflict. We saw that youngsters in the grip of problems typical of their age and life circumstances sometimes found a satisfactory solution in religious conversion, satisfactory in the sense that it was consistent with further emotional growth and life fulfillment. On the other hand, we encountered cases in which conversion had consequences that were constrictive and frustrating and was associated with symptoms of emotional illness of such severity as to require psychiatric treatment. And the success of this treatment, as we noted, appeared on occasion to be bound up with the elimination of the conversion drive; not the elimination of religion altogether, but its transformation into a mature form of expression. We saw also that the conversion of one partner to the religion of the other in interfaith marriages calls attention to the fact that such marriages themselves may be a symptom of emotional disturbance, and that the religious leader should be aware of this before he undertakes premarital counseling.

Almost always present in religious conversion is a mystical component deeply charged with emotion. Brief as the actual duration of the mystical experience may be, it leaves behind so profound an impression that the memory of it provides a lasting impetus to religious fervor.

The Nature of Mysticism

THE mystical experience, whether religious or not, consists of a state of consciousness marked by certain distinguishing qualities.[1] Above all, the experience has "ineffability." According to the mystic it is inexpressible and indescribable; it is impossible to convey what it is like to one who has never had the experience. Equally characteristic of the mystical state is its "noetic quality," the feeling that the mystery of the universe has been plumbed, that an immense illumination or revelation has occurred. Along with this may go a curious sense of authority, the conviction that one is privileged to lead and command. The classical examples here are the Biblical prophets. As for the revelation itself, it consists of layer upon layer of "truth," which as it unfolds may find expression in some familiar thought, but one which the devotee has found suddenly pregnant with new meaning. Common sayings from Scripture are especially liable to this change in the mind of the mystic. On the other hand, the revelation may be expressed in words that are unintelligible, even to the speaker.

Another characteristic of the mystical state is its "transiency." It may last only a moment or go on for an hour or two, but when the experience ceases the particular quality of feeling it aroused is only imperfectly reproducible in memory. Yet it is as unforgettable as it is highly treasured, and colors all subsequent activity.

Still another marked feature of the mystical state is its "passivity." There is an abeyance of the will, as if the subject were in the grip of a superior power to whose direction he is highly responsive. He experiences a sense of unity with this power, which is felt as infinite. This sense of unity with something outside the self may be artificially induced, as by mescaline. Aldous Huxley describes how, under the influence of this drug, he lost himself in the contemplation of a chair with bamboo legs. Looking at the tubularity of the legs and their smoothness in a kind of ecstasy, he achieved a timeless state in which he was unable to decide whether the experience of the bamboo legs lasted a few minutes or several centuries. He describes himself as not merely gazing at the bamboo legs, but actually being them, "—or rather being myself in them." [2] Henry Susso, the fourteenth-century Christian mystic, compared his ecstasies to drunken states in which he would lose himself in God, pass into Him, become one spirit with Him in all respects. All mystics are agreed that the sense of unity with God —or the Absolute, as nonreligious mystics sometimes say—is the very heart of the mystical experience.

The sense of unity in the mystical state is accompanied by a capacity to reconcile opposites, or what appear to be such to the ordinary understanding. In Huxley's feeling of timelessness, minutes and centuries were all one. A mystic will speak of a darkness that dazzles, of voices of silence, of a nothing that is deeper than anything. In the transports of a mystical experience, the doctrine of the Trinity, for example, despite its complex character, presents no difficulties; indeed, it becomes crystal-clear. Nothing troubles the mystic less than the rules of logic. In this respect, it is possible to see mysticism as in part a reversion to childhood habits of thought. Take, for example, the following conversation between two four-year-old girls, Nancy and Amy. Nancy has been told nothing about God. "You know, if you kill someone, God will punish you," said Amy. "Who's God?" asked Nancy. "Oh," said Amy, who was very clear on the point, "God is dead and He's inside of you." [3] Like the child, the mystic shows little concern for ordinary logic, embraces opposites without difficulty, and has no sense of time.

Although the circumstances in which the mystical state may arise are various, they all involve a retreat from reality, withdrawal from one's fellow men, and a sense of union with the ineffable Absolute. It is well known that there are many chemical substances capable of facilitating such withdrawal. Depending on the size of the dose, they partly or wholly cut consciousness off from reality and thus induce the mystical state in all or most of its typical features. And they are often employed for this purpose. Many accounts exist of religious ecstasies brought about by the use of chloroform, ether, or nitrous oxide (laughing gas). A group of Indians of Christian faith living in the West conduct their religious ceremonies under the influence of a drug (peyotl or mescal) derived from a cactus plant. In the reverie induced by the drug they devote themselves to the contemplation of God. This clouding over of the mind, which appears to be a prerequisite of the mystical experience, may also be induced by isolation from other people, by fasting or self-inflicted physical hardship. It was in the desert, fasting and praying, that the Hebrew prophets experienced their greatest mystical transports, as did many of the later Christian mystics. St. Ignatius Loyola's revelation came to him when he was suffering from physical exhaustion due to a leg wound. Isolation and meditation figure prominently in the quest for mystical experience, a quest which in its meditative aspects has more than once been carefully codified, as by St. Ignatius in his famous Manual of Spiritual Exercises. In this work the disciple is advised gradually to rid himself of all sensation and to imagine holy scenes in its stead. At its most successful this discipline results in a semi-hallucinatory state in which the figure of Christ or of the Virgin Mary occupies the mind to the exclusion of all else. Certain Jewish mystics of the Middle Ages tried to free themselves of all earthly thoughts, and to this end turned their minds to the evolution of mathematical puzzles arising out of the assignment of numerical values to the letters making up the words of a Biblical passage. The poet Tennyson would undergo a mystical experience by repeating his name to himself silently, "till," he says, "all at once, as it were out of the intensity of the consciousness of individuality, individuality itself seemed to dissolve and fade away into boundless being . . . where death was an almost laughable impossibility—the loss of personality (if it were so) seeming no extinction, but the only true life." [4]

The literature of mysticism is full of accounts emphasizing the suddenness with which the mystical experience comes about. One such account, cited by William James, concerns a free-thinking French Jew, M. Ratisbonne, who converted to Catholicism in Rome in 1842. In a letter to a clerical friend written a few months after his conversion, he gives a dithyrambic account of its circumstances. As for the predisposing conditions, they appear to have been slight. Ratisbonne had an elder brother who had been converted and was a Catholic priest. He was himself irreligious, and nourished an antipathy to the apostate brother and generally to his "cloth." Finding himself at Rome in his twenty-ninth year, Ratisbonne fell in with a French gentleman who tried to make a proselyte of him, and succeeded after two or three conversations in getting him to hang a religious medal around his neck (half jocosely), and to accept and read a copy of a short prayer to the Virgin. Ratisbonne represents his own part in the conversations as having been of a light and chaffing order, while noting the fact that for some days he was unable to banish the words of the prayer from his mind. The night before the crisis he had a sort of nightmare in which a black cross appeared to him with no Christ upon it. Until noon of the next day he was free in mind and spent the time in trivial conversations. Then, while visiting a church with his friend Monsieur B., Ratisbonne was suddenly and without warning overwhelmed by a shattering mystical experience and at that moment his decision was made to convert to Catholicism.[5]

What concerns us especially in this account is Ratisbonne's claim that his conversion happened to him unexpectedly, that he was in an "undisturbed" mental state at the time. Yet he himself provides us with evidence of emotional disturbance, even while he protests his inner tranquillity. Actually, the playful proselytizing of which he speaks was not altogether playful. So he was unable to banish from his mind the words of the prayer which his friend had prevailed upon him to read. Further, preceding the actual conversion was the nightmare in which the crucifixion figured. In the relationship between Ratisbonne and his friend there was first a struggle of wills, and only a partial surrender. The obsessional prayer and nightmare represent a continuation of the struggle, and the mystical experience its culmination. In this, as in most other cases of conversion, there is evidence of a preceding state of mental conflict, usually of exhausting intensity. And it is that which sets the stage for the mystical experience.

The Root of the Matter

WE SHOULD like now to inquire whether the insights of psychoanalysis do not provide a unifying principle under which the diverse qualities of the mystical state can be brought together. As was apparent from the discussion of the "illogical," or better, the prelogical aspect of mystical thought, what characterizes such thought is the revival of a mental state characteristic of early childhood. Mystics themselves have described their experience as a reversion to the original innocence, which is beyond good and evil, of a newborn child. And the mystic's sense of unity with God, a unity between "a smallness and a vastness," as it has been described, is comparable to the child's sense of being enveloped by God the Parent. Compare these words of a mystic, "I have the sense of a presence strong and at the same time soothing, which hovers over me. Sometimes it seems to enwrap me with sustaining arms," [6] with those of a girl on the occasion of her first communion, "There was in me such a great fullness, of blessedness and of holy, pure joy. Every fiber of my feelings belonged to my Creator. At that moment I would like to die. Die! Oh, it is no real death, it is only just the releasing of our poor body in order that the soul thus freed may hasten back to the arms of its first Parent, the Creator." [7]

Feeding is central in the development of the earliest phases of the child's relationship to its mother. If we hypothesize that the mother-child relationship reawakens in the mystical state, we should expect that the taking of food would in one form or another figure largely in the mystic's account of his experiences. And so in fact it does. Thus St. John of the Cross refers to the mystical revelation as "the mysterious and sweet-tasting wisdom," and says that "in this abyss of wisdom, the soul grows by what it drinks in from the well-springs of the comprehension of love." In the Book of Ezekiel, it will be recalled, God says, " 'Son of man, I send thee to the children of Israel, to a rebellious nation, that have rebelled against Me . . . And thou, son of man, hear what I say unto thee: be not thou rebellious like that rebellious house; open thy mouth, and eat that which I give thee.' And when I looked, behold, a hand was put forth unto me; and, lo, a roll of a book was therein: And He spread it before me, and it was written within and without; and there was written therein lamentations, and mourning, and woe. And he said unto me: 'Son of man, eat that which thou findest; eat this roll, and go, speak unto the house of Israel.' So I opened my mouth, and He caused me to eat that roll. And he said unto me: 'Son of man, cause thy belly to eat, and fill thy bowels with this roll that I give thee.' Then did I eat it; and it was in my mouth as honey for sweetness" (Ezekiel, II:3, 8–10; III: 1–3).

The child, when it has satiated its hunger at the mother's breast, goes off to sleep, so that for the infant contented sleep and the feeding process are associated. And here too, as we should expect, references to sleep are numerous in mystical literature. So Saint Teresa writes, "In the prayer of union the soul is fully awake as regards God, but fast asleep as regards the world and herself. During the short time that this union lasts, she is deprived of all feeling whatever, and even if she wishes, she could not think on any subject. Thus no effort is needed here to suspend the thoughts. They remain so inactive that she knows not how she loves, nor whom she loves, nor what she desires. In short, she is dead entirely to this world and lives solely in God." [8]

Eating, sleeping, and sinking into the very substance of the loving mother are called by the psychoanalyst the "oral triad." [9] The child at the mother's breast or in other feeding situations experiences a satisfaction amounting to ecstasy as his imperious demands for food are fulfilled. In the warmth and softness of the mother's bosom and arms the child acquires its first memory traces. And they are lasting. The experience of this infantile paradise, since it occurs before the child has learned to speak, will always seem to him inexpressible when he recalls it in later life and tries to put it into words. The "recollections" of absolute security and contentment, of inexpressible ecstasy, of union of a tiny self with a greater being which gave it life and could be depended on for protection and for the provision of its every want, are in fact "recollections" of the infant's feeding situation. And it is these "recollections" that charge the emotions of mystical experiences in later life. As for the intimations of immortality and glimpses into eternity of which the mystic speaks, they may also be a "recollection," namely, of the child's awakening from contented sleep into the world of the ever present and loving mother.

Each time the child ecstatically surrenders its consciousness in the arms of a protective loving mother, its attitude of trust is reinforced. As its various needs are repeatedly and dependably provided for, the groundwork of optimism and faith is laid down. Optimism and faith become part of the character structure of the infant, and they help to underlie the mystical experience as well as religious faith in general. For religion, mystical or not, is essentially optimistic and affirmative, even if it is a constant reminder also that man must mend his ways if he is to be saved. The point is that he can be saved.

Nothing testifies more poignantly to the place of "recollections" in the mystical experience than the feeling which commonly overcomes the mystic of having "been here before," of *déjà vu,* as the French call it. The feeling has been well expressed by Tennyson:

> —something is or seems
> That touches one with mystic gleams,
> Like glimpses of forgotten dreams—
> Of something felt, like something here;
> Of something done, I know not where;
> Such as no language may declare.

Is it far-fetched to see in this experience that "no language may declare" an unconscious recall of those ecstatic moments that precede the nursing child's sleep? Here perhaps is the root of that "ineffability" that is so typical of the mystical state. In the same way its noetic quality, the feeling of being in possession of ultimate knowledge, is reminiscent of the infant's satisfaction before it falls asleep. So all the qualities of the mystical experience, its transiency, passivity, sense of unity between the small and the great, and prelogical character—all these we may say have as their model mother and child in the feeding situation.

This is not to say that all mystics without exception express themselves in language that recalls the mother-child relationship. For there are some who express the state of mystical union in terms of the sexual union between man and woman. Indeed, it has been argued that these terms are the most appropriate of all. Thus R. C. Zaehner in a recent scholarly study of mysticism states that in the soul's highest union with God ". . . its role can only be that of the bride; it must play the woman, because, as far as its relations with God are concerned, it must be entirely passive and receptive . . . Hence it must recognize its essential femininity . . . The soul, then, at this stage is comparable to a virgin who falls violently in love and desires nothing so much as to be ravished, or annihilated, and assimilated into the beloved. There is no point at all in blinking the fact that the raptures of the theistic mystic are closely akin to the transports of sexual union, the soul playing the part of the female and God appearing as the male. There is nothing surprising in this, for if man is made in the image of God, then it would be natural that God's love would be reflected in human love, and that the love of man for woman should reflect the love of God for the soul. . . . This is absolutely appropriate, for just as the human body knows no sensation comparable in sheer joyful intensity to that which the sexual act procures for a man and a woman in love, so must the mystical experience of the soul in the embrace of God be utterly beyond all other spiritual joys. The sexual image is, moreover, particularly apt since the man both envelops and penetrates the woman, is both within and without her, just as God, Who dwells at the deepest point of the soul, also envelops it and covers it with His infinite love. It is for this reason that the Virgin Mary is as perfect an image of the soul in grace and in love as it is possible to find— Mary, enveloped and penetrated through and through by the Holy Ghost and made pregnant of the eternal Wisdom of God." [10]

Yet this employment by mystics of imagery derived from adult sexuality does not in the least undermine the hypothesis that the root of the matter lies in the mother-child situation. It is the hypothesis that accounts best for the typical features of the mystical state and of the phenomena that most frequently arise in connection with it.

Perhaps the most important precondition for the emergence of a mystical state is the desire to escape from what is thought to be an intolerable reality. To the person in the grip of such a desire there is every incentive to search back in his memory for a time in his life when he felt the security he has now lost. In other words, a form of psychological regression takes place. Regression is a phenomenon that occurs in varying forms in all people in times of emotional stress, for it is a form of psychological adaptation. Viewed psychoanalytically, the clinical cases cited throughout this book all illuminate forms of regression—and all involve a serious dilemma, a state of unresolved emotional conflict. One young man struggled with the guilty belief that his wishes had caused his father's death; a boy longed for a loving father in the place of his own rejecting alcoholic father; still another fought against an infantile attachment to his mother that had sexual overtones. A young woman, childishly attached to her parents, tried desperately to free herself from the need to masturbate. In these and in countless other instances the subsequent awakening of religious feeling represented an attempt to solve a purely personal problem. We have compared the prolonged search for a solution, with its accompanying anxiety and depression, to an underground fire that spreads and mounts in its fury, and yet remains hidden from view all the while. Commonly the dilemma involves cherished ideals on the one hand and horrifying wishes on the other. The life experiences of the individual may be such as to impart a certain momentum to the conflict so that it proceeds to a crashing climax, and the climax may be a mystical experience of the sort we have been describing.

The mystical experience represents psychological regression at its extremest. The individual travels back as far as it is possible for him to go, to the very beginnings of his conscious psychological life. The reversion is a kind of ultimate counsel of despair. As he travels backwards in memory, finding no one on earth to whom he can turn for help, the individual comes at last to a time of contentment, a time that preceded conscious awareness of other human beings as such. In such cases the mystical experience may provide a way out, one which preserves the subject's sanity and even saves his life.

There are various ways, religion among them, in which a repressed and therefore unconscious wish achieves an acceptable form of expression. That which was desired but consciously rejected may now be transmogrified into a divinely ordained command. And with this the struggle comes to an end at last. In its place there is complete and absolute surrender to a higher power that cannot be resisted, that envelops, overwhelms, and compels. Just as the insoluble dilemma led to feelings of pessimism and doom, so the solution, felt to be a gift from God, brings with it feelings of optimism and rebirth. It is no wonder that a person going through such an experience speaks of himself as having been "saved," and recalls his salvation with such intense gratitude that it effects a lasting change in his life.

The psychological reality of mystical experience is something that can scarcely be doubted, even by those who have never partaken of it. And for the mystic himself, as James points out, its authoritativeness is indubitable. He goes on to say, "If the mystical truth that comes to a man proves to be a force that he can live by, what mandate have we of the majority to order him to live in another way? We can throw him into a prison or a madhouse, but we cannot change his mind—we commonly attach it only the more stubbornly to its beliefs . . . The mystic is, in short, *invulnerable* and must be left, whether we relish it or not, in undisturbed enjoyment of his creed." [11]

No doubt James is right in saying that neither prison nor madhouse will change the mind of the mystic, but this by no means proves the mystic's invulnerability. It only proves the inadequacy of punitive measures. We have already seen that an essentially nonreligious conflict is often at the basis of the mystical experience and the religious fervor to which it gives rise. And we have seen further that psychoanalysis, in throwing light on the elements involved in the conflict, enabled the patient to view his religious experiences in a nonsupernatural way, the result being that his excessive religious fervor subsided. Not that psychoanalysis in such cases either aimed at or resulted in the destruction of the religious impulse. Rather, it was disentangled from infantile wishes and so set free to express itself in ways more in keeping with emotional maturity.

As has been widely recognized, the mystical experience has resulted in practices that are devoid of love and that have shut the mystic off from God as well as his fellow men. If religious mysticism goes back, as we have argued, to the experiences of earliest infancy, if it is indeed the case that the mystic is as a newborn child, it is clear that the ideal of service to man must sometimes fall by the wayside. Suffering and prayer, absence of mind and ecstasy—these often are the whole life of the religious mystic. The founder of the order of the Sacred Heart,

Margaret Mary Alacoque, became so absorbed in mystical reverie that she was incapable of attending to her practical duties. The authorities assigned her to work in the infirmary, but without success. In the kitchen, everything she picked up dropped out of her hands. In the school, little girls eager for religious relics cut pieces out of her clothes. Unable to take care of themselves, many mystics would have died if it were not for their admiring followers. Infantile dependency had become a way of life, which is not surprising in the light of what we have seen concerning the role of infantile "recollections" in mystical experience.

Once it becomes fixed as a way of life, regression is the hallmark of mental illness. It is not surprising, therefore, to find that the religious mystic's behavior in some ways resembles the symptoms foreshadowing an attack of schizophrenia. We may cite here the well-known case, studied by Freud,[12] of Daniel Paul Schreber, one-time president of the Senate in Dresden. In 1903, Schreber published a detailed account of two episodes of mental illness in his life, one of which has some aspects that are suggestive of the mystical experience. Just before the onset of his second illness Schreber lay in bed one morning in a state between sleeping and waking. Suddenly the idea occurred to him that after all it really must be very nice to be a woman submitting to the act of copulation. Now sleepless, he began to imagine himself persecuted by unnamed persons who were handling his body in all kinds of revolting ways. This was followed by experiences in which he saw miraculous apparitions, heard holy music, and believed that he had a mission to redeem the world. If he were to perform this mission, however, he would first have to be transformed into a woman. It appeared to him also that as a result of this sexual transformation he would acquire the capacity of being impregnated by rays from God and thus give birth by immaculate conception to a new race of men. No question but that these delusions exhibited a mystical religious character, but they were delusions nonetheless, and they were the harbingers of an illness that required hospitalization.

Resemblances between the onset of acute schizophrenia and religious experience are almost a byword. No one has brought this out more vividly than Anton T. Boisen.[13] His observations on an episode of mental illness in himself, as well as his study of the schizophrenic patients to whom he ministered in his work as a mental hospital chaplain, are of the first importance. People recoil from the real world in the face of an unendurable emotional hurt. Some destroy themselves without ever rallying from the blow; others, after a period of retreat, reestablish contact with the world, but in a tentative, fearful way. Indeed, the fear may be so great that the contact is only through the distorting veil of mental illness. These people return to the world, but a world which has been twisted out of shape by their imagination in order to fill some personal need. It may seem to them that they are reborn, but if so it is into a world which is isolated from God and their fellows.

But there are the few who, buffeted into retreat from the world, undergo, in some way that science is unable to probe, a genuine spiritual rebirth. When these people reestablish their bonds with the real world, they bring with them a great message, one which their contemporaries accept as if they had been waiting for it, and which, when it comes, stirs them to the depths. Indeed, it is just this passionate acceptance by others that brands this type of mystic vision. The Biblical prophets had it,[14] and embraced by their people it gave them unity and strength, and a new concept of right and wrong. Hence it is that the mystic vision at its best may usher in a new stage in the moral evolution of a people.

A mystical experience has religious value to the degree to which it speaks to all of mankind. When it is expressive merely of the personal needs of him who has the experience, it is more likely to be revelatory of a mental disease than of a spiritual truth. When the mystic's message appeals only to a group, it may inspire the rise of a religious sect, or of a movement that envisages special needs, such as those of the alcoholic or the mentally ill. Nothing, however, compares with the vision that is understood by all men. It is the supreme expression of religious mysticism.

Conversion and Emotional Instability

WE HAVE emphasized that the religious conversion which grows out of some form of mystical experience is often the product of mental conflicts that are nonreligious in nature and are associated with actual or impending mental illness. This possibility should always be present in the mind of the religious leader in dealing with the convert who comes to him for help. He will remember also that an important factor in the sense of personal identity derives from identification with one's own religious group; so that a proneness to religious conversion may indicate a lack of this sense of identity. Thus, in a study of the psychological factors which interfere with the social rehabilitation of physically handicapped people, it was found that religious conversion had occurred more frequently among those who were emotionally immature and whose neuroticism perpetuated their chronic invalidism.[15] On the other hand, studies of the Nazi concentration camps show that an unswerving belief, a devotion or an allegiance, whether religious, nationalist, or political, was a powerful force for survival. The camps were full of people who lapsed into a mental torpor in which nutrition and personal hygiene were neglected, and many of them died. But there were others who were fired by a belief, and they were the ones who rallied first and made up the larger part of the remnant that survived. The devoutly religious were especially prominent in this group.[16]

Religious conversion is often the expression of a disorganized personal life and the pursuit of constantly changing goals. A case in point is that of a man who was brought up in a devout Presbyterian home and married a young woman of the same faith. Although brilliant scholastically, he was unable to decide on a career. He changed from one graduate school to another, distinguishing himself for his aptitude but never for his actual accomplishments. Till middle age his interests were confined to the humanities, but he then switched over to medicine. This inability to take a stand with regard to himself professionally was paralleled by an instability with regard to his conception of himself as a religious person. For along with his decision to embark on a belated career as a doctor, he converted to Judaism. Although detailed psychological data are lacking in this case, there is evidence of emotional instability.

Another illustration worth citing is one culled from Samuel Freuder's autobiography, *My Return to Judaism,* which appeared in 1915. It is a perfect example of how a chaotic inner life may express itself in an equally chaotic variety of religious experiences. Born in Hungary into a Jewish family of more than ordinary piety, Freuder numbered several distinguished rabbis among his uncles. One of these uncles supervised his religious training. In the course of this tutelage the boy delighted in fooling his uncle by reading non-Jewish books which the latter had forbidden him to read. When he entered the Rabbinical Seminary of Berlin, he encountered a curriculum in which the study of the non-Jewish classics and of philosophy went hand in hand with the reverent study of the Talmud. Yet liberal as this curriculum was, Freuder's distaste for Jewish studies grew till he decided against a rabbinical career. Owing to the anti-Jewish agitation of the time, he left Germany for America. His fellow Jewish passengers on the ship were the objects of his contempt, and so was a German passenger who gave him a letter to Rabbi Isaac M. Wise, the founder and president of the Hebrew Union College of Cincinnati. Rabbi Wise advised him to resume his rabbinical studies at the Hebrew Union College, which he did, though he would go to church every Sunday, pretending that his object in doing so was to improve his English. He failed in his rabbinical studies.

Not long afterwards he was baptized in an institution founded "to spread the Gospel among the Jews and to bring God's ancient people to the feet of Christ." Just as he had been dissatisfied with what he felt were contradictions and intolerance in Judaism, so now he began to discover the same faults in Christianity. Although he made efforts to hide his conversion from his father in Hungary, the news got out and sent the old man sorrowing to his grave. It was the memory of his father, he states, together with the circumstances of his death, that spurred Freuder's return to Judaism. But before this happened he led the wandering life of a lecturer for years, visiting most of the large cities of America, lecturing on the way in which he "was led to see the truth as it is in Jesus." A Congregationalist for a time, he changed over to the Protestant Episcopal Church because "it shows a special reverence for Jewish customs and traditions and has always cherished a feeling of admiration and love for the Jewish people." Ordained deacon, he became a member of the clerical staff of the Grace Episcopal Church in New York City. But not for long. At a meeting of missionaries he made a theatrical renunciation of his Christianity, and subsequently occupied his time with lecturing and writing to prove that the work of proselytizing to the Jews was enveloped in deceit and falsehood. He now turned his hand to a variety of unskilled jobs in all of which he failed. Next he gave English lessons, wrote an article or two and then his autobiography. The book was an act of expiation. In it he says, "I am extremely happy in the thought that I have done my bit for Judaism, to the service of which I now earnestly dedicate the remaining years of my life."

Ironically enough, Freuder was concerned all his life with dishonesty in others. He relates one of his earliest memories as follows: "One day, looking out of the window, I saw the Rabbi, our next-door neighbor, enter our yard with a basket, into which he started to put some linen from off the clothesline. Unaware of the fact that an increase in the Rabbi's family had caused an extension of his clothesline into our yard, I began to rap on the window with all my might and to shout at the intruder. As the Rabbi, curious to learn the cause of my excitement, approached me, I shook my finger at him, exclaiming: 'You thief, don't you steal our things!' There was in this incident an almost prophetic foreshadowing of my future, when I often stood up for the right, and yet was wrong."

As we can see, Freuder's own life was filled with deceit. He began with his uncle, continued with his teachers at the Hebrew Union College, and as an ardent missionary indulged in the very "lies" which he was later to denounce in Christianity. Anti-Semitism caused him to leave Germany, yet on his own showing he was an anti-Semite himself. Presumably it was to free himself of the company of Jews that he became a Christian, yet he chose a career as a Christian which was designed to bring him into contact with Jews. It would appear that he hated Judaism, which did not prevent him from joining the Episcopal Church because of its special friendliness to Judaism. He wished to hide his conversion from his father, yet somehow let the news get out to him. The latter's death helped bring him back to Judaism, but the process stretched out over a span of five years. At every point we are confronted with two Freuders, neither one conspicuous for honesty, striving against each other. He lived out his life isolated, homeless, friendless, with no roots anywhere. Freuder's incapacity for normal love, as revealed in his autobiography, his lack of tender feelings, his intense conflict of mind, and, associated with this, his inability to enter into human relationships—all indicate to the psychiatrist the presence of a grave emotional disorder. And it is these things that are often predisposing causes of mystical experience, of apostasy and conversion, so that they concern the doctor no less than the religious leader.

We have been concerned in this chapter to emphasize the psychological aspects of religious mysticism and conversion. They are not the only aspects, but it would be a mistake to overlook them. We found that the mystical state is commonly preceded by an unbearable emotional conflict which results in a retreat from reality and in psychological regression, and that in many ways the mystical state harks back to the experiences of earliest childhood. It was in this light that we reviewed the several characteristics of the mystical experience. The experience is a resolution of the mental conflict that preceded it, but the reestablishment of contact with reality to which it leads may be of such a distorted character as to place the experience in the domain of mental illness. At the same time we have emphasized that the mystic may achieve insights which not only solve his own problems but possess validity for mankind generally. No psychological probing, of whatever sort, can undermine the mystical experience at this level. But mystical experience at this level is rare, and hardly needs the encouragement of the religious leader. At any other level it is suspect, and where it forms the basis of a religious conversion, the religious leader will look at it with a realistic eye.

RELIGION AND THE AGING

9.

SCIENCE HAS PROLONGED AND PROMISES TO PROLONG
still further the life span of man, and consequently holds
out new possibilities and inspires new hopes in millions of
hearts. At the same time the prospect of living beyond three
score and ten years, in the face of the realities of contemporary
economic and social life, has thrust upon the helping and healing
professions and aging people themselves a heavy burden of
new problems. Poetic imagery describing the latter years of
life as "the teeming, quietest, happiest days of all, the brooding
and the blissful, halcyon days" has come to sound purely
utopian. To the religious leader concerned with the purpose
and value of life in all of its phases and through all its years
and ages, certain questions are pressing. While science has
added years to life, what has religion done to add life to man's
years? How has religion helped aging men and women to
achieve inner peace and a sense of fulfillment as they approach
the end of their days? What role can religion play in the emotional and spiritual enrichment of our aging population?

The answers to these questions are of supreme significance.
Whereas in 1900 about 4 percent of our population was sixty-
five or over, it is conservatively estimated that by 1980 the
figure will have risen to about 15 percent. That religious institutions have a responsibility towards this growing body of
older people is unquestionable, yet religious leaders of all
faiths and denominations admit that their ministry to the aging
has been neglected. On the other hand, the scientific and social
contributions to the welfare of the aging by the other helping
professions, described under the broadly inclusive word geron-

tology, have been growing. It is against the background of modern gerontologic knowledge that we can most profitably explore the potential but long overdue contribution of religion in this field.

The Needs of the Aging

NO SECTION of the population has been more profoundly affected by the social changes of our time than the aging. Indeed, their situation and attitudes have been transformed, as have the attitudes towards them. Before we consider this phenomenon in relation to religion and religious institutions, let us first summarize its chief features. The first thing to be said here is that compulsory retirement from work at the age of sixty-five or earlier condemns many men and women to social and psychological oblivion. Nothing can quite replace the satisfactions associated with the accomplishment of a specific task. Pride of craft and a feeling of certainty about one's powers give direction and purpose to life. Working with a product or performing a service links a person to his fellow workers and gives him a sense of social belonging. He develops a feeling of indispensability to his organization, to his family, and at times to society at large, all of which are a source of self-esteem. Moreover, social life tends to develop around one's occupation. People who work together commonly choose to relax and play together. Wives and children are drawn into this fellowship. Labor unions embrace not only members but their families. Union headquarters is often a social center where workers congregate for leisure-time activities or during periods of unemployment. And management is beginning to recognize the importance of the social aspect of union organization.

Further, in our culture the acquisition of money is probably the major incentive to work. A man's earnings are one measure of his manliness. His tools are part of him. Work also gives him a chance to sublimate aggressive and destructive impulses; it strengthens self-esteem; it counteracts feelings of guilt and gives rise to virtuous feelings. In the words of Freud, "Laying stress upon importance of work has a greater effect than any other technique of living in the direction of binding the individual more closely to reality; in his work at least he is securely attached to a part of reality, the human community." [1]

Given the role of work in the psychological economy of man, it is not surprising that retirement, especially if it involves a total loss of occupation, creates an immense void. The psychological complications of retirement are many and serious. It is striking, for example, how often couples can accept each other so long as the man is away at work for the larger part of the day. When the man is no longer employed, the couple may have to face, late in life, serious incompatibilities in their relationship. That emotional disorganization can occur in a man following retirement is well known, but it is perhaps not so widely recognized that older women can also develop severe emotional disorders coincident with the retirement of the husband. In most cases, retirement means accepting a substantially reduced standard of living, with a consequent loss of self-esteem. Against the usual rule of retirement at a fixed age, regardless of the physical state of the worker or his desire to work, a more flexible approach is being developed, which is in closer accord with psychological reality. Thus the Consolidated Edison Company of New York saved $110,000 out of its pension funds by the simple expedient of not retiring eighty-two workers who preferred to continue working. Another useful if limited remedy for the unemployment problem of older people is the sheltered workshop [2] where people who are not able to work a full day can be gainfully employed. Medically trained supervisors regulate the production schedules so as to protect the health of the infirm worker. His working hours can be decreased at will and immediate medical attention is available to him. Such arrangements, since they increase the well-being of the aged, will of course have the support of the religious leader. He may even pioneer their initiation in his community. Above all, he will understand and convey to his parishioners that the later years open new opportunities for artistic and cultural pursuits which contribute to self-realization. Nor will he overlook the fact that money may also be an incentive to work at this time.

Much of the stress and tension which older people experience is the result of such factors in our industrial age as the increasing mobility of the general population, particularly the shift of families from farms to cities. On the farm it is possible to be productively employed well into old age; the man is more clearly head of the household and retains that status or a semblance of it for a longer period of time. Living accommodations are more available and the practice of reserving comfortable and accessible rooms for grandparents is general. In contrast, urban populations are compelled to live in small houses and smaller apartments. Older people who cannot afford their own quarters may have to live with their children in overcrowded conditions or may be compelled to move into custodial institutions.

Another factor in the position of the aged, one peculiar to this country, is the conflict between the oldest generation and their children. The young immigrants who arrived here between 1890 and 1914 constitute a large part of our old people today. The older age group among the foreign-born is often still loyal to the precepts and customs of the foreign culture, whereas their middle-aged children have drawn away from their parents. They tend to identify themselves with their own more Americanized young children. In the United States it is taken for granted that sons will enter occupations requiring more education and commanding higher salaries than the occupations of their fathers. For the son's sons still more education is planned and a still further push upward on the social and professional ladder. In the upward social climb, the climber not only affiliates himself with the class level above him and assimilates its culture, but breaks with the class level left behind, which is most often represented by his parents. Hence social-class difference is a factor which creates tension between old people and their upwardly mobile children. The trend is to keep the generations apart in separate living quarters, with institutional nursing homes supplanting the familial dwelling as the self-sufficiency of the aging parent declines. And this no doubt helps to decrease personal conflict. As a makeshift solution older people are frequently urged not to identify themselves too closely with their children and to seek friends of their own age. Each is to lead his own life. Yet such advice is at odds with the religious emphasis on family unity.

In recent decades financial needs, medical care, suitable recreation, adequate housing, and retirement planning have all been in some measure provided. But the fact is that the most fundamental need of older people is for intimate, affectionate contacts in a stable group, just as the need of the child is for a wholesome family and of the adolescent for the society of his contemporaries. The companionship and social life that go with marriage are cherished aspects of the institution. But suddenly in old age men and women long accustomed to the satisfactions of group life, especially within the framework of the family, become isolated and unneeded. The religious leader will have to address himself to this situation in order to restore and keep alive treasured family values for the aging.

With advancing age, old friends and spouses die and life becomes a series of bereavements. The social circle shrinks and the opportunities for companionship outside the home decrease. Loneliness settles like a pall over the oldest generation. The physical, psychological, and social resources for coping with bereavement become progressively impaired, and in time the older person becomes as vulnerable as a young child to the death of a loved one. At the same time he becomes less and less capable of overt expressions of grief. Bereavement may cause an apathetic state from which the older person rallies slowly, if at all, or he may protect himself against such a state by a flight into physical disease. The resulting invalidism secures for the fragile aging personality physical protection and care as well as needed human contacts of a sort. During the mourning period the religious leader, if he times his interventions properly, can mobilize human relationships in social and vocational situations, and so stem the process of regression in older people and prevent the consolidation of abnormal mourning reactions.

Women have come increasingly to constitute the majority of those in our population who are over sixty-five years of age. The life span of women has been prolonged by several years over that of men, with the result that there is a growing number of widows. Many women identify completely with their husbands and are dependent upon them. With the husband gone, the woman is bereft of a major aspect of her concept of self, and suffers a shattering blow to her self-esteem.

Approximately one-third of all men and two-thirds of all women aged sixty-five and over are widowed. By the age of eighty-five, 60 percent of the men and 85 percent of the women are widowed. These are the people, old and stranded, who speak of loneliness, of no one caring for them, of neglect by children and of the uselessness of living. Besides this group, there are the old couples. So long as all these old people remain physically self-sufficient, their need for love is not poignantly apparent. But when ill health and failing strength supervene, they feel the same need that a child feels for the sympathetic and protective care of someone who is attached to them by affection and loyalty. Until recent times the family has been the group expected to supply that love and protection. With the loosening of family bonds, the older person has become increasingly isolated and left to his own devices to find a satisfying group experience. As never before, perhaps, the need to belong is the key need of older people.

Along with the loss of one's group there goes a loss of the sense of personal identity. Men and women accustomed to a lifetime of self-sufficiency and even authority within the family and in other groups may find themselves in their old age dependent and powerless. Hence the older person's preoccupation with maintaining his sense of self. He treasures photographs of his relatives and delights in displaying evidences of his membership in a family group. Much of the "anecdotage" of the old is a compulsive turning back to a happier time when they figured significantly in the society of their fellow men. The widow who dwells in detail on the virtues of her departed husband is often struggling to win acceptance and esteem for herself in the eyes of others. In the chapter on bereavement we spoke of the process of idealization of the deceased as part of the normal work of mourning. While such idealization is in part a device to combat guilt feelings, it is also, especially in older people, an attempt to raise one's sagging prestige. One elderly woman always sported a rather conspicuous and somewhat battered red hat. The offer of a new hat was indignantly refused because the familiar one was a part of her past which she treasured. A "home of one's own" is a very substantial part of a concept of self, and an essential part of a home of one's own is the constant presence of familiar objects which are cherished more and more as the years go by. No one can regard a place as a home unless it is saturated with the familiar, and this needs to be borne in mind when new living arrangements are made for an older person. An old and battered chair may be treasured more than a modern comfortable one because the old one belonged to a husband. Insensitivity to this need may cause impatience when an older person seems to insist foolishly on overcrowding a room with knickknacks.

The task of providing equivalents for what they have lost is central to all program planning for the aging, and the religious leader is in a unique position to deal with this problem. Earlier we described the way in which the church and synagogue can function as substitute families for isolated individuals of any age. For the oldest age group this role of the church assumes special importance. Through the pastoral and priestly offices of the religious leader, the aging parishioner is provided with a replacement for long-lost parental figures. In group activities with fellow parishioners he is provided with opportunities for leadership and companionship which to a degree reproduce aspects of family life.

The Mind of the Aging

PLANNING for older people must start with a realistic appraisal of their physical capacities. Even where health remains unimpaired, advancing age brings a decline in strength, a decreased speed of reaction in emergencies, and lessened endurance. These changes restrict the environment in which the older person can live. He can no longer, or only with extreme difficulty, climb stairs to rooms on upper stories. He becomes accident-prone. Getting in and out of a bathtub becomes a special hazard. And if he injures himself, he heals more slowly.

The physical degeneration of the aged is not necessarily matched by equal mental decay. Further, many of the confused reactions of older people are the result of anxiety and tend to clear up when the source of the anxiety is removed. For example, older people admitted to a general hospital for a physical illness may become mentally confused, a condition that disappears in a day or two as they become accustomed to their new environment and less fearful of what is in store for them. It has been found possible to treat and clear up a variety of so-called senile symptoms and to restore apparently hopeless old people to the community in a much improved condition.

However, the brain of an old person does differ from that of a young one. While it functions like a youthful brain, it does so in "slow motion," so to speak. An older person can learn new material almost as well as a younger one, though it may take him longer. He may even, at times, learn it better. The minor psychological accidents of everyday life—forgetting names, mislaying objects—occur in young and old. Freud pointed out long ago that these psychological accidents are not haphazard, but occur rather in response to specific wishes or needs. In old people these accidents tend to occur more often and are less speedily corrected. The tendency to see similarities between new faces and old, between new places and old haunts, may occur in the young as well as the old. To the young man in love, many women remind him of his sweetheart when he is separated from her. To the homesick traveler, details of a landscape or a street in a strange land may evoke recollections of the longed-for homeland. Such experiences are more apt to occur under emotional duress, and usually the error is in a direction which diminishes anxiety. Whereas the younger person readily corrects this mistaken first look, older people do this more slowly. In its extreme form this results in a more or less sustained case of mistaken identity which we call a delusion. A familiar-looking orderly on the ward of a hospital may then be taken for a favorite nephew, the hospital room perhaps for a room at home or at a favorite resort.

Drastic changes of environment such as those attending hospitalization or admission to a home for the aged may release an intolerable amount of anxiety, and initiate senile changes from which the aged subject never rallies. Visits by the religious leader at such times may be of critical importance. As a familiar figure and as the carrier of specific anxiety-allaying influences in his pastoral ministrations, he may facilitate adjustment to an otherwise forbidding environment.

In addition to the needs of the aged in general, there are the special needs which arise from the particular emotional bent of the individual. For the most part, the behavior of old people is simply an exaggeration of lifelong patterns. The so-called second childhood of senility is characteristic primarily of those who never successfully resolved their first. For instance, the emotionally immature individual who was inclined all his life to act rigidly or impulsively will display these characteristics more readily with advancing age. On the other hand, for the more emotionally mature the leisure of the latter years provides opportunities for knowledge and esthetic fulfillment which were impossible during the busier years of youth. Or, as sometimes happens, there may be a welling up of previously unsuspected creative powers, as in the famous case of Grandma Moses. Such powers, of course, do not first come into being in old age: it is simply that they have been long submerged. Although the matter has not been studied with any thoroughness, there are some grounds for believing that the most striking examples of delayed creativity are more apt to occur in women than in men. The reason may be that, unable to bear children any longer, and with more leisure time, the older woman experiences a need for other forms of creativity. Aware that there are as many problems as there are older people, the religious leader will adapt his approach to the specific personality traits of each person. He will assume a supportive, parent-like role towards the immature, and in the case of the mature he will encourage continued intellectual and spiritual growth through Bible study, social action, and other forms of religious expression.

Emotional Needs of Older People

THERE are many opinions among clergymen and informed laymen about the effect of religious faith and activity on the lives of the aging. Although no scientific studies of the subject have been made, it is possible to draw some conclusions from existing data on the role of religion in the emotional crises of old age.

Given the stresses to which the elderly are subject, one would imagine that in old age there is an upsurge of religious interest. Yet it seems that people over fifty attend religious services less than they did at earlier periods. A study covering four hundred aged communicants in a parish in St. Louis, Missouri, showed that 25 percent attended mass less frequently in their latter

years, as compared to 16 percent who attended more frequently. Two-thirds of the group took no interest in the church
at all except for religious services; they had no part in clubs,
guilds, and societies.[3] Physical factors play a role here, of
course. For example, the St. Louis study showed that 25 percent had difficulty in getting to church, or were unable to climb
stairs. But physical disabilities are not the whole story. Other
factors are at work. Among these are the melancholy feelings of isolation that take the form of shame with regard to the
appearance of one's clothing; inability to afford money for the
collection; the loss of family and friends with the consequent
sense of being surrounded by strangers.

Even when we take all these factors into account, it is still
apparent that the religious leader's failure to concern himself
with the specific needs of the older group is largely to blame
for the falling off of church attendance among them. For if
church attendance among the aging drops off, they read the
Bible at home and listen to religious radio programs more than
ever. And even among those who express hostility to the church
one often finds an underlying attitude of religiousness. Further,
despite the fact that many of them stay away from church, people over sixty years of age still constitute 25 to 40 percent of all
religious congregations and parishes. In any case, there exists
a vast population of religiously inclined older people who for
various reasons have not been involved in organized religious
activities.

Clergymen of all faiths frankly admit that their emphasis on
youth and the family has resulted in a neglect of the elderly.
Religious services are available to all age groups, of course, but
the aging seem to have been left out of the churches' and
synagogues' specific plans. "The church for years has been the
place where older people came as a kind of meeting place but
practically nothing was done for them," said one religious
leader. "These people built most of the parishes. It's time something was done for them."

The Role of the Religious Leader

IN ORDER to come to grips with the growing physical,
emotional, and spiritual needs of the aging, it is essential for clergymen to consider carefully the nature and implica-

tions of their role. The religious leader is a natural rallying point for the activities of his congregation or parish. Individuals and groups look to him for guidance in carrying out their programs or solving their particular problems. He may be in a position to delegate some of his responsibilities to a social worker, an associate, or volunteers, but the chief responsibility for dealing with the emotional needs of the aging within the framework of his institution rests upon him.

A complicating factor is the age difference which ordinarily exists between the religious leader and the elderly who seek his help. In most people, their elders arouse feelings which their parents aroused in childhood. Thus a religious leader whose relationship with his mother suffered disturbance may have special difficulties in working with older women, or if his relationship with his father was similarly affected, he may have trouble working with older men. Many old people also arouse protective impulses, so that those who seek to help them are disinclined either to accept their independence or to try to stimulate it. And the belief that older people have already lived their lives or that they are rigid and unchangeable may induce an attitude of cynicism or indifference. But it is in this area that the religious leader has his most important contribution to make. In his equal treasuring of all human beings, regardless of their physical strength or material success, he provides the spiritual motives to inspire himself and others to work more effectively with the aging in order to give the life of the latter meaning and fulfillment.

The desire of the elderly for help takes devious forms. For example, the older person may react with authoritarian attitudes towards a youthful religious leader, attitudes that are entirely out of keeping with his actual powers and which make him resistant to the help which he actually desires and needs. At the opposite extreme, the older person may pretend to a helpless dependency in order to compel more attention. Such resumptions of childlike postures in the aged person may cause him either to attribute unrealistic qualities of omnipotence to the religious leader or to rebel and reject his help in a manner reminiscent of a child or adolescent in a fit of temper. We have already discussed this phenomenon under the name of transference. Expressions of hostility or indifference by an older congregant or parishioner must not be taken too literally, nor should the religious leader allow himself to be discouraged when his offers of help are refused. To establish a sound relationship requires not only patience and sensitive understanding of the needs of the aging, but the need to master one's own reactions. For example, a religious leader with a strong need to control and direct may not give elderly people the chance to fulfill their own need to exercise leadership. A rigid, authoritarian approach to the elderly has a particularly crushing effect upon them. Another danger is that in striving to meet their emotional needs the religious leader may do too much for them. The highest spiritual fulfillment in the oldest no less than in other age groups is to be found in service to one's fellow man, but various countertransference attitudes may lead the religious leader to deprive his aging followers of opportunities to use their capacities to the fullest.

Out of the complicated attitudes of the aged, the religious leader must forge a sound relationship. If he understands the older parishioner's needs and stands guard on his own transference problems, he can achieve such a relationship. On the other hand, if he adopts an authoritarian or patronizing attitude, he will intensify emotionally immature attitudes in the older person. An attitude based on genuine compassion, understanding, and respect will not require the use of false praise, euphemisms, or evasions.

Individual Religious Counseling

THE pastoral and priestly functions of the religious leader in relation to the aging emerge in both individual and group relationships. Let us consider first the problems of counseling the individual.

The most trying time for the elderly person is when he is alone. However carefully activities with social content are planned to fill the hours of his day, a time always comes when he must search within his own spiritual resources for help. What he finds there will determine whether being alone must necessarily mean being lonely.

In our earlier discussion of religious counseling we mentioned confession, in its broadest sense, and prayer as the unique and special instruments of the religious leader. Since it requires the presence of a confessor, confession is not as constantly available as prayer, yet the old, no less than the young, are in need of the outlet it provides. Older people may suffer frustrations in their family life which create bitterness and guilt-generating hostility in them. Or they may be dogged by a sense of failure or a concern about unfinished business. All of which is to say that the confessional can be of help to them, provided that the barrier of disparity in age between them and the confessor is circumvented. Some elderly parishioners refuse to confess to a young religious leader, feeling as they do that greater comfort is to be derived from the ripened wisdom of an older man. Others, on the contrary, prefer a younger confessor, depending on him to instill them with hope and to give their lives more meaning. One elderly woman complained that her priest, himself old and aware of the infirmities of old age, was too lenient with her, whereas a young priest to whom she went disregarded her age and exacted penances that accorded more with her sense of guilt. But great as the complications often are in connection with the aged, the confessional offers counseling opportunities of the first order. When older people are excessively preoccupied with themselves, as is frequently the case, the confessional can so direct their activities as to involve them in contact with their fellow men and in service to the community.

Along with needs that are primarily spiritual, the religious counselor often finds himself obliged to deal with the material problems of his elderly parishioners. For example, they may require glasses, dentures, special diet or medication, orthopedic shoes, hearing aids, etc. Or they may need home-nursing care, or a housekeeper or homemaker. Disputes with members of the family may have to be mediated. It may be necessary to arrange for different living quarters, such as a foster home, more in keeping with the physical and economic circumstances of a parishioner. There are the problems that arise when a referral to a home for the aged is indicated. Or the problem may be one of finding a home which is prepared to provide highly specialized services. In most of these cases the religious leader will invoke the help of a social agency.

The older person is not always aware of the many helping agencies there are at his disposal in the community, and the simple act of telling him that they exist does him a service. It assures him that in the event of an emergency he has somewhere to turn for financial, medical or nursing aid, or shelter, and the mere knowledge greatly allays his fears. The religious leader, acquainted with the welfare and psychiatric resources of his community, is in an unusually good position to alert others to their existence. If he finds that referral to a family agency is indicated, he will make the referral in accord with certain principles. First and foremost, his task is to evaluate the problem brought to him by the aging person and to estimate that person's needs in the context of the needs of those about him. Usually the request for help is made in his behalf by his children or friends, who are likely either to have a preconceived idea of the form this help should take, or else to be overwhelmed by the problem. The fact is that relatives, enmeshed in problems of their own, are hardly ever capable of the objectivity necessary for resolving the problems of their aging kin. But whatever the solution, it is one that must take into account the needs of all concerned, and the services of a competent caseworker are hardly to be dispensed with in arriving at such a solution.

The wisest course for the religious leader is to establish direct contact with the agency and explore with its staff the ways in which they can best serve the parishioner's needs. Once this groundwork has been laid, he can then take up the problem of getting the parishioner to accept help. Unless the latter is psychotic, the religious leader does not plan for but with him. In the case of the lonely elderly person the family agency can become for him an additional group experience, another branch, as it were, of his substitute family.

Let us consider now a few typical examples of problems which require referral to a social agency.

Among those problems none is more frequently encountered than that of living arrangements. Apart from the hardship imposed upon an older person with special emotional needs who lives in an overcrowded household, physical illness requiring nursing care may complicate the situation still further. And economic problems introduce yet another complication. How involved the problem may become is illustrated by the following case.

A sixty-four-year-old woman lived in a small apartment with her seventy-year-old husband. A heart attack obliged him to stop working. When doctors recommended hospitalization, he refused because of a fear of being separated from his wife. She did home sewing to meet their expenses, but in spite of hard work they ran into debt. The wife's health meanwhile began to fail because of overwork. Their children, two sons and a daughter, who lived in the same city, were unable to take them into their homes because of lack of space, nor could they provide financial assistance because of their own straitened circumstances. They consulted their minister, who discussed the matter with a family agency, and the children met with the caseworker. She ascertained that the father was indeed seriously ill and in urgent need of hospital care, and at her suggestion the minister worked with the husband, whom he finally induced to accept hospitalization. To the patient's great comfort the minister visited him regularly. Meanwhile the caseworker found that the couple were not receiving the old-age assistance to which they were entitled. The matter was straightened out, so that the woman, no longer overworked, soon recovered her health. When the patient returned to his home eight weeks later, he and his wife were able to live in reasonable comfort.

Another commonly encountered problem is that of finding living quarters for aged people who are widowed and homeless. Thus a seventy-eight-year-old woman, widowed for three years, was living with one of her married daughters. Because of cramped quarters she shared a room with two small grandchildren, and her constant complaints about their shouting and activity were a cause of family dissension. In addition, her presence strained the limited financial resources of the family. The woman consulted her minister about finding work as a baby sitter, feeling that all the family troubles would subside if she could only contribute towards her keep. Learning more about the family unhappiness from the daughter, the minister took up the problem with a caseworker in a family agency, who found that the old lady's other daughters were no better able to care for her and felt that placement in a home was indicated. When the minister first broached the subject to his elderly parishioner, he was met with a refusal, but as he told her more about the home, which belonged to the church, she became interested. At a day center for elderly people, also operated by the church, the minister got her into conversation with another old lady, a former member of the center who now lived in the home, and as a result of this talk she became more amenable to the idea. Finally she was persuaded to visit the home, and after some indecision she made the move. When she visited her relatives the following Christmas, the warmth and affection there made a happy contrast to the anxiety and depression that had caused her departure for the home.

It is commonly believed that the advent of a psychosis in an elderly person marks the termination of his or her life in the community. But this need not be so, for with proper supervision the older person so afflicted can continue to function in relative liberty. So we have the case of the seventy-five-year-old woman who lived in a shabby roach-infested room behind a store in a poor neighborhood of New York. She did not eat properly and had become so suspicious of people that she refused to let anyone in to visit her, even the insect exterminator. She accused the landlord of trying to poison her and sometimes even locked the door against her relatives, apparently not recognizing them. Her family had the minister call on her, and in a few visits he succeeded in establishing a trusting relationship. With the family and a social agency, he worked out an arrangement whereby a daughter-in-law would clean the room weekly and keep the shelves stocked with canned goods, and the sons agreed to visit regularly and to supplement her old-age assistance. The visiting nurse provided by the family agency brought about an improvement in the old lady's eating habits. Delicately balanced as the whole situation was, it lasted a year, and might have lasted longer if the woman had not fallen and injured her shoulder. At this point it seemed clear that she had become too frail and unsteady to live alone in safety, so the family agency placed her in a boarding house with an experienced proprietor who was particularly successful with eccentric old people. Although she may eventually have to be hospitalized for mental illness, this woman has been maintained in the community for several years.

The fact that the common pessimistic attitude towards mental illness in older people is not always justified is further exemplified by the following case. An elderly woman had been in mental hospitals, clinics, and convalescent homes intermittently for much of her adult life. At the age of sixty-eight she took a turn for the better, and no longer underwent episodes of illness requiring hospitalization. Her visits to the psychiatric clinic became less frequent and finally ceased altogether. At the same time she became more and more interested in her church, attending services regularly. With the encouragement of the minister she participated in the group activities of the church, though in times of emotional stress she would withdraw from her fellow parishioners for fear "they might make trouble for me." A family agency arranged her summer vacation for her, smoothed her relations with the public-assistance agency, and drew her into a day center program. But it was religion that appeared to be the most important factor in stabilizing this woman's life after years of emotional imbalance and mental illness.

When both physical and emotional health are impaired, the latter may have to be dealt with first, before anything can be done about the former. Thus we have the case of a seventy-five-year-old widow who lived with an unmarried daughter, her sole support. Although the woman suffered from a severe heart condition, she refused to accept a housekeeper's assistance, and several housekeepers whom the daughter hired were driven away because the mother was irritable and argumentative. As a result of frequent heart attacks, her life hung in the balance, but in spite of the seriousness of her condition the woman refused hospitalization. Her daughter in turn was overwrought emotionally, and overworked in order to pay for nursing care at home. Although mother and daughter argued constantly, they were deeply attached and clung to each other in an unwholesome excess of dependency. In the course of several pastoral visits the minister sized up the situation and referred the daughter to a family agency. With the help of the caseworker the daughter began to free herself from her ambivalent attachment to her mother, and as the daughter became more self-sufficient the mother, too, underwent a striking improvement. She readily accepted the caseworker's recommendation for placement in a nursing home, and when a suitable one was found, financial assistance was obtained to help the daughter with the expenses. In this case the psychological problem raised by the guilt-ridden, ambivalent mother-daughter relationship had to be resolved by skilled casework before proper medical care could be instituted.

Although in such cases as this the issues are personal rather than religious, they nevertheless become the concern of the religious leader since he is the one commonly consulted in such emergencies. But he must bear in mind the importance of prompt referral to a family agency, if he is not to get himself hopelessly involved. For example, a religious leader became entangled in a network of contradictory plans as a result of allowing a parishioner to draw him into taking responsibility for his problems in regard to housing, money, social activities, and family disputes. Such secular involvements interfere with the religious leader's real role. The fact is that a parishioner who is referred to a social agency will often develop a spiritually more meaningful relationship to his church, precisely because he works out his practical problems with a competent caseworker. This is especially true when the caseworker accepts and encourages the religious interests of her client and cooperates actively with the religious leader in her plan of treatment.

It might be supposed that whatever problems plague the life of older people, marital problems are not among them, that the personality differences between an aged couple must have been ironed out by now. Yet this is far from being the case. Besides the important changes that retirement causes in the psychological balance of a marital relationship, the stabilizing influence of growing children may be withdrawn as they achieve maturity and move away. Or the menopause may be responsible for unprecedented emotional stresses. And sex continues to play a significant role. Even though the actual drive to gratify sexual passion is diminished, the tender component of sex remains, and indeed may become stronger than ever. Marriages, and even elopements, occur late in life. In one day center for older people there were eleven marriages in less than a decade.

Courtship, jealousy, marital intrigue with its train of infidelity, unhappiness, and broken homes are not unheard of among the aged. One religious leader writes: "It would seem that some of the basic thinking about marriage and family life which has dominated Western culture must be redone in the light of our new situation. We would not be exaggerating much to say that, until sometime in the nineteenth century, the average parent died at about the time the youngest child left home to found a family of his own. The spiritual assumptions made in discussing marriage and family life centered naturally around parent-child relationships and responsibilities. Now, for the first time in human history, nearly half the time of the average marriage will soon be spent in a childless state, the children having grown up and moved away. Western sex ethics, also concerned primarily with parent-child relationships and the protection of children, may have to consider anew the meaning of many of its precepts, for example, the meaning of adultery to people who have already produced and reared their children. The problems of the new situation have to be seen along with the potentialities. It would be easier—and I have the disquieting feeling it is happening often—for older couples, with children grown and independent, to fall into an outwardly blissful but inwardly unproductive mutual dependency which does not fulfill them nor help to fulfill anyone else. And this is the group which, from the point of view of economic security and other external matters, is on the more fortunate side. Freedom from child-rearing, as every active parent knows, is a consummation devoutly to be wished about half the time. But unless this leads to productive use of the freedom . . . there may be only loss and no gain." [4]

The problems attending a second marriage late in life may be no less complicated than those which attend the first. Interestingly, it is not so much within the marriage itself that difficulties are apt to arise as in families of either partner or both. A devoted daughter or son, with children of his own, may resent a step-parent. Often the peculiarities of one partner, while they do not offend the other, offend the step-children. Comforts or luxuries provided for the step-parent may be compared bitterly to the more modest arrangements which the deceased parent enjoyed; indeed, such invidious comparison is so common that one can only conclude that children as a rule identify with the deceased parent. It is not unlikely that family estrangement over such matters will come at a time when the older folks crave family life and the joys of grandchildren more than ever. The religious leader of course will do what he can to achieve a rapprochement.

The "shut-in" parishioner presents the religious leader with a special group of problems. It should be said at the outset that shut-in is a relative term, and that with proper motivation many older people otherwise confined to their homes can be involved in community activities. For example, an elderly couple who had been members of a church for years lived on a farm about two miles out of town. They had no car and were unable to attend services. Then a sect group came to town and organized a new church. The elderly couple became ardent members, and walked or managed to pick up a ride into town several times a week. What attracted them to the group was the warm, friendly welcome they received from people who, like themselves, were mostly on the economic fringe of society. They now acquired a new sense of participation and responsibility which stood in the sharpest contrast to their experiences in the church to which they had originally belonged. There they would not have been considered for any office or post of responsibility, whereas in the informal atmosphere of the sect they found an emotional release from the frustrations of a rather barren life, and achieved in their own eyes a special social status. Motivated as they had not been before, these erstwhile shut-ins became quite mobile.[5]

Motivation appears to be crucial in determining whether an older person becomes a shut-in or not. For example, a study of a day center has shown that, when the people who play an active and creative role in its activity die, most of them die of sudden illness; [6] that is to say, properly motivated they carried on to the last, not incapacitated by physical or mental deterioration. It would appear that a program which gives purpose and direction to the lives of the elderly acts in some sort as a shield against the invalidism to which so many of them are prone. A case in point is that of a man who first joined a day center at the age of sixty-eight. He at once joined the poetry group, where his memory for Irish poems and his own verse-making, together with his humor and genial personality, made him very popular. The fact that he was an Irishman in a predominantly Jewish group did nothing to detract from his luster or the friendships he made. Nor did he confine himself to poetry; he painted in the art group and acted with success in the drama group. These activities also enhanced his prestige with his daughter and grandchildren, in whose house he lived. He carried on for four years, in spite of a chronic arthritic condition which would certainly have incapacitated him except for the motivation which his activities in the center provided. At the age of seventy-two he had a stroke and lay for some days in a coma. A day before he died he suddenly rallied and wrote down some verses which he asked his daughter to take to the day center where he had spent so many happy hours. The poem was a tribute to the center, to its friendly atmosphere and its activities.

Through conversations with the family doctor, the religious leader will inform himself of the physical state of a shut-in parishioner. He will inquire into the parishioner's life circumstances, too, taking note especially of such things as loss of home and loved ones, whether others members of the family exist, and if so what their role—actual and potential, constructive or negative—is in the life of the shut-in. He will inquire into the parishioner's past, whether there have been episodes of incapacitating mental illness which may account for his withdrawal or may indicate referral to a social agency for special help.

To emphasize the need for the religious leader to reconsider his approach to the aging, we cite a survey by a team made up of physicians, social workers, nurses, occupational and physical therapists, and hospital chaplains, of ninety-five unselected aged patients in New York City municipal hospital wards. It was found that only seven of the ninety-five needed continued hospitalization. Whatever medical care or rehabilitation that the remaining eighty-eight patients needed could have been provided on an outpatient basis. Yet these ninety-five people had spent a total of more than a quarter of a million days in municipal hospitals, with a cost to the city that ran into millions of dollars.[7] Not so easily calculable is the spiritual loss, moral deterioration, boredom, frustration, and general breakdown of morale.

In acquainting himself with the previous interests of the aging recluse the religious leader lays the ground for establishing contact with him. It is to be noted that the counseling situation here is of a special sort. Instead of himself being sought out, the religious leader seeks out the parishioner in his own home, which is likely to make the task of establishing a relationship with him all the more difficult. We have already indicated some of the special problems of transference and counter-transference that arise in connection with the religious counseling of the aged. Now let us consider the techniques that are available to the religious leader in meeting the emotional needs of the shut-in parishioner.

A simple and effective technique is the birthday card, which may be accompanied by a subscription to a magazine. Another is sending postcards which call attention to religious broadcasts or telecasts of unusual interest. Still another device for making the shut-in feel less isolated is that of assigning him such special tasks as telephoning, sending out cards, addressing letters, or crocheting for the annual fair or bazaar. In one city the shut-ins were made members of the regular Bible class, received the same lesson material as the others, and were visited by other members of the class who discussed the lesson with them. Some of the class socials were held in the homes of these shut-ins, with the result that they had a real feeling of being participants in the group rather than mere passive recipients of its favors. Radio and television classes are helpful, too.

People confined to their homes or beds feel the need of worship. To meet this need, one minister has inaugurated a series of informal cottage prayer meetings in the homes of his parishioners. In this way shut-ins have the opportunity not only to pray with their minister but to participate in a group activity and even to take some responsibility as a host or hostess. At these meetings informality is the keynote. For example, the minister found an older woman who could play the piano, and though she knew only the old familiar hymns, it is the kind of music that the elderly enjoy and sing best. He asks one member of the group to select and read a passage from Scripture and uses her reading as a basis for the discussion. At the close of the meeting, plans are made for the next, a place chosen, a person selected to read, and the members asked to suggest activities they would like to take part in. Some churches bring private communion to shut-ins on Sunday afternoon, following a morning communion service in the church. An experiment in which parts of a communion service were recorded and used for private communion for shut-ins, suggests immense possibilities for the future.[8] The increasing efficiency and lowered costs of recording machines may soon put them within the budgetary reach of most religious institutions.

Still, it must not be imagined that mechanical devices are a panacea for the aged. The St. Louis parish study brings out clearly that older people are lonely people and that above all else they need the companionship of fellow human beings. And so we are brought back to the vital function of the church and synagogue as a substitute family, an enlarged and indestructible family, one that is permanently and everywhere available, whatever the adversity. When the people in the St. Louis survey were asked for suggestions about the activities they would like to see their church promote for them, friendly visiting by parishioners was placed at the top of the list. Personal visiting is fundamental to the life of a religious institution. It is of course out of the question for the religious leader to conduct all such visits himself, but he can organize them on a neighborhood-block basis. Nothing that falls within the purview of religion is of more vital importance than such personal service to the aged, blind, and chronically ill.

Not infrequently a shut-in can become a functioning member of a community by a change of dwelling. Some new housing developments are including special apartments for the aged which provide them with physical conveniences and easily accessible medical care, and with a variety of opportunities for group life, such as community dining halls. Where such developments do not exist, the religious leader will do what he can to sponsor them. In any case, he will make every effort to provide facilities for worship that are physically accessible to the aged. If his parishioner is disabled and requires constant care and medical supervision, his referral to a nursing home will not be at random. For such homes have to be selected with care, and one of the criteria is the religious needs of the patient.

Some type of "sheltered care" often holds out the best prospects for the shut-in aging person. Crowded quarters, temperamental and cultural differences owing to differences in age, can create havoc in family life. But placement of an older person in a home for the aged usually involves a period of great trial for the family. It is sometimes said, with too little justification in fact, that the middle generation shirks its responsibilities, so that aging parents are relegated to a home too often and too casually. No figures exist on the subject, but surely nothing is commoner than the unwillingness of children to place their parents in a home for the aged, and this because of a sense of guilt rather than because of resistance on the part of the parents. It is part of the religious leader's role to assuage such feelings of guilt, if he thinks they are unwarranted, just as he can help the caseworker in the selection of a home that meets the special needs of the person concerned. Once the selection is made he can arrange to have residents of the home visit the new candidate in order to acquaint him with what life is like there, and he can see that the candidate in turn visits the group he is about to join. But important as it is to pave the way for the new move, the final decision to enter a home should rest with the aged person, assuming of course that he is mentally competent. In the home itself there is every likelihood of his finding new friends and new opportunities for personal fulfillment. Since a large percentage of them are church sponsored, homes for the aged lend themselves readily to a well-developed religious program. We repeat, then, that the religious leader, in providing a new home and a new family for the aging parishioner, is fulfilling one of his chief functions.

Death is virtually an everyday event in any social group of elderly people, and what strikes the observer is the matter-of-fact way in which the old react to the news. While the death of a husband or wife or anyone upon whom he is deeply dependent has a shattering effect upon the elderly person, the death of acquaintances or friends leaves him relatively calm. Death is not a morbid preoccupation with him, though he may talk about it a great deal, probably in order to minimize its importance and so lessen his fear of it. Thus an eighty-nine-year-old woman worked out in detail all the things she wanted done upon her death, such things as burial dress and all arrangements to make her "look right when the funeral director arrives."

Of great concern to older people is that the dead should be properly honored, and this means above all else that they be buried in accordance with the religious rites of their church. The day center provides ample illustration of this concern. If no members of the family are available, the staff of the center makes the funeral arrangements and gets in touch with the appropriate religious leader to conduct the services. These services are always well attended. Sometimes there is no alternative to burial in a municipal cemetery, and in such cases every assurance should be forthcoming that such public cemeteries are well cared for and that the stigma of "potter's field" no longer attaches to them. A small burial-insurance policy, commonly provided as part of the membership in a benevolent society, is a very comforting possession for an older person.

Failure of the younger counselor to bear in mind the realistic attitude to death that is characteristic of old people may prevent him from entering into an effective working relationship with them. Paradoxically, younger people tend to overreact to the presence of death, and in their discussions of the subject with the old they are likely to indulge in euphemisms and evasions, which the old are quick to detect and which may give rise to anxiety or resentment where none existed before.

Psychiatry seems constantly to be rediscovering that the deepest longing of human beings is for affection and acceptance. But this fact, while it has been immensely documented for the younger age groups, is just now coming into its own with respect to the elderly. The young, even those trained to work with the aged, are always surprised to find that the latter are like themselves, experiencing much the same temptations and frustrations, not at all devoid of ambition or pride. Some aspire to leadership, others are content to be led, and there is rivalry among them. What is perhaps most astonishing of all is the aging person's capacity for change in the direction of further maturity. In one day center there were a number of older people whose self-centeredness led to their rejection by the group, but who with the help of the staff were able to see the error of their ways and over a period of years became, not more crotchety, but more serene and lovable.

Group Programs for Older People

T H E remark by an eighty-six-year-old man that the thing he found hardest in being old was to have outlived everyone whom he loved and who loved him sums up the central dilemma of the aged. Since the major problem of the old is their loneliness, the greatest service the religious leader can render them is the exploration of group programs in their behalf. Unfortunately, the religious institutions have shown a lack of enterprise here, for the fact is that the day-center program, which has proven itself so valuable in the spiritual rehabilitation of older people, originated and developed under secular auspices. It is only lately that such centers have been set up under church sponsorship. What is probably the first of these centers was established in the Bronx section of New York City in 1943. Set up in old Borough Hall, the Hodson Center, as it was called, began as a small social club of unemployed elderly recipients of financial relief who had nowhere to go and nothing to do after the receipt of their weekly check, except to retire to a lonely room or to a park bench when weather permitted. Using both private and public funds, the club grew rapidly into a large educational, recreational, and craft center. It has become a model for similar clubs all over the country and in other parts of the world. Club activities are run largely by the members, who are democratically organized in a self-governing group, though trained social workers are employed to give help if needed. The center, although it is now quasi-public, has a relatively independent status. Different groups are responsible for such activities as catering, theatrical productions, summer-camp vacations, adult education, skilled occupations, art, painting, and recreational programs. Visiting shut-ins at home and in hospitals is arranged, and so is civil-defense work. It is a measure of the efficacy of the center's program that among its members the incidence of emotional illness requiring hospitalization is a small fraction of that in comparable age groups in the same section of New York City. Even more dramatic is the fact that within a decade the number of members haunting the medical clinics of the city with a variety of physical complaints was reduced by 40 percent.[9]

An instructive demonstration of the need for fellowship which a group of this kind satisfies is the story of a man who came day after day to a center for older people and sat by himself in a corner, refusing to join in any of the activities. Instead he devoted himself to reading. After a time, he confided to the social worker that he was having trouble with his daughter-in-law, with whom he lived. The social worker, after looking into the matter, suggested that the man move to a different part of the city, to live with another son under much better physical and emotional circumstances. His immediate reaction to the idea was, "Why, I can't do that. I wouldn't be able to come to the center." Even though he had shown no apparent interest in the group, it meant so much to him that he was willing to endure discomfort and inconvenience for its sake.

Another important program from which we can learn is the Detroit center for the aging, which was started in 1954. The city took over a big armory-like hall and converted it into a club and classrooms, a clinic, an exhibition room for arts and crafts, a gift shop, a dining room, and a stage. Community cooperation has been evident in all phases of its work. A doctor and a nurse come every week from the Detroit Board of Health. Local attorneys offer legal advice and give generously of their time. Each month one of Detroit's prominent clubs sends over a supply of bus tickets for members who live too far from the center to walk. Exhibition-sales of the old folks' handiwork draw great crowds as a result of the wide publicity given them by the city's newspapers. Many members attend daily services at a nearby church, and a clergyman conducts a day of meditation each month.[10]

In New York City the municipal day centers for the aging are nonsectarian, which does not mean, however, that religion fails to figure in their programs. In winter, Christmas and Hanukkah, and in spring, Easter and Passover, are celebrated together, and religious leaders of all faiths are invited to the center on these and other holiday occasions. Now and then a chorus or dramatic group from a center is invited to participate in the social programs of one of the churches, and such exchanges have resulted in emotional growth for all concerned. The centers conduct tours to the leading churches and synagogues, emphasis being placed on the beauty that characterizes the observances of all denominations. The religious center itself is presented as a refuge from the workaday world where people may search for solace within themselves through meditation and prayer. Many New York churches have offered their physical plants for the operation of such municipal centers. When some of these churches have initiated sectarian programs, they have attracted older people of all creeds who by their very warmth and unity give the programs a nonsectarian character, though the particular form of sectarian worship remains available to those who desire it.

In neighborhoods with several churches, day-center programs have been set up at different hours and on different days so as to obviate competition between them. What usually happens is that the same group goes from one center to another, and they are thus kept occupied with a varied and interesting series of programs. Several churches have set up summer camps open to members of the day centers, who often attend them without regard to creed. They take part in the camp's religious services and so affirm within the framework of their own religion the basic fellowship of all men in God.

Of paramount interest to the religious leader is the recrudescence of religious interest that regularly occurs in these day centers. Many older people who have not attended religious services for years resume the practice. They inform the religious leader of this change in them and credit the day-center program with bringing it about. No doubt the lapse came about in the first place owing to a loss of self-esteem on the part of the older person, a feeling of not being wanted. In restoring these things to him, the day center restores him to religion. Workers in the day center agree that the lives of the members are enriched by this renewal of religious activity. The sermon is discussed during the week, and religion generally comes to supplement the other activities of the center. It is clear that the relative nonparticipation of older people in the church is no measure of their capacity or readiness for religious experience.

Religious interests also express themselves in the center's program of arts and crafts. One man who survived a Nazi concentration camp found his self-esteem returning as he worked away at a beautiful representation of a Jewish star on a copper plaque. Another man in his late seventies, who had undergone an acute religious awakening some fifteen years before, busied himself painting Bible verses on wooden plaques in exquisite illuminated lettering. Such awakenings are probably more frequent among older people than is commonly supposed. In this instance the man was left with the impulse to spread God's word, but was unable to act on it till he joined the center, where his daily stint in the shop gave him the feeling that he was engaged in just that mission.

Day centers provide us with still other instances of religious awakening among the aged. A man who had worked all his life as a skilled cabinet worker found himself homeless, friendless, and penniless in his middle seventies. He lived in a shabby rooming house in a poor section of the city, and was dependent on old-age assistance. All around him he saw men who had wasted their lives and were sleeping off their remaining days in alcoholic stupor. He experienced a sudden desire to help these people, to save them, while there was still time, from finishing their lives in utter futility. He began attending religious services in the neighborhood mission, where he assisted in distributing food and cleaning up. In due course he was given a room in the mission and assumed responsibility for keeping the place in order. He became more than ever preoccupied with the welfare of those who came there, and he did evangelical work with them. The minister of the mission permitted him to conduct some of the prayer meetings, and to take his place on occasional evenings when he was unable to attend. Meanwhile the man attended several day centers. In one of them a volunteer worker awakened in him an interest in music, which had died out many decades before. He started composing music and set several old hymns to new melodies. He then took to illuminating his musical manuscripts with religious pictures, and wound up by becoming, in addition to all else, an active worker in religious arts and crafts.

In one church a "couples" club composed chiefly of people in their forties and fifties invited older couples to join. Several did so, to their great pleasure, and the younger members were astonished to find their seniors participating creatively in the group's activities. The benefits have been mutual. As a result of this mixing of age groups it became possible democratically and in a friendly fashion to introduce a more flexible program of church administration, for hitherto the church board had been made up mostly of older men who held office for years and kept control in their own hands. In general, older groups enjoy working with younger groups, provided the latter make allowance for stiffened joints, bad hearts, or other physical infirmities. Nor can cultural background and training be left out of account, for these in some measure determine interest and response.

There are many advantages in mixing age groups, but it would be a mistake to suppose on this account that one need have no special program for older people at all. The development of a program for older people often depends not so much on the initiation of new interests and activities as on reviving old ones that were relinquished largely because of the responsibilities that accrued with the middle years.

Group study of the Bible is a traditional religious activity which is ideally adapted to the needs and abilities of the aging. In addition to intellectual growth, there is a positive emotional exchange as the members of the study group learn from each other and inspire each other. Such group study may be properly counted as a mode of worship. Indeed, the sermon itself, which is so vital a part of the religious service, had its origin precisely in this activity. According to one religious leader, "the exalted feeling of having well done a task divinely appointed, a task, too, in which man proves himself most God-like, that comes from having mastered a particularly difficult bit of the Bible," is one of the most fulfilling forms of religious experience.[11] And he goes on to observe that William James was guilty of a serious omission in not including it among the varieties of religious experience which he describes in his classic work on the subject. The significance of religious study is illustrated in the case of an elderly Jew who supplemented his activities at the neighborhood day center with a full program at his synagogue. He would get out of bed at sunrise and hurry to attend morning services before breakfast. After attending the day center he would return to the synagogue for afternoon prayers and participation in a Bible and Talmud study circle which was the high point of his day. He would follow the texts closely and eagerly join in the discussions of their interpretation and deeper meanings. The exchange of ideas and shared insights lingered in his mind afterwards and gave meaning to everything he did. When his married daughter, with whom he lived, invited him to move with her family to her new home in the suburbs, he chose instead to rent a room and board with a family in the neighborhood of the day center and synagogue.

Just as a religious program for children or youth is designed to meet their needs, so a program designed for older people ought to meet theirs. It is along the right lines to have, as a few churches and synagogues do, a Half-Century Club composed of people who have been members for fifty years or more. Their admission into the club is signalized by a certificate of honor, presented at services. In making the presentation, honor and recognition are given for achievement, past and present, especially for decades of service to the religious institution and the community.

In some churches golden wedding anniversaries are occasions for special celebration during which the place of older people in the life of the family, the church, and the community is emphasized. Not only wedding anniversaries, but birthday remembrances—a card, or a small present, or a visit—give older people a sense of personal identity, group belongingness, and self-esteem. One minister asked some of his older people to write out statements on "What Religion Has Meant to Me." In a series of Sunday morning services he preached sermons in which these testimonies figured. The sermons made a deep impression on the congregation, and gave the older people a renewed sense of the value of their experience to others as well as themslves.

The sermon provides an important opportunity for the religious leader to address himself constructively to the needs of the aging. Since so much of Scripture is addressed to the ways in which human beings may approach losses of one kind or another, it makes sense in a sermon to consider the loss of youth and the losses associated with it. Without ignoring the physical losses of aging, which are obvious anyway, the religious leader will dwell upon the spiritual gains which are not so obvious. Again the opportunity to fulfill worthwhile aspirations that had to be abandoned owing to the responsibilities of middle life may require illumination from the religious leader to make its presence clear. A person may no longer be able to "keep up with the Joneses," but his fundamental worth as measured by religion remains unchanged.

THE CHAPLAIN IN CONTEM-
PORARY SOCIETY

10.

UNTIL THE SECOND WORLD WAR, THE SERVICE OF CLER-
gymen in medical, military, and penal institutions was
of a restricted character; in the years following the war there
has been an enlargement of their activities, with the result that
the chaplain's work has assumed greater significance than
ever before. Approximately 3 percent of the clergy function,
full- or part-time, on the staffs of hospitals, prisons, colleges and
universities, military establishments, and penal and other institutions; that is to say, about twelve thousand institutional
chaplains minister to more than five million people in the United
States. Many of these people are under stress, so that chaplains have to cope with a variety of major problems.

All religious counseling has in common the ideal of bringing
help and fostering spiritual growth. But the methods employed
to this end are divergent, and the divergence is determined most
of all by the environments in which chaplains counsel their fellow men. For one thing, the number of people the chaplain is
called upon to serve exceeds that of any congregation or parish
—for example, the armed forces generally provide one chaplain per thousand men. Besides this, the chaplain, although ap-
proved by his own church, is responsible to an institutional
authority and perforce functions as a member of an official
hierarchy. Unlike other clergymen, he is neither paid nor appointed by the people he serves, and in many instances he
ministers to more than one denomination or faith. Finally, the
chaplain ministers to special groups in special situations: to
those confined in penal or corrective institutions; to the mentally

ill in hospitals; to a particular age group, as in colleges or homes for the aged; or to an integrated, secularized group like those in military service. Each of these presents a distinctive situation and requires a different application of the basic principles of religious counseling.

The Chaplain in the Mental Hospital

THE chaplain in a mental hospital or the psychiatric ward of a general hospital finds himself confronted with a special class of problems. To encounter neurotic and psychotic patients en masse is quite different from occasionally facing an irrational congregant or parishioner. The mentally ill arouse uncanny feelings in all who are technically uninformed about psychiatry. Bizarre behavior and strange remarks are only too likely to induce a "snake-pit" reaction of anxiety in the novice who witnesses them, and the common view that all mental patients are potentially dangerous and given to sexual abnormality creates dread. Every attempt may be made to conceal the feeling, yet the underlying impulse to withdraw is there and it is quickly sensed by the highly sensitive, as the mentally ill are. Our words and actions may be unexceptionable, but our misconceptions give us away. Until deep-seated prejudices are uprooted by education and actual clinical experience—above all, until the mind is freed of anxiety, which alone makes genuine acceptance of the mentally ill possible—the chaplain will not be ready to minister to them properly. Although it is doubtful that a personal psychoanalysis should be a routine part of theological training, it is certainly true that there are mental-hospital chaplains for whom it is the only way they can achieve the degree of emotional maturity essential for effective work in this setting.[1]

The exacting demands of a mental hospital population will challenge the psychological and spiritual resources of even those who are adequately trained and have the necessary emotional maturity. Psychotic patients have an uncanny skill in detecting one's weaknesses. In a state of inner struggle and divided within themselves, they react quickly to dissensions among staff members. Their greatest need is for a conflict-free environment, yet they have an incomparable capacity for sowing seeds of discord among those whose responsibility it is to help them. The chaplain must not only stand guard lest he contribute to this discord, but in his role as a compassionate and consistently accepting figure, he will help others to create the kind of equable atmosphere the mentally ill require.

Many who work with the mentally ill, the chaplain no less than the others on the hospital team, tend to imitate the psychiatrist; personal anxiety or professional inadequacy leads them to borrow his techniques to their own disadvantage. For the religious leader, the result is not only unsatisfactory psychotherapy, but the loss of his specialized spiritual contribution, which is vital to the overall treatment program. If religion plays as important a part in the functioning of the normal mind as we have indicated in these pages, it is obviously a potentially powerful instrument for the rehabilitation of the mentally ill. To employ the chaplain in any role except that of religious leader is to provide "therapy" of questionable value and to deprive religiously inclined patients of the specific help of religion.

The chaplain will find reassurance in the thought that there are times when even the most mature and highly trained person experiences some anxiety in working with psychotic patients. As a way of achieving personal and professional competence he will participate in staff conferences, and the training program of the mental hospital should acquaint him as well as all personnel with all the phases and activities of the treatment program. For teamwork is of the first importance. A patient may communicate something to the chaplain which the social caseworker or psychiatrist should know, or he may communicate something to the recreational therapist that the chaplain should know. Hence the chaplain will inform himself of what every staff member is trying to accomplish in order to relate his service to theirs and to the operation of a therapeutic community. For example, in conjunction with the recreational-therapy department the chaplain will organize a choir and arrange for rehearsals for religious services and special holiday celebrations. With the help of the occupational therapist he may have an altar built, an ark for housing the Torah for Jewish services, chairs and other objects for use in the chapels. In problems involving family relationships the chaplain can often assist the social-service department. Or he can help carry out the psychiatric plan for a particular patient. When he thus coordinates his work with that of other departments and services, the overall effectiveness of the treatment program is enhanced.[2]

Almost every pastoral and priestly function is important for patients in mental institutions. There is the need for private and public worship; ministering to the physically ill, the aged, and the dying; providing for religious education; improving family relations; and interpreting needs and programs to the neighboring community. In addition to the counseling practices discussed in earlier chapters, which are applicable here as well, the chaplain in a mental hospital setting has the psychotherapeutic aim of helping the patient reestablish contact with reality through worship. That is why it is essential for him to understand the manifestations of psychopathology, as well as to bear in mind his specific religious task in relation to the treatment program.

Besides conducting group services, the chaplain will have numerous contacts with individual patients. The most crucial of these contacts, and perhaps the most difficult, is the first, when he takes the newly admitted patient's religious history and seeks to establish a relationship with him. Usually frightened and cowed, the patient may react to the chaplain with suspicion, hostility, or indifference. He may harbor as part of his illness bitterly antireligious feelings or he may be in the grip of grandiose religious delusions and so inclined to dismiss the chaplain with contempt. Or he may protect himself from what he regards as a dangerous world with odd behavior. But this commonly is a façade for his helplessness and yearning for protection, and if the chaplain is not put off by these initial psychotic maneuvers he can usually develop a sound human relationship with the patient.

Patients frequently complain that they have been "shanghaied," insisting that they are perfectly well and have been incarcerated by the doctor and family as part of a plot. The patient may state his case with the greatest plausibility: he does not belong here but will be imprisoned here forever. In this event the chaplain can assure him of competent professional care whose sole object is to return him to his home. To the patient who is plagued by a deep sense of shame about being in a mental hospital, the chaplain, like any other member of the staff, will point out that for all of us there is a breaking point, that we can take only so much strain. He will tell the patient that the mind no less than the body has its limits of endurance, though in the one case as in the other these limits vary from person to person. He will tell him also that it takes strength to request help from a hospital or a psychiatrist, just as he will bolster the patient's self-esteem by explaining that under certain stressful conditions mental ill health is the rule, that it is not the weakness of a particular individual. In all this the chaplain is helping the patient to overcome his sense of shame and at the same time establishing rapport with him.

With regard to the feeling of forsakenness, the mentally ill patient is especially vulnerable to it and, like a child, is in need of protective care. Here the chaplain who is from the first a good parent surrogate is of immense help to the patient. All his words and actions are directed to making the patient feel that he will be cared for, that far from being isolated and abandoned by man or God, he can depend on the chaplain's concern and assistance. Of course the psychiatrist and caseworker will have reassured the patient, but if he is of a religious turn of mind the reassurances that will count most are the chaplain's.

Besides establishing a relationship with the patient, itself a major contribution to his rehabilitation, the chaplain may receive at this interview information which the patient has failed to tell anyone else. For example, it not infrequently happens that a patient who refuses to talk to his doctor on admission will tell his story to the chaplain. Thus a chaplain in one hospital, while interviewing an army officer returned from combat in a deep depression, was the first person to learn that the patient was concerned about his critically ill wife who did not even know that he was back in the United States. Accordingly the chaplain got in touch with the family, and this was an important step in the treatment process. Another instance in which information given to the chaplain proved to be important for the overall treatment plan is that of a Catholic youngster who, on being admitted to an institution for disturbed boys, promptly told the chaplain of his determination to become a Protestant, and indulged in a bitter attack on his oppressively overprotective parents. The boy was not moved by any positive religious impulses, his determination to change being rather an expression of adolescent rebellion. The information thus acquired was passed on to the social-service department and it was vital in determining their approach to the boy's family. It will be evident from this that the chaplain functions as part of a team, and that the positive steps he takes in the patient's behalf are part of an overall plan, whose formulation is the responsibility of the physician.

Any other approach except this cooperative one is likely to have undesirable consequences. In a large metropolitan mental hospital a young chaplain was making pastoral ward rounds when he was approached by a patient in his early thirties, whom he had never seen before. The man had an engaging personality and spoke in a completely rational manner. He stated that he had become nervous because his wife was constantly threatening to leave him and take their four children with her. The threat, he said, had caused him occasionally to drink to excess, and that was why he was in the hospital. He begged the chaplain to speak to his wife and to prevail upon her to take him home. Deeply moved by the patient's story, the chaplain made no further inquiry but proceeded at once to telephone the wife. At his urging the wife came to the hospital and signed the patient out against the advice of the doctors. Three months later the patient was back in a mental hospital, guilty of killing his youngest child in a drunken fury and severely assaulting his wife. It was only then that the chaplain learned that the patient had suffered from periodic alcoholic excesses over a period of years, with progressive physical and psychological deterioration. When sober he presented a deceptive mask of sanity, and appeared humble and contrite. Under the influence of alcohol, however, and dominated by the delusion that his wife was unfaithful to him, he was subject to outbursts of rage, which were directed especially at his wife and youngest child. Although the doctors had warned about the dangers of releasing him, his condition at the time was not such that he could be compelled by legal means to remain in the hospital. If the chaplain had consulted with the caseworker and the psychiatrist he would never have been a party—an unwitting party, it is true—to this tragedy; on the contrary, under the guidance of the physician he might have used his religious authority to persuade this dangerously ill person to continue with his treatment.

In his first contacts with a patient the role of the chaplain as sympathetic listener is paramount, and this without aping the techniques of the staff psychiatrists. Since his counseling is at all times of a religious nature, the language and illustrations he employs are different from those of the psychiatrist. The Bible and prayer are his means of calming fears and inspiring hope. When he acts as a confessor to the patient, his attitude will not be one of apparently acquiescent silence, but one that helps the patient to accept forgiveness and inspires him to better living. Because of the large population he must serve and the relatively small number of staff chaplains in mental hospitals, he is obliged at times to practice nondenominational and sometimes nonsectarian counseling. Obviously, a chaplain cannot counsel patients of different denominations and faiths unless he places human needs before religious dogma, but his qualifications should include a sound knowledge of the history, doctrine, and ritual of all branches of Christianity and Judaism.

If his initial interview with the patient has resulted in a friendly, supportive relationship, the chaplain is ready to proceed to the next phase of his work with him. He will continue to see the patient, and will make brief written reports, based on information that he has gathered. He will present these reports at special staff conferences, where he himself will gain a deeper insight into their meaning. In order to minister to the patient's need for security, the chaplain will mobilize all the religious resources at his command; his use of them, however, must at all times accord with the treatment prescribed by the psychiatrist. Although the influence of the chaplain is primarily religious, it is also psychotherapeutic to the extent that it contributes to the patient's rehabilitation. But such an effect of his ministrations is always, we cannot emphasize too strongly, a by-product of his role as a religious leader.

Yet on occasion the chaplain may have an opportunity to participate directly and intimately in the psychotherapeutic process. Just how is concretely illustrated by a case at the Winters Veterans Administration Hospital in Topeka, Kansas. The patient, a man of thirty-five, had been born on an Iowa farm and reared in a strict Lutheran family. He attended church and Sunday school from childhood. He left high school after two

years, at the insistence of his father and against his own inclination, to help on the family farm. At the age of twenty-two he
joined the Navy, "to get more education." After two years of
combat service in the South Pacific, he fractured a leg and
became subject to attacks of cramping pains and severe diarrhea. During combat he had killed many Japanese soldiers
and on occasion killed them "unnecessarily out of revenge." He
was given a medical discharge in 1945 and soon thereafter
married a warm, understanding girl from his home town. He
studied agriculture at a nearby university and at the same time
acquired and ran a modest dairy farm. For the following five
years he was subject to headaches, attacks of diarrhea, ab-
dominal and leg pains, and insomnia; he "jumped in response
to sudden loud noises." Admitted to the hospital, he was
thoroughly examined and his symptoms turned out to be emotional in origin. In the course of treatment—he revealed to the
psychiatrist something he had never told anyone before—
that he had been having frequent nightmares of "blood, violence, and murder," connected, he thought, with his murder of
Japanese soldiers who managed to survive from shot-down air-
planes and with his standing by on board a boat while a buddy
kicked a Japanese prisoner of war into the sea. Besides his terrifying dream, he had the delusion that "Japs would come and
take over the farm." In order to get these killings out of his
mind and by way of amends for them, he had attended church
regularly, overpaid his farm help, acquired livestock beyond its
market value, and been generous to excess with family, friends,
and community contributions. When the therapist agreed with
him that he must reestablish control over his hostile impulses,
the patient interpreted this as a confirmation of his feeling
that he would "burn in hell."

At this point the patient broke off the interviews with his
psychiatrist and of his own accord sought out the chaplain,
whom he had refused to talk to before. Not only did he tell him
about his misdeeds as a soldier, but he also expressed hostility
against his father and against the therapist for implying that he
would burn in hell. It was agreed between the chaplain and the
therapist that the one should take as his goal the resolution of
the patient's guilt feelings within the framework of Lutheran
theology, while the other would concern himself primarily with

the repressed hostility against the father. Thus the chaplain was able to reassure the patient by reminding him of the Pauline injunction about obedience to the ruling government and the obligation to bear arms at its order. War, he said, often releases instincts that result in wanton killing which cannot help arousing feelings of guilt, but such acts, although not condoned, are forgiven by God—a concept that was part of the patient's belief in atonement and forgiveness. All this brought the patient emotional relief and reduced his pain, but he still felt that he wanted "something to do." Accordingly the chaplain suggested that instead of overpaying for his livestock, he might increase his contributions to the church and earmark them for Japanese missions. In this way he would make his atonement within the church. The patient was now glad to resume relations with the therapist, who was able after a time to resolve the patient's hostilities. Visiting him on his farm five months after he had left the hospital, the chaplain found that his physical ailments had disappeared. He was less nervous, slept well, and was happy in his work and family.[3]

Here, then, we have a case in which the chaplain took a hand directly in expediting the treatment program. Through his efforts the patient's guilt and anxiety were lessened, and the road paved for his return to the psychiatrist. And all along the chaplain maintained his role as a religious leader, even to the point of carrying on his counseling in a denominational context different from his own.

Psychiatrists are coming to be more and more impressed by the emotionally beneficial effects of certain group experiences. Here, too, the religious leader is able to make an important contribution, not directly as a group therapist, as some religious leaders have proposed, but indirectly through the healing influence of group religious experiences. If isolation and estrangement from their fellows is the common lot of psychotic patients, nothing could be more beneficial than to bring them together in an emotionally meaningful situation. And few things, it seems, can effect this better than a religious congregation. The repetition of carefully selected prayers in unison, responsive readings, and the singing of hymns, instrumentally accompanied, are all calculated to draw lonely people together. The doctors, nurses, and attendants also have a contribution to make here, for their presence at the religious service can only heighten its effectiveness. Since the religious services have this therapeutic effect, it follows that no effort should be spared to foster and intensify the religious feelings of the lonely patient.

Regular worship services are the mainstay of the chaplain's contribution to the mental hospital. All holidays ought to be celebrated, with maximal regard for color and beauty of observance, and they should be led up to by weeks of anticipatory activity. There will be sermons on the subject and suggestions to patients that they take part in such preparations as choir rehearsals and work on decorations. Every encouragement will be given them to join in the services to the fullest extent, in responsive readings, group singing—especially of old familiar hymns—in distributing and collecting prayer books, posting announcements of services, and so on. In planning the religious program, it should be borne in mind as a guiding principle that the psychotic patient can be more effectively reached through symbols and concrete acts than through the spoken word alone. Services should not last more than forty minutes, and if possible arrangements should be made for services in the mother tongue of foreign-born patients. Sermons should be brief, not over fifteen minutes, and devoted to topics readily understandable to the patient, and close to his current needs—love, friendship, health, loyalty, work, ambition, home, family. It is to the feelings of the patient that the chaplain will address himself, using simple parables and concrete illustrations. For many mental disorders are characterized by an impairment of the capacity to think in terms of abstractions. In order to mark the unity of purpose among all those who have to do with the patients, prayers will be offered up for the doctors, nurses, and attendants; in a word, for the entire staff of the hospital. For patients too ill to go to chapel, the services might be broadcast over the public-address system. When television is available, it should also be used to bring religious comfort to patients who are confined to their beds or wards. How important group worship may be as a source of emotional security is evident from the fact that patients often return for Sunday services even after they have been discharged to their homes.

Finally, among the special functions of the chaplain in a mental hospital is that of teaching. As a specialist in religion his work in an institutional setting offers him many opportunities to impart his specialized knowledge and experience. By means of the background material he assembles and the religious significance he extracts from it, the chaplain is in a position to contribute to the formulation of treatment plans at staff conferences. He is the authority on religious behavior, and it is as such that he collaborates with doctors, caseworkers, attendants, occupational and vocational therapists, nurses, and volunteer aides. For example, in one hospital the chief nurse was in the habit of informing the chaplain of the arrival of a deceased patient's family; she did this because the chaplain had reminded her of the guilt which assails relatives at such times and of the specific comfort which he could give them. Theological students receive some clinical training as part of their field work in pastoral counseling, and the chaplain can add to this training by conducting a teaching program for clergymen in neighboring communities, so that they may better understand the special spiritual needs of the mentally ill and the released patient.

The Military Chaplain

IN CONSIDERING the work of the military chaplain, whose history dates from ancient times, we move into an environment very different from that of the mental hospital. For one thing, the military is an arm of the state and its chaplaincy is a state-supported institution. Part of an institution that is eminently hierarchical in character, the chaplain corps is identified with its military aims and subject to its regulations. At the same time, from the viewpoint of the commanding officer the chaplain is an appendage to the fighting machine rather than a functional part of it. It was a long time before chaplains were granted equal rank, and even longer before they were given equal pay with other officers. All in all, the military chaplain is obliged to live in a highly secularized environment and his life is regulated at every step.[4]

In a milieu where everything exists for the sake of war, the role of the religious leader necessarily undergoes modification.

Although religion, along with all other resources of the community, is mobilized by the state in time of war, it is nevertheless true that the killing of human beings is contrary to the moral teachings of Christianity and Judaism. It is impossible to reconcile commandments like "Thou shalt not kill" and "Love thy neighbor as thyself" with the command to "kill or be killed." The result is a moral conflict for the chaplain. He must relinquish for the time being notions of universal brotherhood, love, and peace and identify himself with military ideals of duty, honor, and country. He must choose between the claims of his religious fellowship and submission to military authority. It is a dilemma [5] which in a small way is illustrated by a unit chaplain who reprimanded a soldier in the presence of the commanding officer for failing to salute, and afterwards privately apologized to the soldier. Overall, the chaplain is in the position of having to subordinate his conception of divine justice to the ends of military justice. Although his military status does not destroy his symbolic role as a religious leader, it limits it severely.

Most chaplains succeed somehow in resolving this conflict, many of them even choosing the military as a permanent career. On the other hand, as in the last war, there were ordained ministers who refused commissions and entered the ranks and preferred combat duty. The Protestant minister Dean E. Hess, author of the popular autobiography *Battle Hymn*, became one of the deadliest fighter pilots in the Korean war. Those who have seen the film *Gung Ho* will recall the young minister-infantryman in Colonel Carlson's Raiders, a group of marines especially trained as jungle killers in the Pacific area. It may be surmised that the very dilemma of the military chaplain is a contributing factor in these feats of extraordinary heroism. In the main, chaplains identify themselves with the military hierarchy and feel little conscious conflict between military duty and religious conviction. Yet in a study made of a group of seventy-one chaplains and ex-chaplains in 1952, it was found that their reasons for entering military service included "the opportunity to render a service, the moral and spiritual challenge offered by the military situation, personal satisfaction, the existence of a need, and a missionary call." And the truth of this is borne out by the experience of millions of soldiers and sailors as recorded in the documents and literature of the great wars of the twentieth century. Here is one instance. On June 15, 1943, the U. S. Army transport *Dorchester* was torpedoed in the North Atlantic, and sank so rapidly that there was little chance to don life belts or launch lifeboats. Four chaplains assigned to the ship, Father John P. Washington, Rabbi Alexander Goode, and Reverends George L. Fox and Clark V. Poling, gave their life belts and gloves to four trapped soldiers, who then jumped into the cold sea. As the ship sank, the survivors saw the four chaplains go down arm in arm, reciting prayers.[6] The very intensity of faith here displayed may be, as Karl Menninger suggests, the outcome of the moral dilemma and of an unconscious struggle against disbelief in military ideals. There is the touching story of a chaplain who served in a front-line infantry battalion in the Second World War. On the eve of an attack, a soldier detailed to a reconnaissance patrol approached him and said he would not return alive. When he requested the chaplain to pray with him, the chaplain replied, "I will not only pray with you. I will go with you."

Whatever the military chaplain's state of mind, and however indecisive he feels, it is above all in his symbolic role that he appears to the enlisted man. Whether it is the cross worn by the Christian chaplain or the tablets of the Decalogue of the Jewish chaplain, it is the power of these emblems, rather than the officer's uniform, that communicates itself to the soldier, especially in situations of stress and tragedy. And it is conduct in keeping with these emblems that intensifies and concretely expresses the symbolic role of the chaplain. Evidence of this is plentiful, but a single illustration must suffice here. This story is told in detail in Father Joseph T. O'Callahan's *I Was a Chaplain on the Franklin.* Apart from the engrossing character of the account, the book is a matchless document for the study of the role and conduct of military chaplains.

On the afternoon of March 19, 1945, the carrier U.S.S. *Franklin,* part of Task Force 58, which had engaged in an offensive action against the Japanese Home Islands near Kobe, Japan, was hit and severely damaged by enemy air attacks. The ship was rocked by violent explosions, the magazines flooded, and decks and below-decks raged with fires. Many men were maimed, trapped, and killed. Religious belief was widely prevalent among the personnel, not only during the actual calamity but in the days preceding the battle. The numbers of men who sought consolation in prayer seemed to bear out the saying that "there are no atheists in foxholes." Nor was it only Catholics who applied to Father O'Callahan, though his accounts deal largely with their reactions, but numerous non-Catholics accepted his aid with evident gratitude. As the situation came to look hopeless, Father O'Callahan showed no qualms about resorting to prayer at the same time that he set an example of courage and selflessness. No one could have found evidence of indecision in the way he offered the consolation of prayer to all whom he encountered in that veritable inferno, Catholics, Protestants and Jewish alike. Throughout, filled with a sense of mission, he sought to mobilize all that was most noble in the men about him. "I realized distinctly," he writes, "that my actions in the present emergency would greatly influence the boys for good or ill."

We had occasion earlier to note the power of religious observances and prayer in promoting group feeling. Father O'Callahan describes an incident which may be taken as a dramatic illustration of this. In the midst of the smoke, fire and explosions on board the *Franklin*, Negro crewmen tried to drag a tow cable. Their extremest exertions failed till they broke out into a work chant. Whereupon a new kind of power appeared to emerge among them, and the tow cable gave way to efforts that seemed to be more than human. We may say that these men were fused into a group by an activity akin to prayer. In Father O'Callahan's mind there was no doubt that their chant was inspired by religious feelings. And he testifies as well to the efficacy of direct group prayer in recounting how by its means the crew's panic was stilled.

There emerges from Father O'Callahan's narrative a clear picture of the military chaplain's functions. These functions encompass all the pastoral and priestly duties that have been discussed in earlier chapters. The chaplain conducts individual and group prayer, helps the sick and wounded, builds up morale, encourages communication between the men and their families, endorses compassionate leave, imparts instruction, administers last rites to the dying and services for the dead, and in times of crisis and catastrophe takes the part of a leader. In addition to all this there are counseling problems peculiar to the military chaplaincy, which demand consideration.

Whether a chaplain is assigned to a training camp, permanent post or ship, military hospital or prison, or a combat unit, he finds that the task of counseling in connection with personal and welfare problems is of supreme importance and is very different from counseling in civilian life. He is a unit in a carefully regulated chain of command, and is under the authority of a single individual, the commanding officer, who may or may not be cooperative. The majority of those who seek the chaplain's guidance are enlisted men, and since they are frequently in conflict with authority, his problems are more complex and his solutions more restricted than in civilian life, where the pressures of boards, vestrymen, sisterhoods, sodalities, and the like, great as they may be, are not as authoritarian. Even his priestly functions are in some measure controlled, as we shall have occasion to see in discussing conversion and evangelism. Yet the opportunities for counseling are immense. Chaplains have said that they learned more about human life and its problems in a few years in the armed services than they could have learned in a parish in fifty years.

Apart from the difficulty of adjusting to a new environment, it is the serviceman's separation from family, home, and community that is his greatest difficulty. In their more benign forms homesickness and marital troubles cause only temporary hardship. They disappear soon after the basic training period and become a subject for the kind of humor that has helped books like Jareslav Hasek's *The Good Soldier Schweik* and Marion Hargrove's *See Here, Private Hargrove* to become popular classics. But chaplains, no less than medical and line officers, are aware of how harassing and disabling family hardships may become and of how seriously they affect the morale of the serviceman and his unit. The plight of A.W.O.L. soldiers is often caused by long absence from home and concern for their families.[7] Sexual infidelities that are often destructive of a previously stable marriage are a common problem when servicemen have been stationed overseas for long periods of time. Then there are the vicissitudes of the family at home, such as illness, death, unemployment, or legal involvements. In these crises the serviceman, especially if he feels that it is futile to apply to other officers, will often appeal for help to the chaplain.

In this situation the chaplain, anxious to do something at once, has to contend with his dual role as pastor and officer. In the former capacity his prime desire is to resolve the problem; in the latter, he is under the necessity of conforming to military regulations. To him as to the troubled serviceman, "red tape" is a stumbling-block. If he merely makes a referral to the Red Cross worker or a military social worker, the serviceman is likely to accuse him of "passing the buck" and in his disappointment take things into his own hands, even at the risk of a serious breach of regulations. The chaplain not only has to establish a trusting relationship with the petitioner, but must understand and then formulate his problem. Failure in the latter respect is common, and it leads to complications all round. The chaplain must get the facts, which it is not easy to do, especially in the circumstances of overseas duty, or in the midst of war or the threat of war. Any action of his based on incomplete knowledge or downright misinformation may have serious consequences, as the following case brings out. A chaplain was consulted overseas by a sailor who said that his wife, from whom he had been separated for several years, had written to his commanding officer, complaining that she was ill and needed him at home. Claiming that he had supported his wife by an allotment of his salary throughout their period of separation and that she was a hypochondriac, he convinced the chaplain that he ought to remain at his post. At the chaplain's personal request the seaman was permitted to remain on duty. Soon afterwards a communication from the Navy Department, together with a statement from a local family agency and a medical diagnosis, asked why the commanding officer had taken no action. The fact was that the wife had become acutely psychotic, so that her husband's return was imperative if arrangements were to be made for her commitment and the care of the child. Accordingly compassionate leave [8] was immediately granted and the seaman ordered to go home. Plainly this chaplain had failed to make sure of the facts, and his ill-advised counsel embarrassed his superior officer and caused a delay in dealing with an acute family problem. If the chaplain had proceeded more circumspectly, he would have checked the seaman's story with the Red Cross or the military social worker, and finally with the medical officer, whose word in such matters is, according to regulations, practically final.

It is not only the difficulties arising from causes outside himself that are liable to bedevil the life of the serviceman, but his own psychological problems as well. The same abnormal behavior patterns that appear in civilian life appear also in military life. Psychoses, neuroses, sexual perversions, addictions, mental deficiency, antisocial behavior, all are to be encountered. The abnormality may be nothing more than inability to take orders, or to adjust to the monotony and loss of freedom which is the lot of every serviceman. Or it may take the form of expressing dissatisfaction with one's unit or a specific assignment. A man may be able to adapt to military service under one officer and fail completely under another, or he may belong to a unit which is overwhelmed with problems; that is to say, a unit suffering from poor leadership. Cases of psychological inadequacy make their appearance for the most part during basic training, although men with longer experience are not immune to breakdown. They may go into a panic on receiving overseas orders, either because of fear of combat or because they cannot tolerate separation from home.

Unfortunately, the chaplain is usually able to interview only after a man has already been hospitalized for abnormal behavior or has been subject to disciplinary action. It would be better practice if the referral were made to him earlier, so as to give him the opportunity to forestall the crisis through religious counseling, if possible.

In military as in civilian life, one of the dangers that the religious counselor needs to be wary of is getting himself emotionally involved. The chaplain may become an uncritical partisan of the enlisted man in trouble, or he may identify with the officer who is pressing the charges. Above all, the need here is objectivity and action based on all the available facts. Not all chaplains are as gullible as the one who, in the course of a visit to a station hospital, talked to a patient who said that he had been granted a weekend pass to visit his family, but that he did not have the thirty dollars for expenses, and immediately lent him the money. Actually, the soldier had not been given leave at all. Managing to get out of the hospital, he visited a bar in a nearby city and then in a drunken stupor exposed himself to rain and cold. He was brought back by the military police, stricken with pneumonia, and almost died. When he recovered, he was court-martialed. If the chaplain had not given way to an impulse, he might have consulted the medical officer, from whom he would have learned that the soldier was a chronic A.W.O.L., and a gambler and drunkard. No one benefited by the act of generosity, least of all the chaplain himself, for it vitiated the good relations he had established with staff and enlisted men through months of hard work.

How complex the issues in a military disciplinary action may be is well exemplified by Herman Wouk's account in *The Caine Mutiny* of a court-martial and of the events leading up to it. Our own examination of almost two hundred records of chaplains who counseled servicemen in an overseas disciplinary barracks between 1951 and 1956 shows that 70 percent of these men were sentenced by courts-martial for forgery, larceny, manslaughter, and other offenses committed against civilians during absence without leave. To illustrate the highly constructive role of the military chaplain in these circumstances, we cite the following case history. The commanding officer of a disciplinary barracks, who was known among the prisoners as strict but fair, summoned the post chaplain, a Methodist, to discuss two new admissions. He showed him two letters from parents, begging help for their sons. He gave the chaplain the record files, and asked him to speak with the two young men and report on his findings. One of the soldiers belonged to an Anabaptist sect [9] and the other was Jewish. They had been tried together in a general court-martial for several crimes and given long sentences that good behavior on their part would shorten. After several lengthy visits with them over a period of weeks, the chaplain put together a revealing history of the two men. The boys had met in a paratroop unit for which they had volunteered soon after basic training. They had gone "over the hill" numerous times and committed theft, arson, and finally manslaughter in an auto accident. Both were physically robust and had scored over 125 on their army aptitude tests. Their backgrounds and characters were dissimilar. The Anabaptist, now nineteen, had been drafted a year before, after graduation from high school. He had been brought up, he said, by "fanati-

cal" parents to conform with the beliefs and rituals of the Anabaptist sect, which forbade movies, smoking, drinking, dancing,
popular music, and stressed hard work. A few months before
his induction, he had indulged in some of these pleasures and
been stricken from the rolls of the church. He felt "different"
from the other men during basic training and made no friends
until he met his partner in crime, whom he found to be as
friendless as himself. During one of their sprees he had secretly
married a Catholic girl, sixteen years of age and pregnant.
Although he now "felt badly about his wrongdoing," he expressed to the chaplain a marked hostility towards his parents
and their "moralistic ways."

The other soldier had been brought up in an orthodox Jewish
home and graduated from a metropolitan high school, where he
had achieved a superior scholastic record and become an outstanding basketball player. He entered college on an athletic
scholarship but withdrew against his parents' advice after four
months, and at the age of eighteen enlisted in the army for
three years. He showed no interest when the chaplain told him
of his parents' letter. In the disciplinary barracks he associated
with no one and seemed to prefer tasks that were solitary and
menial.

The chaplain recognized that both cases involved psychological problems that were beyond his depth, and he accordingly
recommended to the commanding officer that the two men be
remanded to a nearby army hospital for psychiatric examination. Treatment of the Anabaptist youth over a period of six
months centered primarily upon his rebellious attitude towards
authority, and began with his hostility against his fanatically
religious father. Returned to the disciplinary barracks in a
considerably improved condition, he pursued the rehabilitation
program zealously. On the recommendation of the psychiatrist,
the chaplain arranged military approval of his marriage, officiated at a second, formal wedding, and helped his wife find
lodgings and work in a neighboring town. It was found that he
had great aptitude for figures and bookkeeping, and, assigned
to headquarters, he developed an original technical device
that was adopted by the army. His sentence was considerably
reduced and he finally procured an honorable discharge from
the service.

The Jewish youth was diagnosed as a schizophrenic. Symptoms that had begun to appear in early adolescence had gone unnoticed by his family and teachers largely because of his scholastic and athletic achievements. He was frightened by homosexual impulses in himself, and his flight into the service, especially his choice of paratroops, was an attempt to prove his manhood. In the paratroop training unit his failure to make friends was noticed, and he was regarded as a "queer duck." Eccentric as he was, he might have completed the training successfully, had he not come under the influence of his accomplice, who was in rebellion against officers and the rigorous training schedule. Under his leadership they launched out on the series of escapades which culminated in their arrest and sentencing. In the military hospital to which the Jewish soldier was transferred from the disciplinary barracks, it was found that he suffered from depression and delusions of persecution. Transferred to a hospital nearer home, where he remained under treatment for two years, he improved somewhat, and was finally given a medical discharge. At the hospital a Jewish chaplain referred him to a veterans' counselor of the Jewish Welfare Board, who helped him with his family problems and to find a job. The chaplain induced him to attend religious services and participate in an adult study group, and both of these activities continue to engage his interest as a civilian. With the help of the counselor and of a psychiatrist whom he visits now and then, he manages to maintain a precarious adjustment in the community.

As these cases show, the military chaplain performs a multiplicity of functions and performs them within a religious framework, or if he steps outside, it is only in order to enhance the value of his religious counseling. He is thus in touch with command and medical officers, and on good terms with them. While he keeps to his role as a religious leader, he seeks to gain insight into functions other than his own. Through his pastoral activities he enlarges the interests of his men and strengthens their self-identity. Whatever the denomination, sect, or faith to which a man belongs, the chaplain's counsel is knowledgeable and sympathetic. He writes to anxious parents about their sons' welfare. Able to avail himself of information from a variety of sources—medical, social, and military—he can do much to ameliorate the serviceman's hardships. And he continues to help even after discharge, by referring the ex-serviceman to the proper civilian agencies when necessary. We may add here that the notion now prevailing of the military prison as a place for rehabilitation is in keeping with psychiatric thought and religious morality.

Once the chaplain has resolved the conflict in his mind between the ideals of religion and the demands of war, he can minister to the well-being and mental health of servicemen, irrespective of their faiths and denominations. Yet not all military chaplains, whether because of misunderstanding or excessive zeal, observe this catholicity. They see themselves as evangelists. While there is nothing either in military regulations or in chaplains' manuals which forbids such activity, there exists an unwritten law, a kind of gentlemen's agreement, that chaplains are not to proselytize. Missionary activity, whatever its form, is not among the duties of the chaplain. The chaplain who has been trained for just such activity, however, finds it hard to resist the opportunities that present themselves in the course of military life. When missionary activities are carried on among native populations overseas, the commanding officer is inclined to close his eyes to it, unless there are complaints from the natives themselves. Colonel Hess, in his heroic efforts in behalf of Korean children, did not look into their religious affiliations. And it is probably the case that missionary activity among native populations has not been a major problem for the overseas commands.

In connection with the proselytizing chaplain, it may be pertinent to reaffirm our thesis about conversion—namely, that it points to emotional conflict. Accordingly, the serviceman ready to be converted should be scrutinized from the point of view of possible psychopathology before the chaplain sanctions the step. We have seen that a change from one religion to another may be motivated by reasons that are essentially nonreligious. This case history presents a familiar story to the reader, but in a military setting. A young woman of twenty-three who was brought up an Episcopalian in a small Midwestern town left her home after completing college to live with young friends in Chicago, and then joined the Marines. At her station there was no Episcopal chaplain so she attended Catholic mass, and after several months was converted by the chaplain to Catholicism. Within a year she was discharged on psychiatric grounds as unfit for military life. She resumed her former civilian life, and was soon faced with an out-of-wedlock pregnancy. Applying for help to a family agency, she was urged to undergo psychiatric treatment, which she refused to do. Her history included several attempts at suicide in her teens, but she had not informed the Marines of her neurotic background. On becoming pregnant, she left the Roman Catholic Church because, in her own words, it was "too restrictive," and returned to the Episcopal Church. During the next six months she alternated at least three times between Catholicism and Protestantism. A chaotic mental state was reflected in a chaotic religious history. If the chaplain had understood this woman's problem, he would have urged her to defer her conversion until she had received psychiatric treatment.

The military chaplain sometimes finds himself in a situation that requires resort to canon or rabbinical law. Such situations, while they are not common, raise problems that are of a delicate and often tragic character, and so are especially important. Great understanding and skill is required of chaplains who minister to servicemen who as a result of war wounds become sexually incapacitated. Should a man who is sexually incapacitated be permitted to marry? And if he is already married and incapable of sexual and social life, should divorce be permitted? Moral issues of the most difficult sort are involved here. To take an example: A chaplain visiting a veterans' hospital was consulted by a devoutly religious soldier whose lower body was paralyzed and his genitals partly mutilated. He had been married a few months before entering the service, and he and his wife loved each other; both were extremely anxious to preserve the marriage. However, the wife complained that the enforced sexual abstinence was upsetting her and injuring her health. The chaplain learned from the medical officer that the soldier could avail himself of an artificial device or prosthesis that would make it possible for him to have sexual intercourse. Informed of this, the man asked the chaplain to ascertain if such practice was in accord with religious law. The chaplain sought the opinion of an authorized chaplaincy commission and was informed that on the basis of the principle that any type of sexual relationship between man and wife is permitted, "the methods created by modern science to enable these paraplegic and mutilated men to maintain family life are not objectionable." [10]

We think we have said enough to show that despite the restrictive, authoritarian, and aggressive character of the military environment, the military chaplain can exert a positive religious influence. If he is responsive to the needs of servicemen; if he consults appropriately with command and medical officers and welfare personnel; if he can understand and accept transference manifestations in a predominantly male society without resorting to authoritative countertransference—he should be able to redirect the rebellious responses of servicemen into constructive religious channels. Perhaps his chief ally throughout is the medical officer, who will supply him with data which, together with his own resources, prepare him to deal not only with the problems of the servicemen, but with these problems as they affect his family.

The Prison Chaplain

I F T H E military chaplain is on the horns of a dilemma as between his religious ideals and the demand of the military, the dilemma of the prison chaplain is even greater. Modern students are in agreement that criminal law as it now exists is more punitive than rational and just, expressive of hostility against the criminal rather than of concern for the safety of society.

Prison is a continuation of this bad state of affairs. Punishment is rationalized as being a deterrent, yet it is highly doubtful that punishment, especially by itself, can eliminate crime. Those who have studied the matter are inclined to think that punishment as a device to control criminal behavior is futile, that if it accomplishes anything it works to intensify the criminal pattern. Thus Gregory Zilboorg contends that the psychological make-up of the criminal is such that punishment, itself an aggressive act of society, has the effect of aggravating the criminal's own aggressive impulses. In prison he becomes more antisocial than ever.[11] Our penal system is in need of further reform, and of the kind that will allow the religious leader to play a more constructive role within it. And it is a reform which he himself must help to bring about.

Changes are already in progress, changes that have been prepared for by the discoveries of modern psychiatry. What these discoveries have brought out and emphasized is that every criminal, even the most brutal, has a conscience: a sense of guilt, carefree and callous as he may appear to be; a sense of community, no matter how antisocial his behavior. The typical criminal is not so much antisocial as he is "pseudo-social" —unable to achieve normal contact with society.

The prison chaplain has been hampered by the existing penal system, although as enlightened legislation makes headway it may be hoped that his role will become increasingly like that of the chaplain in the mental hospital. To the chaplain the revolution in penological thought and, in some measure, practice represents a fundamentally religious point of view. Indeed, some of this point of view prevailed in the first state prison in New York, founded in 1797. In those days the idea of "reforming" a prisoner was understood entirely in religious terms. The prison chaplain placed a Bible in every cell and ministered to prisoners in the hope that under religious influence they would undergo a spiritual conversion. There is psychiatric evidence that this kind of approach, appealing as it does to the prisoner's sense of guilt, is superior to one which is primarily punitive.

What has been accomplished so far by way of reform affects such a small portion of the total prison population that the chaplain must carry on in a situation that is inimical to his pastoral and priestly role. In keeping with the philosophy of socialized treatment, the modern probation system places some offenders under supervision in the community, but concomitantly with this the correctional institutions unfortunately receive the offenders who offer the least promise of successful treatment by our present methods. Herein lies the challenge to the modern prison chaplain, as well as the source of his frustration. But his religious role is clear-cut: he is the representative of a forgiving society and the symbol of divine compassion.

It is a role that he must never forget, even when bombarded by thoughtless statements that every prisoner who insists upon his innocence is guilty, that the decisions of judge and jury are always fair, and such commonplaces. To succumb to these is to do the prisoner an injustice. Men have served long prison sentences because nobody, including the chaplain, would believe that they were the victims, for example, of a false identification. It was only when a public-spirited lawyer or newspaper took up their cause that they were ultimately vindicated and released. On the other hand, it frequently happens that chaplains, allowing sentiment to prevail over judgment, overidentify themselves with clever convicts, and so fall into the trap of countertransference. The literature of penology is full of examples of prison chaplains who invested great but misguided effort in persuading judges, governors, and other officials to reduce sentences and release "model convicts." If he is not to go astray on this, the chaplain must possess an acquaintance with criminal psychology, and above all he must learn to cooperate with the prison staff.

Modern prisons and correctional institutions make provision for all the priestly and pastoral functions of the chaplain. Wardens set aside rooms for public worship, and in many instances energetic chaplains have succeeded in securing funds for chapels for all faiths, sometimes built by the prisoners themselves. Through the efforts of religious and lay leaders, attendance at public worship in prisons has become voluntary, and many wardens have been persuaded to eliminate the presence of armed guards. Such changes have helped to endow the religious services with a friendly, moral atmosphere in which prisoners feel a sense of liberation, of being in touch with the outside community. As a link between the prisoner and normal family and community ties, the chaplain is in a strong position.

While it is good policy to allow prisoners to employ what special talents they may have, as for example in the decoration of places of worship, it is well for the chaplain to bear in mind that he may be moved to such commendable activities by motives that are decidedly mixed. Thus there is the case of the counterfeiter at Leavenworth, a favorite prisoner of the chaplain, who built a wooden altar in the chapel and painted several reproductions of religious masterpieces to cover two ugly walls. In the course of this genuinely artistic labor, which went on for two years, he was made a trusty and served as the chaplain's chauffeur on his visits to a cathedral in Kansas City. Just a month before the man's scheduled release, it was discovered that he had employed his materials for other than artistic purposes, that he had set up a press behind one of the pictures and made dummies and plates which he passed on to a contact man not far from the cathedral. The shock to the chaplain was not lessened by the fact that through his good offices a job reproducing works of art for a museum had been waiting for the prisoner on his release. The chaplain was not without a sense of humor, and in relating the story remarked, "I think in my declining years it would give me considerable peace to have less artistry and more piety behind me at the altar." [12]

Not all chaplains, however, are able to take a betrayal of their confidence in this spirit. More often than not their reaction is one of embittered disillusionment and a demand for redoubled punishment. Yet the fact is that such betrayal is an indication of a mental disturbance, and the chaplain should regard it in that light. Criminal behavior is actuated by a variety of motives, not the least of which is fear of the society of free men. Lawbreaking may be a way of obtaining the security of the prison. Or the criminal may be hounded by unbearable guilt feelings which punishment in prison serves to relieve. If he is a thief, there may enter into his motives unconscious factors of sex and aggression. The point is that the psychology of the habitual criminal is not a simple matter, reformable by punishment alone. Since his motives are often unconscious and give rise to behavior beyond his control, he is a subject for the psychiatrist.

The criminal's frequent relapses are proof enough of the inadequacy of merely punitive measures. Take, for example, the case of the woman in her early thirties who was serving a second term for theft. This time she attended a lettering class in prison, and discovered in herself a genuine talent for drawing. Further, she was receiving psychiatric treatment for kleptomania, and was responding well. Through the efforts of the chaplain, together with a church visiting committee, arrangements were made to teach the prisoner dress design and interior decorating. Upon her release, the chaplain obtained a job for her with a large dressmaking establishment. Five years later she had become a leading designer, and she now began to make annual contributions to the work of the church committee that had visited her in prison. Apart from illustrating how effective an enlightened approach to kleptomania may be, this case is a nice example of collaboration between chaplain, prison staff, and community.

The evidence is that prisoners derive spiritual solace and concrete help from individual pastoral counseling. Inmates of prisons with resident chaplains have access to them upon request. When the inmate is one who has been sentenced to death, the chaplain is often his mainstay, especially during the "last mile." Prisoners undergoing agonizing personal crises often call upon the chaplain, who by the exercise of his moral authority, his use of prayer, Scripture, and confession, brings relief and comfort. It sometimes happens as a result of such consultation with the chaplain that a prisoner will make a clean breast of his crime and so absolve others who were erroneously implicated. The chaplain can be a comfort, too, to the prisoner who has been bitterly disappointed by the decision of a parole board or governor. How effective religious faith may be in this situation is illustrated by Nathan Leopold, who after serving thirty-three years of a life sentence for murder at Statesville Penitentiary in Joliet, had his appeal for release rejected by the parole board and the Governor of Illinois. "I am disappointed but not crushed," he said to reporters in the prison chapel. "In my religion, we have a prayer, the 'Kaddish,' which magnifies and sanctifies the Name of God. For many years in this prison I have wondered why this prayer should consist solely of the glorification of God and not contain one word about the grief the Lord suffers. I now understand that grief today because I stand at the open graveside of my hopes for clemency . . . As in every religion, we too have the saying, 'Thy will be done.' The Governor's action apparently was His will." When Leopold was later granted freedom, he wrote, "I am grateful first of all to God, for man can do only what God permits him to do."

In a prison without social service facilities or with inadequate facilities, the chaplain may be the person consulted by the prisoner whose wife or family may be ill or in economic straits. The chaplain of course will enter into these problems with the greatest sympathy, communicating with the family concerned, even visiting them if possible. Yet in prison no less than in congregations and parishes, problems of this sort call for a knowledge of and referrals to the agency resources in the community. The caseworker alone is trained to deal with them adequately.

Enlightened wardens, like Lewis E. Lawes of Sing Sing Prison and Joseph E. Ragen of Joliet, have stated that they were guided in the improvements they instituted by complaints about living conditions, work assignments, behavior of guards, and so on, as reported to them by chaplains. It is interesting to note in this connection that chaplains in England were responsible for the abolition of dehumanizing prison wards and the introduction of cells. Chaplains have also been instrumental in broadening recreational, educational, and vocational facilities, all of which are important instruments of rehabilitation. Besides the examples already cited, there are numerous others showing that as a result of the chaplain's interest prisoners have left penal institutions as artists, artisans, musicians, athletes, and technicians. Great opportunities are also open to the chaplain in connection with the allotment of living quarters to prisoners that are more in accord with their age, background, sex, and temperament. And he can take a hand in such things as the quality of food, the conduct of mess halls, the inauguration of programs of self-government, and the humanization of probation methods. We may add that jails call for especially vigorous chaplains, for jails are often "the preparatory school of crime" at the same time that they house young and first offenders who are psychologically more receptive to religious counseling than their hardened elders in prison.

Custodial reforms and the institution of rehabilitative programs have been aimed at helping the prisoner to adjust to a normal environment. Yet these largely external changes will prove of little value unless they are accompanied by an internal change in the convict. Which is to say, as Warden Lawes puts it, that rehabilitation must come from within. In this respect, religious counseling can be crucial. The chaplain, in lending support to the prisoner, fostering his education, assuming towards him an authoritative role that he can accept, is adding to the prisoner's psychic strength and arousing a new hope in him. Each success here means the salvation of a human being and the enhancement of the mental and moral health of the community.

The Chaplain on the Campus

T H E college or university chaplain, whether the institution he serves is small or large, public or private, coeducational or not, moves in a much freer atmosphere than his counterparts in mental hospitals, military services, and prison. Since he is in touch with the young men and women who in due course will provide the cultural, business, political, and professional leadership of their country, he is also in a position to affect the quality of religion in our society.

Those who attended college some years ago can have only the dimmest notion of the chaplain's role today. They will recall the visiting preacher whose weekday or Sunday sermons reached a negligible part of the student body and affected their intellectual life hardly at all. This situation has changed drastically in the years since the Second World War. Now the chaplain is an official of the staff and his duties bring him into intimate association with the cultural and social life of the student body. Reports from educational institutions throughout the United States show that students are becoming increasingly concerned about religion. At Barnard College the number of students enrolled in courses on religion increased from 5 percent in 1936 to 14 percent in 1956. The Student Council at Harvard University, after conducting a ten-month study of religion in college life, found "an increasing concern for religious questions," and recommended additional courses in the history and philosophy of religion. No less important than the college chapels are the educational and social programs conducted by chaplains under the auspices of student associations such as Newman Clubs and Hillel Foundations, many of them housed in impressive new buildings on or near the campus.

Whether these facts are indicative of a truly religious revival is not easy to say. What can be said is that a climate more congenial to religion has come into being. At the same time this change of climate has not been accompanied by any change in the fundamentally scientific and secular approach of modern education and scholarship. It is within this context that the student radicalism of the twenties and thirties has changed to the conservatism of the forties and fifties. The student is preoccupied with his general studies and the decisive influence upon him is that of his teachers, so that the chaplain is faced with much the same secular pressures that exist outside academic society. His task therefore is to inspire moral vision and create a spiritual ferment. Needless to say, it is not an easy task to fulfill, even within academic walls. For today, as educators point out, many are trained but few are educated.

It is only too easy for the campus chaplain to fall an unwitting victim to secularism. The matter is perhaps best considered in connection with the chaplain's counseling role. At a seminar on religious counseling the following case was presented. One midafternoon a chaplain at a small midwest college received a telephone call from a student, requesting an appointment the same day. To use his own words, the chaplain, who constantly referred to himself not as chaplain but as "counselor," "granted the counselee an interview." It lasted an hour or more. The student, twenty-four years of age, wanted advice on a vocational choice that involved a decision about his further education. He was plagued by lack of self-confidence, which he tried to explain in terms of family, friends, and vocation. Although he felt grateful to his family for their self-sacrifice in helping him to obtain an education, he at the same time felt alienated from them. He lived in worlds apart, owing to his parents' lack of education and culture. They were interested in their church, while he, because of his rationalism, could not stomach their "parochialism." Lack of money was thwarting his ambitions, the jobs he saw only inspired dislike, and he was failing more and more of his examinations. Other members of his family were doing well, as were the young men in his neighborhood, and this was causing him distress and embarrassment. Both at home and at school he was becoming uncommunicative and withdrawn. At the end of the interview the student suddenly revealed that he must decide whether or not to take a midterm examination that very afternoon. The "counselor" expressed sympathy for the young man's problems and "tough breaks," while emphasizing the need for making a vocational choice, unfavorable as the circumstances were. The chief thing was to make up his mind, for only so could he solve his problems and find any satisfaction in life. Finally, he put it to the student that having done most of the reading for the course, he ought to consider taking the examination, even if he did not achieve the sort of grade he would like. The student "seemed to agree."

Such was the story the chaplain told. When he was asked in the seminar why he preferred to be called "mister" and "counselor" rather than pastor, he replied that he thought students would be more likely to come to him if he dropped the religious designation. Now, as we have insisted before, this abdication of a religious for a secular role is neither seemly nor effective. Available to the young man at his college was an excellent mental-health service staffed with qualified psychiatrists and student counselors. Yet he chose to apply to a minister for help. Noteworthy, too, is the fact that the student himself brought up the issue of religion. The chaplain's failure to pursue the subject was all the more egregious on that account. It amounted to divesting himself of the symbolic power inherent in his role. And he failed in still another respect. Given the young man's history, he should have enlisted the specialized help of one of the other members of the mental-health team.

It will pay us to look a little further into this case, for the problem it presents is one which, in one form or another, is constantly cropping up. Here was a young man who on his own showing was the victim of a conflict. It was therefore incumbent upon the chaplain to take cognizance of this conflict and try to understand the elements that went into its making. A self-confessed rationalist, the young man professes to find his parents' religion repugnant; at the same time he chooses to seek aid, not from a psychiatrist, but from a minister. In other words, it would appear that his need to draw closer to his parents was stronger than his need to draw away from them. Accordingly the chaplain might have dwelt on the fact that his parents, if they were uneducated themselves, yet recognized the value of an education, as their financial sacrifices in his behalf showed. Further, by citing examples from the history of religious thought the chaplain might have shown the young man that his rationalism was not as incompatible with religion as he supposed. He might in this way have allayed the student's doubts about religion and helped him find his way back to his parents, or to find in the chaplain himself a parent substitute whom he could rely on and respect. The chaplain was in a strategic position to exercise his authority as a religious counselor and so to be of immediate help to his charge. It will be recalled that the interview ended with the student's announcement that, though he had an examination that very afternoon, he was unable to decide whether or not to take it. Such postponement of a vital matter to the very end is a common occurrence in the counseling situation. With regard to the young man's inability to make up his mind concerning a vocation, the chaplain rightly emphasized the need of a decisive step. If he had taken a similarly unmistakable position with regard to the examination, he would probably have relieved the young man of much of his anxiety. Moreover, it should have been obvious that the young man's problem could not be handled in a single interview, yet no basis was laid, it seems, for a continuing relationship. The initial interview raised a variety of issues which it would have taken several meetings to follow up. Again, the chaplain's assurances showed a tendency to minimize the actual gravity of the problem. The student's evident anxiety, his withdrawal and self-depreciation were all signs that he would need the help of a caseworker or a psychiatrist, if he was going to achieve a working solution of his problems. If the chaplain has unreservedly accepted his religious role and knowledgeably applied the principles of religious counseling, he might have offered this student a kind of help that he could have got in no other quarter.

A word once more about premature referral. It is as much a danger on the campus as off it. Dr. Orville Rogers, a former director of the Department of Health at Yale University, found that a widespread fear of psychiatrists exists among the student body. Partly it was owing to the fact that many job questionnaires ask, "Has this student ever had consultation with a psychiatrist?" Students had the quite rational fear that an affirmative answer might have the effect of disqualifying them for a position irrespective of their abilities. Nor was this feeling altogether allayed when the psychiatrists issued assurances that they were bound to respect the confidences of students no less than other patients, keeping secret the very fact of consultation itself. The result is that many students who need, even want, psychiatric help, avoid it.

It is of first importance that teachers, including religious counselors, should themselves be in good mental health. If school and religious authorities have failed to resolve their own resistances, biases, and fears concerning psychiatry, and are under compulsion to assume an omnipotent role, their advice to students to seek psychiatric help will hardly carry conviction. But irrational fear of the psychiatrist is as widespread among students as in any other group, even if in their case there may be practical reasons as well. It is commonly related to a widespread fear of insanity, which goes back to early childhood misconceptions.

It often happens that students desperately in need of psychiatric help and yet fearful of psychiatry turn to the college chaplain for help. Now if the chaplain makes too hasty a referral to the psychiatrist, the student may get the impression that he is being rejected and forced into the arms of the psychiatrist whom he fears. So a too precipitate referral should be avoided. But one too long delayed is equally undesirable. It may result in transference and countertransference problems which have the effect of intensifying the emotional disturbance. When he is appealed to for help, therefore, the chaplain's first task is to provide warmth, sympathy, and reassurance—in a word, to fulfill his role as a religious pastor. Once a trusting relationship has been established, the chaplain can guide the disturbed student towards treatment.

The chaplain also can be of great assistance to the student who is undergoing treatment, both as guide and friend, just as in cooperation with psychiatrists, caseworkers, and counselors he can reassure and help the parents. The student at college or university has a large measure of freedom in ordering his life, but even so, such institutions assume some measure of custodial responsibility, especially in situations of illness, injury, marriage, or death. The fact that these situations occur on the campus calls for no alteration in the counseling methods of the chaplain. Yet the chaplain is confronted in the day-to-day life of the student with peculiar and often perplexing problems. Thus a seventeen-year-old student in a sectarian college, where chapel attendance was mandatory, was called to the chaplain's study and asked why he had been absent from services. The boy was of superior intelligence, industrious, a good athlete, and had many friends. He confessed to the chaplain that whenever he entered the chapel he experienced palpitations and breathlessness and broke out into a sweat. Although he made every effort to control his feelings of panic, it was to no avail, and he would flee in fear from the chapel. The college physician, having made a thorough physical examination and finding no evidence for organic disease, suggested that some emotional problem was involved, and the chaplain persuaded the boy to visit a psychiatrist. Treatment uncovered a familiar pattern. The oldest of five children, the boy was a victim of subtle but crushing parental supervision. His father, an industrial leader, came of a proud, aristocratic family and, deeply devoted to his son, was determined that he should live up to the standards of his forebears, all of whom had attended the college in which the boy was now enrolled. If he thus expected his son to uphold the family prestige and tradition, the father exercised no gross pressure, but, being a gentle and affectionate man, his method was that of sweet reasonableness. Yet the pressure was there quite as much as if it had taken a punitive form.

The psychiatrist succeeded in establishing a working relationship with the boy, as a result of which the latter confessed that his unhappiness was owing to a lack of opportunity to develop his own interests, and that those interests were not in the family tradition. This confession, made rather tentatively, was accompanied by expressions of guilt on the one hand; tears, anger, and complaints on the other. Extremely fond of his father, he was ashamed of his rebellious impulses against him, and struggled to repress them. The required daily chapel attendance came to represent the very quintessence of his mental conflict, except that at this point the conflict was not only with parental authority, but with college authority, and further still, since he was a religious youth, with the highest authority of all, with God. Unable to separate in his mind these different levels of authority, the boy foundered on what was to him an insoluble conflict and so found refuge in illness. His physical symptoms both expressed and after a fashion resolved his conflict, but only after a fashion, and an unwholesome one, as is evident from the intensity of his suffering. And in the end he asked the chaplain for help.

As the psychiatric treatment progressively revealed the elements in his conflict, the boy's attitude towards his father underwent a change. He came to accept, without feelings of guilt, his right to develop his own individuality. At a suitable point in the treatment the psychiatrist revealed his findings to the chaplain and suggested that he meet with the father. A few friendly discussions were sufficient to convince the father that he was bringing undue pressure on his son, and he acted accordingly. It was also arranged with the director of the summer camp, where the boy was a counselor, that he be given increased opportunities for exercising personal initiative. The boy, now better aware of the nature of his symptoms, achieved on his side a happier relationship with his father. The fear of attending chapel soon subsided, though for a while he had to sit close to the chapel door in readiness for a rapid exit. At last, however, he was able to take his proper place with his class in chapel devotions. So here again we find psychiatric treatment opening the way for a happier and more fulfilling kind of religious experience. Nor are cases like the above at all rare, a fact which is not surprising when one considers that conflict with authority is a major psychological problem in adolescence and that compulsory chapel attendance, especially in a school setting, can come to represent a fundamental symbol of authority in general.

More serious cases of mental illness among students may come to the chaplain's attention, especially those that take a hyperreligious form and exhibit a preoccupation with mysticism and conversion. Such a preoccupation, as we have seen, may herald the outbreak of a serious emotional disorder, and the chaplain who is aware of this possibility is in a position to make an appropriate referral before irreparable damage ensues.

The changing character of the college student body has created many problems that are new to the campus. For one thing, there has been an enormous increase in college enrollment, which has reached the figure of almost three million in the nineteen fifties and is expected to increase still further in the decades to follow. Another even more significant development is the increasing number of marriages among undergraduates, which began with returning veterans of the Second World War and showed no decline even after the veterans disappeared. In 1957 it was estimated that about one-fourth of the college student body were married and that more than half of those married were parents. The change in attitudes and relationships ushered in by these developments are of great import to all academic counselors. Studies at six colleges of varying size and character are unanimous in concluding that married students lack the spirit of adventure, that they are more settled and conservative than the unmarried students. Their problems are chiefly of a marital character and run the same gamut as in the general community. They are problems that involve the chaplain, particularly when they raise such issues as birth control, intermarriage, and divorce. And since the chaplain is here dealing with people who are young, flexible, and of a higher than average intelligence, his opportunities for effective counseling are particularly great.

In the new context of today's colleges the chaplain figures prominently in a team which more than ever requires the collaboration of teacher, psychiatrist, psychologist, caseworker, and student counselor. The number of college psychiatrists, caseworkers, and counselors has doubled in the years following the Second World War.

At no time has the chaplain been under a greater necessity of exercising his own role, of teaching the great insights handed down by religious tradition and of applying them to the currents of contemporary thought. Here, too, however, the chaplain is obliged to reckon with the attitudes and convictions of the student population. Not that these are easy to make out, for the evidence bearing on the subject is contradictory and elusive. It would seem that the commitments, emotional and intellectual, of the college student today have never been more diverse. Nor will it do to draw comparisons with his counterpart of the twenties and thirties, for new motivations have come into being among the young since then. A new environment has emerged, one characterized by the paradox of material security and spiritual insecurity. As Reinhold Niebuhr has described it, our society is "a paradise of domestic security and growing justice suspended in a hell of international insecurity." Conformity tends to loom large among student attitudes, but there are many other tendencies as well. On the one hand, we have the influences of Camus and Faulkner, Dylan Thomas, and J. D. Salinger; on the other, those of Soren Kierkegaard and Martin Buber, Paul Tillich and Albert Schweitzer. There is sober realism, cynicism, and social idealism. No question but what there is a desire among youth for a larger social and spiritual commitment.

It is just this that presents the college chaplain with his supreme challenge. He will not simply ignore but neither will he accommodate himself to the values of adolescent disenchantment; nor on the other hand will he seek refuge in time-honored commonplaces. He cannot but be aware that a faith based merely on authority is no alternative to the empirically tested truths of science. It is only on the basis of the knowledge they are acquiring in the classroom and from their own experience that the chaplain can hope to enrich the moral and spiritual life of his college charges.

NOTES AND BIBLIOGRAPHY

The references below are consecutively numbered for each chapter, indicating specific published or unpublished sources. The emphasis is on studies in professional journals, the general literature being listed in the selective bibliographies for each chapter. Books that have extended bibliographies are starred. The reader will find guides to some of the relevant literature, religious and other, of the last fifty years in the following: Charles T. Holman, *The Care of Souls: A Sociological Approach*, University of Chicago Press, 1932; John Rathbone Oliver, *Psychiatry and Mental Health*, Scribner's, 1932; Seward Hiltner and others, "Bibliography and Reading Guide," in *Pastoral Psychology*, Vol. 4, January, 1954; and Karl A. Menninger, *A Guide to Psychiatric Books*, Grune & Stratton, New York, 1956 (rev. ed.). A comprehensive bibliography, including literature published in Great Britain and Europe as well as numerous unpublished studies, is needed.

1 *The Domains of Psychiatry and Religion*

1. Boisen, Anton T., *The Exploration of the Inner World: A Study of Mental Disorder and Religious Experience*, Harper, New York, 1936, p. 267. Our criticism is not intended to obscure much that is valuable in this remarkable book.
2. Fromm, Erich, *Psychoanalysis and Religion*, Yale University Press, New Haven, 1950, p. 7. Similarly, a psychiatrist claims that he has shown that religion is simply a means, albeit a respectable means, ". . . of attaining the same ends as those for which psychiatry works." See Ian Stevenson, M.D., "Assumptions of Religion and Psychiatry," in *Bulletin of the Menninger Clinic*, Vol. 19, No. 6, November, 1955, p. 202.
3. We omit consideration of a development in Europe known as "existential analysis" (*Daseinsanalyse, Existenzanalyse*); or "logotherapy," a term proposed by Viktor E. Frankl, M.D., in his book *The Doctor and the Soul*, Knopf, New York, 1955. But a neologism is not necessarily a new idea. This school is another expression of the attempt to substitute a religio-philosophical quest for psychiatric treatment. An objective presenta-

tion of the various schools is to be found in Ruth L. Munroe, *Schools of Psychoanalytic Thought*, Dryden Press, New York, 1955.

4. For an uncompromising statement of this viewpoint see Brock G. Chisholm, M.D., "The Re-establishment of Peacetime Society," *Psychiatry: Journal of the Biology and Pathology of Interpersonal Relations*, Vol. 9, No. 1, February, 1946, pp. 3–20. A brief exposition of the opposite viewpoint is given by Sol W. Ginsburg, M.D., "Values and the Psychiatrist," in *American Journal of Orthopsychiatry*, Vol. XX, No. 3, 1950, pp. 460–478.

5. Freud, Sigmund, M.D., "From the History of an Infantile Neurosis" in the *Standard Edition of the Complete Psychological Works of Sigmund Freud*, Vol. XVII (1917–1919), Hogarth, London, 1955, pp. 7–122. The quotations are to be found in pp. 61, 62, 114.

6. Deutsch, Helene, M.D., "Obsessional Ceremonial and Obsessional Acts" in *Psycho-Analysis of the Neuroses*, Hogarth, London, 1932, pp. 175–197. We have found seventeen instances of persons who after completing a psychoanalysis were enabled, as a result, to identify themselves more fully with religious belief and church participation. For example, a brief statement is given by a British psychiatrist: "One would expect . . . that deep analysis would leave the patient less religious than he was before. My own experience has been the exact opposite of this. After an analysis (for scientific purposes) by a leading psychoanalyst extending over ninety-two hours, supplemented by many hours of self-analysis later on, my religious convictions were stronger than before, not weaker. The analysis had indeed a purifying effect upon my religious feelings, freeing them from much that was merely infantile and supported by sentimental associations or historical accidents. But the ultimate result has been that I have become more convinced than ever that religion is the most important thing in life and that it is essential to mental health. The need of forms and ceremonies is another matter, far less fundamental. In many patients whom I have myself analyzed I have found a similar result. Although mere emotionalism and religiosity is diminished, the essentially religious outlook on life remains unimpaired." William Brown, M.D., *Personality and Religion*, University of London Press, London, 1946, p. 134. Cf. also Jack Sheps, M.D., "Re-establishment of Religious Belief Following Psychoanalysis," unpublished paper.

BIBLIOGRAPHY

Allport, Gordon W., *The Individual and His Religion,* Macmillan, New York, 1950.

Braceland, Francis J., M.D., editor, *Faith, Reason and Modern Psychiatry.* Kenedy, New York, 1955.

Cattell, R. B., *Psychology and the Religious Quest,* Nelson, New York, 1948.

Fenichel, Otto, M.D., *The Psychoanalytic Theory of Neuroses,** Norton, New York, 1945 (rev. ed.).

Flugel, J. C., *Man, Morals and Society,* Duckworth, London, 1955.

Freud, Sigmund, M.D., *The Complete Psychological Works of Sigmund Freud,* translated from the German under the general editorship of James Strachey in collaboration with Anna Freud, Hogarth, London. The entire series will comprise twenty-four volumes, of which ten were published between 1953–1958. Cf. also
The Future of an Illusion, Hogarth, London, 1943.
Civilization and Its Discontents, Hogarth, London, 1949.
Moses and Monotheism, Vintage Books, New York, 1955.

Fromm, Erich, *Psychoanalysis and Religion,* Yale University Press, New Haven, 1938.

Herberg, Will, *Protestant, Catholic, Jew: An Essay in American Religious Sociology,* Doubleday, New York, 1955.

Jung, Carl G., *Psychology and Religion,* Yale University Press, New Haven, 1938.

Maves, Paul B., editor, *The Church and Mental Health,** Scribner's, New York, 1953.

Menninger, Karl A., M.D., *The Human Mind,** Knopf, New York, 1957, 3rd ed., rev.

Ostow, Mortimer, M.D., and Scharfstein, Ben-Ami, *The Need to Believe,* International Universities Press, New York, 1954.

Yinger, J. Milton, *Religion, Society and the Individual,** Macmillan, New York, 1957.

Zilboorg, Gregory, M.D., *Mind, Medicine and Man,* Harcourt, Brace, New York, 1943.

2 *Religious Development in Childhood*

1. Allport, Gordon, W., *The Individual and His Religion,* Macmillan, New York, 1950, p. 31.

2. For the development of this point, see Erik H. Erikson, M.D., "Growth and Crises of the Healthy Personality" in Milton J. E. Senn, M.D., editor, *Symposium on the Healthy Personality*, Josiah Macy, Jr., Foundation, New York, 1950, pp. 15–146. See also Phyllis Greenacre, M.D., "Experiences of Awe in Childhood," in *The Psychoanalytic Study of the Child*, Vol. XI, International Universities Press, New York, 1956, pp. 9–30.

3. Cf. Oskar Pfister, *Love in Children and Its Aberrations*, Dodd, Mead, New York, 1924, p. 168 ff.

4. Leavy, S. A., M.D., "A Religious Conversion in a Four Year Old Child," in *The Bulletin of the Philadelphia Association for Psychoanalysis*, Vol. 7, No. 3, September, 1957, pp. 85–90. The story of the conversion of Phoebe Bartlet, aged four years, is told by John Wesley, *Journal*, Standard Edition, 8 vols., edited by N. Curnock, Kelly, London, 1909–1916, Vol. 3, p. 244.

5. Lewin, Kurt, *Resolving Social Conflicts*, Harper, New York, 1948, p. 185.

6. Roloff, Else, as quoted in Kurt Koffka, *The Growth of the Mind*, Humanities Press, New York, 1951, pp. 382–383.

7. Piaget, Jean, *The Child's Conception of Physical Causality*, Humanities Press, New York, 1951, p. 60 ff.

8. While this surmise seems reasonable, it cannot be documented with certainty. A strong case in favor of it is made by H. L. Philp, *Freud and Religious Belief*, Pitman, New York, 1956, pp. 1–6. Ernest Jones, M.D., at the writing of the first volume of Freud's biography, appears to agree. He says, "There was, of course, the Catholic Nannie, and perhaps her terrifying influence contributed to his later dislike of Christian beliefs and ceremonies." However, in the third volume Jones states, "Much has been made of this Nannie by writers who are eager to discover a neurotic origin for Freud's negative attitude toward religion. It is of course easy enough to weave conjectures and speculations on a theme of this sort, but I am not aware of any evidence that might justify one in attributing any lasting influence to the Nannie's theological beliefs, and in any event the contact ceased at the age of two and a half. It has even been suggested that his attitude to religion derived from the circumstance of his losing her at that age. It was only when he was forty-six that Freud learned from his mother the reason for the Nannie's disappearance—her being detected in theft. Yet we have been asked to believe that this precocious two-year-old himself divined that it was the result of her sinning against the ethics of her religion and deduced from this that Christianity was a hypocritical mockery." See *The Life and Work*

of *Sigmund Freud,* Basic Books, New York, Vol. 1, p. 19 (1953) and Vol. 3, pp. 349–350 (1957).

9. Hunter, Edith F., *The Questioning Child and Religion,* Starr King Press, Boston, 1956, p. 83. See also E. A. Loomis, Jr., M.D., "Child Psychiatry and Religion," in *Pastoral Psychology,* Vol. 7, September, 1956, pp. 27–28, 30, 32–33; Reuel L. Howe, *Man's Need and God's Action,* Seabury Press, Greenwich, Conn., 1953.

BIBLIOGRAPHY

Anthony, Sylvia, *The Child's Discovery of Death,* Harcourt, Brace, New York, 1940.

Bovet, Pierre, *The Child's Religion,* translated from the French by George H. Green, Dent, London, 1928.

Erikson, Erik H., M.D., *Childhood and Society,* Norton, New York, 1950.

Griffiths, Ruth, *A Study of Imagination in Early Childhood,** Routledge & Kegan Paul, London, 1935.

Josselyn, Irene M., M.D., *Psychosocial Development in Children,** Family Service Association of America, New York, 1948.

Kanner, Leo, M.D., *Child Psychiatry,** Thomas, Springfield, Illinois, 1955, rev. ed.

Klingberg, Göte, *Studier i barnens religiösa liv** (*Studies in the Child's Religious Life*), Svenska Kyrkans Diakonistyrelses, Bokförlag, 1953.

Mead, Margaret and Wolfenstein, Martha, *Childhood in Contemporary Cultures,* University of Chicago Press, Chicago, 1955.

Pfister, Oskar, *Love in Children and Its Aberrations,** Dodd, Mead, New York, 1924.

Piaget, Jean, *The Child's Conception of the World,* translated by Marjorie Gabain. Harcourt, Brace, New York, 1930.

The Child's Conception of Physical Causality, translated from the French by Marjorie Gabain. Harcourt, Brace, New York, 1930.

The Moral Judgment of the Child, translated by Marjorie Gabain. Free Press, Glencoe, Illinois, 1948.

The Language and Thought of the Child, translated by Marjorie Gabain. Humanities Press, New York, 1952.

Play, Dreams and Imitation in Childhood, translated by C. Gattegne and F. M. Hodgson, Norton, New York, 1951.

Stone, L. Joseph and Church, Joseph, *Childhood and Adolescence,** Random House, New York, 1957.

3   *Religious Conflict and Values in Adolescence*

1. Kuhlen, Raymond G. and Arnold, Martha, "Age Differences in Religious Beliefs and Problems During Adolescence," in *The Journal of Genetic Psychology*, Vol. 65, Second Half, December, 1944, pp. 291–299. See also M. S. Myers, "The Role of Certain Religious Values for High School Youth," in *Studies in Higher Education*, No. 79, Purdue University, 1951.
2. Starbuck, Edwin Diller, *The Psychology of Religion*, Scribner's, New York, 1899, p. 28 ff.
3. Ekstein, Rudolph, "A Clinical Note on the Therapeutic Use of a Quasi-Religious Experience," in the *Journal of the American Psychoanalytic Association*, Vol. 4, No. 2, April, 1956, pp. 304–313. M. Ralph Kaufman, M.D., "Religious Delusions in Schizophrenia," in *International Journal of Psycho-Analysis*, Vol. XX, Parts 3 & 4, July–October, 1939, pp. 363–376.

BIBLIOGRAPHY

Balser, Benjamin H., M.D., *Psychotherapy of the Adolescent*, International Universities Press, New York, 1957.

Gesell, Arnold, Ilg, Frances and Ames, Louise B., *Youth: The Years From Ten to Sixteen*,* Harper, New York, 1956.

Jersild, Arthur T., *The Psychology of Adolescence*,* Macmillan, New York, 1957.

Josselyn, Irene M., M.D., *The Adolescent and His World*,* Family Service Association of America, New York, 1952.

Kupky, Oskar, *The Religious Development of Adolescents*,* translated by William C. Trow, Macmillan, New York, 1928.

Schneiders, Alexander A., *The Psychology of Adolescence*,* Bruce, Milwaukee, 1951.

Starbuck, Edwin D., *The Psychology of Religion*, Scribner's, New York, 1899.

4   *The Basic Principles of Religious Counseling*

1. Some of the dangers inherent in the trend in the direction of setting up psychiatric services within or under the auspices of religious institutions are pointed out in James F. Cooper, "The Religio-Psychiatric Clinic: A Study of the Integration of Religion and Psychiatry in a Psychiatric Clinic," unpublished M.S.

thesis, New York School of Social Work, Columbia University, 1956.

2. Wise, Carroll, A., *Pastoral Counseling*, Harper, New York, 1951, pp. 145–146.

3. The classic work in this field is Mary Richmond, *Social Diagnosis*, Russell Sage Foundation, New York, 1917. A standard contemporary work is Gordon Hamilton, *Theory and Practice of Social Case Work*, Columbia University Press, New York, 1951, (rev. ed.). Another stimulating book, presenting a somewhat different approach, is Helen Harris Perlman, *Social Casework: A Problem-Solving Process*,* University of Chicago Press, Chicago, 1957. For a brief, helpful statement of the methods discussed below, see Alice McCabe, Jeanette Regensburg, Mary Sweeney, Mildred Kilinski, Ruth Schwarz, chairman, *Statement on Social Casework Practice*,* Community Service Society, 105 East 22nd St., New York 10, N. Y., November 15, 1957. The two major schools are known as "diagnostic" and "functional." For a presentation of the two viewpoints in one volume, see Cora Kasius, editor, *A Comparison of Diagnostic and Functional Casework Concepts*, Family Service Association of America, New York, 1950.

4. This case and the following one are based upon the excellent material in Thomas J. Bigham, Jr., "The Function of the Chaplain in the Youth Consultation Service," * unpublished thesis, New York School of Social Work, Columbia University, 1945. Cf. also Samuel Nover, M.D., "Utilization of Social Institutions as a Defence Technique in the Neuroses," in *International Journal of Psycho-Analysis*, Vol. XXXVIII, Part II, March–April, 1957, pp. 82–91; and Marjorie Brierly, M.D., "Notes on Psycho-Analysis and Integrative Living," *ibid.*, Vol. XXVIII, Part I, 1947, pp. 57–105.

5. Freud, Sigmund, M.D., *Civilization and Its Discontents*, Hogarth, London, 1949, p. 26.

6. See special issue on prayer, *Pastoral Psychology*, Vol. 4, September, 1953, pp. 9–67.

7. Among the best studies are Martha Wolfenstein, *Disaster: A Psychological Essay*, Free Press, Glencoe, Illinois, 1957; and J. S. Tyhurst, M.D., "Psychological and Social Aspects of Civilian Disaster," *Canadian Medical Association Journal*, Vol. 76, March, 1957, pp. 385–393.

8. As quoted in Göte Bergsten, *Pastoral Psychology*, Allen & Unwin, London, 1951, p. 79. See also Kirsopp Lake, *The Religion of Yesterday and To-Morrow*, Houghton Mifflin, Boston, 1926, p. 38 ff.

9. See *The Minister and the Social Worker,* Vol. 1, No. 1, issued by the Division for Churches of the Federation of Protestant Welfare Agencies, April, 1943. We are indebted to the author, Alice R. McCabe, for permission to use this case record. Miss McCabe has also written two pioneering papers in this field: "Pastoral Counseling and Case Work," in *The Family,* November, 1943, and "The Church and Social Work," February, 1945, issued in mimeographed form by the Church of the Incarnation, 209 Madison Avenue, New York City. For recent discussion see the symposium by L. H. Woodward and W. Kluge, "The Relationship Between Religion and Psychotherapy in the Adjustment of the Individual," in *Journal of Psychiatric Social Work,* Vol. 18, No. 2, Autumn, 1948, pp. 59–80; Roy Waldo Miner, editor, *Psychotherapy and Counseling,* Annals of the New York Academy of Science, Vol. 63, Art. 3, pp. 319–432; Thomas J. Bigham, Jr., "Cooperation Between Ministers and Social Workers," in F. Ernest Johnson, editor, *Religion and Social Work,* Harper, New York, 1956, pp. 141–154; and Sue Spencer, "Religious and Spiritual Values in Casework Practice," in *Social Casework,* Vol. XXXVIII, No. 10, December, 1957, pp. 519–526.

BIBLIOGRAPHY

Bergsten, Göte, *Pastoral Psychology,* Allen & Unwin, London, 1951.

Hamilton, Gordon, *Theory and Practice of Social Case Work,** Columbia University Press, New York, 1951, rev. ed.

Johnson, F. Ernest, editor, *Religion and Social Work,* Harper, New York, 1956.

Miner, Roy Waldo, M.D., editor, *Psychotherapy and Counseling,** Annals of the New York Academy of Sciences, Vol. 63, Art. 3, New York, 1955, pp. 319–432.

Roberts, David E., *Psychotherapy and a Christian View of Man,* Scribner's, New York, 1950.

Vanderveldt, James, and Odenwald, Robert P., M.D., *Psychiatry and Catholicism,** McGraw-Hill, New York, 1957 (rev. ed.).

5   *Religion in Sex and Marriage*

1. For discussion of birth control and related issues, see Joseph Fletcher, *Morals and Medicine,* Princeton University Press, Princeton, New Jersey, 1954; Dom Peter Flood, editor, *New*

Problems in Medical Ethics, 3 vols., Newman Press, West-minster, Maryland, 1953; and William J. Gibbons, "Fertility Control in the Light of Some Recent Catholic Statements," in *Eugenics Quarterly,* Part I, 3:9–15, March, 1956, and Part II, 3:82–87, June, 1956; M I. Levine, M.D., and Reuel L. Howe, "Pediatrics and the Church," in *Journal of Pastoral Care,* Vol. 3, Fall–Winter, 1949, pp. 39–44; Don J. Hager, "Religion, Delin-quency and Society," in *Social Work,* Vol. 2, No. 3, July, 1957, pp. 16–21; and J. T. Landis, "Marriages of Mixed and Non-Mixed Religious Faith," in *American Sociological Review,* Vol. 14, June, 1949, pp. 401–407.

2. Wittkower, E. D., M.D., and Cowan, J., "Some Psychological Aspects of Sexual Promiscuity," in *Psychosomatic Medicine,* Vol. 6, No. 4, 1944, pp. 287–294.

BIBLIOGRAPHY

Bossard, James H. S., and Boll, Eleanor Stoker, *One Marriage, Two Faiths; Guidance on Interfaith Marriage,** Ronald Press, New York, 1957.

Cole, William Graham, *Sex in Christianity and Psychoanalysis,* Oxford, New York, 1955.

Eisenstein, Victor W., M.D., editor, *Neurotic Interaction in Mar-riage,* Basic Books, New York, 1956.

Epstein, Louis, *Sex Laws and Customs in Judaism,* Bloch, New York, 1948.

Flood, Dom Peter, M.D., O.S.B., editor, *New Problems in Medical Ethics,* 3 vols., translated from the French by Malachy G. Carroll, Newman Press, Westminster, Maryland, 1953.

Flugel, J. C., *The Psycho-Analytic Study of the Family,* Interna-tional Psycho-Analytical Press, New York, 1921.

Hollis, Florence, *Women in Marital Conflict,** Family Service As-sociation of America, New York, 1949.

Skidmore, R. A., Garrett, Hulda, V. S., and Skidmore, C. J., *Mar-riage Consulting,** Harper, New York, 1956.

6 *Understanding Illness*

1. Norris, Catherine M., "The Nurse and the Dying Patient," in *The American Journal of Nursing,* Vol. 55, No. 10, October, 1955, p. 1216. Cf. also R. L. Dicks, "The Religious Function of the Nurse," *ibid.,* Vol. 39, October, 1939, pp. 1109–1112; Helen Cromwell, *ibid.,* "Religion in Nursing Practice," Vol. 49,

December, 1949, pp. 768–770; W. F. Jenks, "Religious Instruction for the Convalescent Child," in *Hospital Progress*, Vol. 33, February, 1952, pp. 56–57.

2. Lebo, Joseph R., as quoted in *The American Journal of Nursing*, Vol. 55, No. 5, May, 1955, p. 548.

3. Lowry, James V., M.D., "Hospital Therapy of Narcotic Addicts," in *Modern Medicine*, October 15, 1957, p. 87.

4. Rosen, Victor, M.D., "The Role of Denial in Acute Post-Operative Affective Reactions Following Removal of Body Parts," *Psychosomatic Medicine*, Vol. 12, No. 6, November–December, 1950, pp. 356–361.

5. Eissler, K. R., M.D., *The Psychiatrist and the Dying Patient*, International Universities Press, New York, 1955, p. 246 ff.

BIBLIOGRAPHY

Cabot, Richard C., M.D., and Dicks, Russell L., *The Art of Ministering to the Sick,** Macmillan, New York, 1957.

Standard, Samuel, M.D., and Nathan, Helmuth, M.D., editors, *Should the Patient Know the Truth?** Springer, New York, 1955.

Oates, Wayne E., *Religious Factors in Mental Illness*, Allen & Unwin, London, 1957.

Stevenson, George S., M.D., *Mental Planning for Social Action*, McGraw-Hill, New York, 1956.

————, *Pastoral Psychology*, Vol. 4, No. 16, October, 1953.

7 Facing Bereavement

1. Freud, Sigmund, M.D., "Mourning and Melancholia," *Collected Papers*, Vol. IV, Hogarth, London, 1946, p. 166. Cf. also Bruno Bettelheim, M.D., "Individual and Mass Behavior in Extreme Situations," in *Journal of Abnormal and Social Psychology*, Vol. 38, No. 4, October, 1943, pp. 417–452; Erich Lindemann, M.D., "Symptomatology and Management of Acute Grief," in *American Journal of Psychiatry*, Vol. 101, September, 1944, pp. 141–149; and Paul Schilder, M.D., and David Wechsler, "Attitudes of Children Towards Death," in *Journal of Genetic Psychology*, Vol. 45, 1934, pp. 406–451.

2. Klein, Melanie, "Mourning: Its Relation to Manic-Depressive States," in *Contributions to Psycho-Analysis, 1921–1945*, Hogarth, London, 1950, p. 323 ff. Cf. also Samuel R. Lehrman, M.D., "Reactions to Untimely Death," in *Psychiatric Quarterly*, Vol. 30, October, 1956, pp. 564–578.

3. Deutsch, Helene, M.D., "Melancholic and Depressive States," in *Psycho-Analysis of the Neuroses,* Hogarth, London, 1932, pp. 215–230. See also Hayim Greenberg, "On Death," translated from the Yiddish by Shlomo Katz, in *Jewish Frontier,* Vol. 22, No. 5 (240), May, 1955, pp. 15–18.

4. Freud, Sigmund, M.D., "Thoughts on War and Death," in *Standard Edition, op. cit.,* Vol. XIV, 1957, p. 296. On this point see also Gregory Zilboorg, M.D., "The Sense of Immortality," in *Psychoanalytic Quarterly,* Vol. VII, 1938, pp. 171–199.

5. Deutsch, Helene, M.D., "Absence of Grief" in *Psychoanalytic Quarterly,* Vol. VI, January, 1937, pp. 12–22.

6. Wise, Carroll A., *Pastoral Counseling,* Harper, New York, 1951, pp. 213–214.

BIBLIOGRAPHY

Eissler, K. R., M.D., *The Psychiatrist and the Dying Patient,** International Universities Press, New York, 1955.

Irion, Paul E., *The Funeral and the Mourners,** Abingdon, New York, 1954.

Freud, Sigmund, M.D., "Mourning and Melancholia," *Collected Papers,* Hogarth, London, 1948, Vol. IV, pp. 152–170.

8   *Religious Conversion and Mysticism*

1. James, William, *The Varieties of Religious Experience* (originally published in 1902), Modern Library, New York, p. 370 ff. For an excellent contemporary discussion of the mystical viewpoints of Rudolph Otto (Lutheran), Father Poulain (Catholic), and Martin Buber (Jewish), see H. J. Paton, *The Modern Predicament,* Allen & Unwin, London, 1955.

2. Huxley, Aldous, *The Doors of Perception,* Chatto and Windus, London, Harper, New York, 1954, pp. 15–16. For other experiences with mescaline and a critique of Huxley, see R. C. Zaehner, *Mysticism, Sacred and Profane,* Oxford, London, 1957, pp. 1–29, 208–226.

3. Hunter, Edith, *The Questioning Child and Religion,* Starr King Press, Boston, 1956, p. 84.

4. James, William, *op. cit.,* pp. 374–375 fn.

5. James, William, *ibid.,* p. 219 ff.

6. Starbuck, Edwin Diller, *The Psychology of Religion,* Scribner's, New York, 1899, p. 327.

7. Kupky, Oskar, _The Religious Development of Adolescents,_ Macmillan, New York, 1928, p. 130.
8. _Obras de la Gloriosa Madre Sta. Teresa de Jesús,_ Madrid, 1752, Tomo II, Morandas Quintas, I, 3, p. 67. Cf. also the description of "L'oraison d'union" in her autobiography, Louis Bertrand, _Sainte Therese d'Avila, racontee par elle-meme,_ Gigord, Paris, 1937, pp. 179–187.
9. Lewin, Bertram D., M.D., _The Psychoanalysis of Elation,_ Norton, New York, 1950, p. 144 ff.
10. Zaehner, R. C., _op. cit.,_ pp. 151–152.
11. James, William, _op. cit.,_ pp. 414–415.
12. Freud, Sigmund, M.D., "Psycho-Analytic Notes Upon an Autobiographical Account of a Case of Paranoia," in _Collected Papers, op. cit.,_ Vol. III, pp. 390–472.
13. Boisen, Anton T., _op. cit.;_ cf. also Leon Salzman, M.D., "The Psychology of Religious and Ideological Conversion," in _Psychiatry,_ Vol. 16, May, 1953, pp. 177–187.
14. Arlow, Jacob A., M.D., "The Consecration of the Prophets," in the _Psychoanalytical Quarterly,_ Vol. 20, July, 1951, pp. 374–397.
15. Ruesch, Jurgen, M.D., _et al., Chronic Disease and Psychological Invalidism. A Psychosomatic Study,*_ University of California Press, Berkeley and Los Angeles, 1951, p. 16.
16. Cohen, Elie, M.D., _Human Behavior in the Concentration Camp,*_ Norton, New York, 1953, p. 148 ff.

BIBLIOGRAPHY

Boisen, Anton T., _The Exploration of the Inner World,_ Harper, New York, 1936.
De Sanctis, Sante, M.D., _Religious Conversion: A Bio-Psychological Study,*_ Harcourt, Brace, New York, 1927.
James, William, _The Varieties of Religious Experience,_ Modern Library, New York.
Leuba, J. H., _Psychology of Religious Mysticism,_ Harcourt, Brace, New York, 1926.
Sargeant, William, _Battle for the Mind,*_ Doubleday, New York, 1957.
Starbuck, Edwin Diller, _The Psychology of Religion,_ Scribner's, New York, 1899.
Scholem, Gershom G., _Major Trends in Jewish Mysticism,*_ Schocken, New York, 1954, 3rd rev. ed.

Zaehner, R. C., *Mysticism, Sacred and Profane*, Oxford, London, 1957.

9 *Religion and the Aging*

1. Freud, Sigmund, M.D., *Civilization and Its Discontents*, Hogarth, London, 1939, fn., p. 34. Cf. Julius Hochman, "The Retirement Myth," in *The Social and Biological Challenge of Our Aging Population*, Columbia University Press, New York, 1950, pp. 130–145.
2. Bellak, Leopold, M.D., *et al.*, "Rehabilitation of the Mentally Ill Through Controlled Transitional Employment," in *The American Journal of Orthopsychiatry*, Vol. XXVI, No. 2, April, 1956, pp. 285–296. See also Blyth Brock, "Sheltered Workshop in a London Borough," in *Old Age in the Modern World*, Livingstone, London, 1955, pp. 599–601; Ruth S. Cavan, "Family Life and Family Substitutes in Old Age," in *American Sociological Review*, Vol. XIV, No. 1, 1949, pp. 71–83; Helen Turner, editor, *A Psychiatric Approach to Institutional Work with the Aged*, Community Service Society, New York, 1955; and Charles V. Willie, "Group Relationships of the Elderly in Our Culture," in *Social Casework*, Vol. XXXV, No. 5, May, 1954, pp. 206–212.
3. ————, *Older People in the Family, the Parish and the Neighborhood: A Study of St. Philip Neri Parish, St. Louis, Missouri.* Catholic Charities of St. Louis, 2331, Mullanphy St., St. Louis 6, Missouri, 1955.
4. Hiltner, Seward, *Religion and the Aging Process*, National Social Welfare Assembly, New York, 1952, pp. 6–7.
5. Maves, Paul B., and Cedarleaf, J. Lennart, *Older People and the Church.* Abingdon, New York, 1949, p. 208.
6. Kubie, Susan H., and Landau, Gertrude, *Group Work with the Aged*, International Universities Press, New York, 1953, p. 200. Cf. also K. Stern, J. M. Smith, and M. Frank, "Mechanisms of Transference and Counter-transference in Psychotherapeutic and Social Work with the Aged," in *Journal of Gerontology*, Vol. 8, 1953, pp. 328–332; Alvin I. Goldfarb, M.D., and Jack Sheps, M.D., "Psychotherapy of the Aged," in *Psychosomatic Medicine*, Vol. XVI, No. 3, May–June, 1954, pp. 209–219; Alvin I. Goldfarb, M.D., "Psychotherapy of the Aged," in *The Psychoanalytic Review*, Vol. 43, No. 1, January, 1956, pp. 68–81; and Frederick D. Zeman, M.D., "Constructive Programs for the Mental Health of the Elderly," in *Mental Hygiene*, Vol. 35, 1951, pp. 221–234.

7. Turkel, Roma Rudd, *Day After Tomorrow*, Kenedy, New York, 1956, p. 138.
8. Maves and Cedarleaf, *op. cit.*, p. 147 ff.
9. There is a brief account of the founding and experience of this pioneer center, written by the founder, Harry A. Levine, "Creative Energy Is Ageless," Department of Welfare, New York City (no date, mimeographed). There is also an excellent professional study of the Hodson Center by two former members of the staff: Susan H. Kubie and Gertrude Landau, *Group Work with the Aged*, International Universities Press, New York, 1953. See also L. Cosin, "The Place of the Day Hospital in the Geriatric Unit," in *The Practictioner*, Vol. 172, May, 1954, pp. 552–559.
10. Turkel, *op. cit.*, pp. 177–178.
11. Isaacs, Nathan, *Study as a Mode of Worship*, Union of Orthodox Jewish Congregations of America, New York, 1925.

BIBLIOGRAPHY

Anderson, John E., editor, *Psychological Aspects of Aging*, American Psychological Association, Washington, D.C., 1956.

Maves, Paul B., and Cedarleaf, J. Lennart: *Older People and the Church*, Abingdon, New York, 1949.

Stieglitz, E. J., M.D., *Predictable Emotional Stresses of Later Maturity*. Report of the New Jersey Neuropsychiatric Institute, Princeton, 1955.

————, *Old Age in the Modern World*. Report of the Third Congress of the International Association of Gerontology. Livingstone, London, 1955.

————, "The Church and Older People," *Pastoral Psychology*, Vol. 5, No. 46, September, 1954. A Symposium: Paul B. Maves, J. Lennart Cedarleaf, Seward Hiltner, Orlo Strunk, Jr., Martin Gumpert, M.D.

————, *Selected References on Aging: An Annotated Bibliography*. Compiled for the Committee on Aging by the Library of the U. S. Department of Health, Education, and Welfare. Washington, D. C., 1955, 64 pp. "Religious Programs and Services," p. 10.

10   *The Chaplain in Contemporary Society*

1. Cf. especially, Ernest E. Bruder, "A Clinically Trained Ministry in the Mental Hospital," in *Quarterly Review of Psychiatry*

and Neurology, Vol. 2, October, 1947, pp. 543–552, and "Training and the Mental Hospital Chaplain," paper presented at the Annual Meeting of the American Psychiatric Association in Chicago, Ill., on May 13, 1957; Alvie L. McKnight, "The Evolution of Pastoral Care in the Army Hospitals," in *The Journal of Pastoral Care,* Vol. VII, No. 3, Fall, 1953, pp. 170–173; A. W. Scully, "The Work of a Chaplain in a State Hospital for Mental Disorder," in *Journal of Nervous and Mental Disease,* Vol. 101, March, 1945, pp. 264–267; Seward Hiltner, "Developing a More Effective Chaplaincy," in Paul B. Maves, editor, *The Church and Mental Health,* Scribner's, New York, 1953, pp. 231–238; David Belgum, "The Role of the Chaplain in the Care of the Patient," unpublished Ph.D. thesis, Boston University, 1952.

2. Gluckman, R. M., M.D., "The Chaplain as a Member of the Diagnostic Clinical Team," in *Mental Hygiene,* Vol. 37, April, 1953, pp. 278–282. Cf. also J. L. Cedarleaf, "The Chaplain's Role with Delinquent Boys in an Institution," in *Federal Probation,* Vol. 18, March, 1954, pp. 40–45, and M. L. Oehrtman, "Chaplaincy Service for the Mentally Retarded," in *American Journal of Mental Deficiency,* Vol. 60, October, 1955, pp. 253–257; Morton A. Seidenfeld, *The Psychologist Advises the Chaplain,* Division of Religious Activities, National Jewish Welfare Board, New York, 1951.

3. Gross, George A., M.D., and Fritze, Herbert P., Chaplain, "The Function of a Chaplain in Psychotherapy," in *Bulletin of the Menninger Clinic,* Vol. 16, No. 4, July, 1952, pp. 136–141.

4. See, for example, the U. S. War Department Technical Manual, TM 16–205, *The Chaplain,* dated 5 July 1944; the Bureau of Naval Personnel 15664 (1949), *The Chaplain's Manual;* and *The Chaplain's Manual,* Veterans Administration Manual, M6–3, Revised, Washington 25, D. C., 1953.

5. For a brief analysis of this dilemma, see Waldo W. Burchard: "Role Conflicts of Military Chaplains," in *American Sociological Review,* Vol. 19, No. 5, October, 1954, pp. 528–535. We are grateful to Prof. Burchard for making available a copy of his unpublished Ph.D. thesis, "The Role of the Military Chaplain," University of California, 1953, which is rich in material and has an extensive bibliography.

6. Of singular interest is part of a letter written by Chaplain Goode to his wife just before embarking on the *Dorchester:* "We are fighting for the new age of brotherhood that will usher in at the same time the world democracy we all want . . . Justice and righteousness as dreamed of by the prophet

who gave the world the democratic spirit will cover the earth as a torrent. Men the world over will have enough to eat, clothes to wear, opportunity for improvement through education, and full employment. Tyranny will no longer be possible in a united world because, before it can gain power, the forces of justice speeded through space by airplane, will have overwhelmed it. Protests against injustice will be heard in every capital of the world the moment it occurs and redress granted at once. What has seemed like civilization up to this point is but a crude effort compared to the era that lies just before us . . ." See I. Kaufmann, *American Jews in World War II*, Dial, New York, 1947, pp. 305–309.

7. This is uniformly true in many studies of A.W.O.L.'s made by the War Department and the Morale Services Division. See, for example, a report made by Dr. Oscar B. Markey (Major, M.C.), a psychiatrist serving as chief of the Consultation Service, Headquarters, Infantry Replacement Training Center, Camp Fannin, Texas, dated 10 May 1944 (p. 2): "The desire for a more liberal furlough policy becomes particularly acute among men who have had an emergency arise at home . . . more than two-thirds of all the men who go A.W.O.L. say that they do so to get home." For a description of the development of casework treatment in the military, cf. Fergus T. Monahan, "Supportive Casework in an Army Setting," *Social Casework*, Vol. XXXII, No. 9, November, 1952, pp. 388–392; and William S. Rooney, *et al.*, "Psychiatric Casework in an Army Setting," *Social Casework*, Vol. XXXII, No. 1, January, 1951, pp. 31–37.

8. Regarding the whole subject of compassionate leaves and reassignment, see James J. Gibbs, and Ralph W. Morgan, M.C., U. S. A.: "Role of Physicians in Recommendations of Compassionate Personnel Actions," in *U. S. Armed Forces Medical Journal*, Vol. VIII, No. 6, June, 1957, pp. 871–882.

9. The authors have observed at training centers a dozen or more soldiers belonging to rigid sects, who displayed remarkable character. They maintained their religious observances and even resisted "Army language" while achieving ratings and commissions for excellent performance. The delinquent soldier in this case (a composite, as is his friend) represents the other side of the coin. The conflicts of parents and the pressures of general cultural patterns on the younger generation leave problems that the sect cannot resolve. For a clinical discussion of this problem, see George H. Wiedeman, M.D., "The Importance of Religious Sectarianism in Psychiatric Case Study,"

in *American Journal of Psychotherapy*, Vol. III, No. 3, pp. 392–398.

10. This case of the use of a wimpus or prosthetic penis and an inflating instrument to cause erection is discussed in *Responsa to Chaplains 1948–1953*, issued in mimeographed form by the Commission on Jewish Chaplaincy, National Jewish Welfare Board, 145 East 32nd Street, New York 16, New York, pp. 3–5.

11. Zilboorg, Gregory, M.D., *The Psychology of the Criminal Act and Punishment*, Harcourt, Brace, New York, 1954. Cf. also Edward Glover, M.D., "Psycho-Analysis and Criminology: A Political Survey," in *International Journal of Psycho-Analysis*, No. 37, July–October, 1956, pp. 311–317.

12. Wilson, Donald Powell, *My Six Convicts*, Rinehart, 1951, pp. 246–252. For other accounts of the activities of prison chaplains, see Gladys A. Erickson, *Warden Ragen of Joliet*, Dutton, New York, 1957; Lucy Freeman, *"Before I Kill More . . ."* Crown, New York, 1955; and Quentin Reynolds, *Courtroom*, Farrar, Straus & Cudahy, New York, 1950. In contrast to the absence of books by American chaplains since the appearance of Hosea Quinby's *The Prison Chaplaincy and Its Experiences*, Concord, New Hampshire, 1873, there are a number of autobiographical works by British chaplains. Cf., for example, P. Middleton Brumwell, *The Army Chaplain*, Adams & Charles, London, 1943; Melville Harcourt, *A Parson in Prison*, Whitcombe & Tombs, Auckland, N. Z., 1942; Clifford Rickards, *A Prison Chaplain on Dartmoor*, Arnold, London, 1920.

BIBLIOGRAPHY

Burchard, Waldo W., "The Role of the Military Chaplain," * unpublished Ph.D. thesis, University of California, 1953.

Elliot, Mabel A., *Crime in Modern Society*,* Harper, New York, 1952.

Farnsworth, Dana L., M.D., *Mental Health in College and University*,* Harvard University Press, Cambridge, 1957.

Hoyles, J. Arthur, *Religion in Prison*,* Philosophical Library, New York, 1955.

Linn, Louis, M.D., "The Chaplain" in *A Handbook of Hospital Psychiatry*,* International Universities Press, New York, 1954.

Menninger, William C., *Psychiatry in a Troubled World*, Macmillan, New York, 1948.

INDEX

DR. LOUIS LINN received his education at the University of Pennsylvania, Rush Medical College, The University of Chicago, and the New York Psychoanalytic Institute. During World War II he served as a captain in the United States Army Medical Corps in Africa, Italy, and France. He is now a practicing psychiatrist and psychoanalyst and Associate Attending Psychiatrist at the Mt. Sinai Hospital, New York City; a Fellow of the American Psychiatric Association and the New York Academy of Medicine; and a member of the American Psychoanalytic Association. Among his writings are over fifty professional papers and a standard text, *A Handbook of Hospital Psychiatry*. He is serving as editor of a collaborative work, *Psychiatric Services in General Hospitals*, now being prepared for publication.

Dr. Linn was born in Newark, New Jersey, in 1914. Apart from his practice, he is engaged in research, teaching, and public activities. He is married and has two children, Robert and Judy.

Born in New York in 1906 and educated at Harvard, LEO W. SCHWARZ has distinguished himself as critic, editor, and historian. His interest in religion and psychiatry began with studies in Semitic languages and literatures under George Foot Moore, Robert Pfeiffer, and Harry A. Wolfson, and graduate work at the Harvard Divinity School. He served for three years as chaplain at the Hudson River State Hospital in Poughkeepsie, New York, when at the same time he was religious adviser to students at Vassar College. He and Dr. Linn met in 1945, when both of them were officers at the Fortieth General Hospital in Le Vesinet, France.

Mr. Schwarz is the author of *Where Hope Lies, The Redeemers,* and *Refugees in Germany Today,* and the editor of *Great Ages and Ideas of the Jewish People;* he has edited five volumes in the Rinehart Judaica Series, and is a contributor to numerous magazines. He has lectured in every state of the Union and traveled abroad often. He and his wife live in New York City.